ANY FOOL'S COUNTRY LIFE

Any Fool's Country Life

JAMES ROBERTSON

Illustrations by Larry

BOOK CLUB ASSOCIATES LONDON

This omnibus edition published 1985 by
Book Club Associates
by arrangement with Pelham Books Ltd

Printed and bound in Great Britain by
Mackays of Chatham Ltd

CONTENTS

Any Fool Can Be A Countryman 7

Any Fool Can Be A Villager 197

Any Fool Can Be A Countryman

To Big Sandy

Chapter One

I FIRST encountered Bill in the small hours of the morning padding round the garden waving a shotgun. The very last thing that you expect to find when you get out of bed in the middle of the night to investigate strange noises is actually to meet the mythical burglar. In fact Bill was not a potential burglar. He was a potential assassin. He was on the lawn in the moonlight staring up at the bedroom window — behind which my wife had probably gone back to sleep — when I opened the french windows and peered cautiously out at the garden and the river beyond.

What is one supposed to do in such a situation? The obvious answer was quietly to shut the window again and telephone the police but the telephone was out of order again because the squirrels had been practising their Tarzan swings on the line and anyway the police station was manned by an answering machine for the entire night and for much of the day as well. So for want of anything else to do I squeaked. I did not actually mean to squeak. I attempted a roar of outrage and would have settled for a decent growl but a squeak was the best that I could produce under the circumstances. The assassin looked at me. 'Shh,' he said, raising his finger to his lips.

He said 'shh' with considerable firmness so I shhed and wondered quite what to do next. I searched my various sources of inspiration but without much success. The stately progress of my life had failed to throw up a similar situation to which I could refer and thus I was unable to decide on a suitable course of action. He continued to stare fixedly at the window.

'Excuse me,' I bravely ventured. He shhed me again with such vigour that, from fifteen feet, his spittle hammered against the french window with the force of hailstones. I fell silent again and watched and listened. The river was gurgling away as it always did and the owls were hooting at each other with their customary enthusiasm, but nothing out of the ordinary was going on. There seemed no obvious reason to have to shh. It was really quite cold and so I shut the window and returned to bed.

'What was it?' asked my wife drowsily.

'A bloke in the garden with a gun.'

'Oh.' She shut up. I was just getting back to sleep when she nudged me in the ribs. 'What did you say?'

'When?'

'Just now. I thought you said there was someone in the garden with a gun.'

'I did,' I replied.

'Well, what did you do about it?'

'Nothing.' It sounded a bit feeble.

'You mean he's still out there?'

'I've no idea.'

'What do you mean you've no idea? You can't just allow people to wander round the garden with guns. What was he doing?'

'Nothing very much. Just standing there looking up at our window.'

'Looking at our window! Didn't you ask him what he was up to?'

'I did try to,' I said. 'But he told me to shh.'

'Why didn't you ask him again?'

'I did, but he told me to shh again.'

My wife sat up in bed and switched on the bedside light. I was not altogether sure if that was a good move. After all, the light would probably be seen through the curtains. 'Look. I said that I thought I heard a burglar, but it was all right wasn't it. It wasn't a burglar, it was just somebody wandering round the premises at 3am waving a shotgun.' I thought I detected irony there. 'I'd much rather it was a burglar. He would just do a bit of stealing and not shoot us in our beds.'

'He seemed quite harmless.'

'Harmless! Toting a gun and telling you to shut up?'

'Shh!' I corrected.

'What is it? Can you hear something? Is he in the house?'

'No. He didn't tell me to shut up, he just said shh.'

'Oh for heaven's sake. Why don't you do something?'

'What do you suggest?'

'I don't know. Tell him to clear off. Try to frighten him away.'

'But he might shoot me,' I said reasonably.

'You are useless.' With that she got out of bed, put on her dressing gown and went downstairs. I followed supportively behind her. She went into the sitting-room, opened the french window and peered out into the garden. He was still there. 'What on earth do you think you're playing at?' she asked. I could have predicted his reply.

'Shh!'

My wife wiped the spittle off her face. 'I won't shh,' she said angrily. 'Why should I shh? How dare you go round people's gardens frightening the wits out of them.' He was certainly frightening me, but I saw precious little evidence that he was frightening her. The gunman started to get agitated.

'Please be quiet. If you make so much noise, you might frighten him away.'

'Frighten who away?' demanded the Boss.

'Hitler.'

'Hitler?'

'Yes. He lives in that bedroom up there.' It took only a small flash of intuition on my part to realise that we were dealing with an armed raving loony and I hurriedly dragged my wife back into the room and shut the window. We passed a peaceful night and, by morning, he had gone. I trotted round to the police station immediately after breakfast for a quick word with the answering machine. It was taking a well-earned break and there was a real policeman on duty, standing in on its behalf. I poured out my horror story, but the policeman was not worried.

'There's no need to get excited, sir,' he said. 'That would be just Bill. You see he's thought that Hitler's been hiding in your house ever since the end of the war, but he never does anyone any harm. He just goes to have a look occasionally.'

'But he was brandishing a gun.'

'It's quite all right. He's got a licence for it.'

'But he could be dangerous.'

'No, not Bill. He'd only be dangerous if you dressed up like Hitler and made a speech at him from your bedroom window.'

'But surely someone like that ought to be put away?'

'There'd be a bloody riot in the village if we did that, sir. Bill's the best mechanic in the area and he only charges his time out at £1.50 an hour.'

'Which proves he must be off his chump.'

Off his chump or not, we rapidly gave Bill the responsibility of keeping our ten-year-old car on the road and it matured peacefully into a thirteen-year-old car under his benevolent care. Bill used to visit us every three months or so in his search for the Führer and we became quite used to him. It was really quite reassuring in its way. An armed guard prowling round one's premises at irregular intervals is something that many security-conscious people are prepared to pay a lot of money for.

There were no good reasons why Bill's appearance should have been much of a surprise. We had lived in the country long enough to know that eccentricity was the rule and not the exception. Our present house was supposed to help to generate an income for the family which was a task at which I had been conspicuously unsuccessful during ten years of married life. It did not worry me very much but it tended to upset other people close to me. We had moved to the village after I had retired from farming due to a surfeit of slurry and occasional exhausting outbursts of hard work. I had rather fancied the idea of moving to a remote village on the coast of Turkey, which some friends had visited on holiday, where I could be a subsistence farmer, putting to use the agricultural skills that I had failed to perfect over the previous decade in a climate that would not dump a couple of million tons of snow on my head every winter.

My wife had vetoed the idea on the grounds that educational opportunities for our two children would have been limited. I argued that a fluent command of Turkish would prove immensely useful to them in their future lives; after all, they would be unlikely to encounter many rivals when they applied for all those jobs that demand that candidates are bilingual in the language. The children agreed with me but we were overruled and we had moved into a nice peaceful English village. There we sat very happily until my wife decided that it was time that she moved to a larger house because she thought she could make lots of extra money doing Bed and Breakfast.

It was actually a very good idea. The village had that certain something that attracted the tourists. It housed about a thousand people and served a much larger rural community in the surrounding area. It had its butcher, its baker and its candlestick-maker whose establishments, mainly under thatched roofs, straggled down from the church, past the village hall towards the river. It was a good quality river, too. Not one of those lowland water courses that oilily meander their way through dreaming cows and dying elms, picking up old prams and effluvia from the towns that they pass through, but a fast flowing upland river that came tumbling down from the moorlands high above the village, crashing round the boulders that strewed its bed to hit the sea about ten miles further downstream. It was home for dippers, kingfishers and even the odd otter or two.

The river was the original reason for the village's existence as it guarded each side of a medieval bridge that had seen the passage of centuries of sheep, cattle and horses cross on their way to markets of the lowlands. The river had also made the village an industrial centre in its day. A massive weir above the village allowed water to be drawn off to power five mills which had once ground corn, weaved cloth, made paper and sawn logs for the locality. Now only the cloth mill remained in production, churning out crude ties and chunky woollen garments that could stop a bullet, over which the tourists picked like starlings when they came to view their rural heritage during the summer months.

The presence of the tourists created a curious atmosphere in the village. In winter, there were very few and the locals could get on with their lives in peace. In summer it could not be. The streets and the surrounding countryside were clogged with them as they peered through the windows of people's houses and gawped at those of us who were trying to get on with our jobs as if we were another species. One could not help feeling a certain kinship with those remote tribes that are suddenly invaded by a BBC film crew or with a pair of chimpanzees in a zoo, busy making sweet love when they suddenly realise that they are being watched by thirty young teenagers from the local comprehensive school. It induced in the villagers a feeling of defensiveness and a tendency to act out the parts that we were expected to play and this certainly helped to breed eccentrics.

The house to which we moved lay at the bottom of the village, fronting right onto the river. It was the last mill on the line, a retired corn mill which had to make do with its water fifth hand after everyone else had powered their wheels from its passage. The millstream forked, for some unfathomable reason, just behind the house and both branches dived beneath it to emerge into the river through holes in the walls which edged the garden.

It was the sort of house that you need to be a bit of a sucker to end up with. It was pretty, certainly, washed white and facing the water with a steeply wooded hillside rising up on the far side of the river, just far enough away to allow the sun to shine through the windows for most of the day. But it was large, leaky and virtually impossible to heat without the aid of a private oil well but with the happy attribute of always seeming able to produce another room just when we thought we had discovered the lot and brought them all into use. The house provided ample room for the family and left the two best bedrooms available to house the B & B guests from whom so much money was intended to flow. It could be made to sound quite attractive in our advertisement 'Riverside Mill, own fishing on salmon river, private bathroom, etc.'. The etc. masked the fact that the private bathrooms had been created by a predecessor by the simple process of raising a stud wall across the already tiny room. The wall neatly bisected the only double-seater fully flushing loo that I had ever come across, created by the legendary Thomas Crapper himself. It was a distressingly intimate experience to use this loo while the stall on the other side of the partition was occupied. The noise which echoed round the plumbing coupled with the raspberries released by one's companion could induce a feeling of great inadequacy.

The other difficulty about maintaining the illusion of luxury that we tried to foster, was that the walls of both the bedrooms grew a particularly vigorous type of fungus which only retreated if the windows were left open in all weathers or it was attacked every other day with a scrubbing brush and bleach. Apart from that and the fact that the roof leaked when it rained and the televisions that we thoughtfully provided in the rooms worked only fitfully, both because of the age of the sets and because the signal from the transmitter had to wend

17

its way across and through miles of wood and hill to reach the wire coathanger aerials, we claimed to offer the epitome of rural comfort.

The first guests turned up before we had a chance to de-fur the bedroom wall and we bounced them on to a neighbour. It is a friendly trade in that we bed and breakfasters scratch each others' backs by passing on to each other customers that cannot be accommodated or look as if they might pinch the towels. The next lot turned up at Easter when we were all ready for them. They actually caught me in my underpants. One of the curiosities of the house is that there is a perspex panel set into the floor of the hall through which one can observe one of the millstreams should the need arise. I had casually glanced through it and seen a five-pound note lying on the bottom of the stream. I whipped off my clothes and was under the house snorkelling for it before it had a chance to drift away. Dripping but triumphant I emerged in time to greet our guests, a French family of six.

Their number presented a bit of a problem as we only had two bedrooms but the thought of all those potential pound notes quickly led to the children being banished to the garage with sleeping bags to share with the dog and the smaller foreigners were installed amid the Lego in their place.

The weekend was nearly a disaster. It all began when my wife produced a spot on the end of her nose just before they arrived. It was not a very large spot, but it was an enormously comic one and she was rather sensitive about it. Madame, one of those dapper little Frenchwomen who are always ruthlessly corseted to maintain their chic, was the official translator for the party and her fractured English broke into smithereens when she was distracted by the glowing presence of the spot and lost concentration on the subject in hand.

Her family took over the house like a bus party loose in a souvenir shop. A couple of their plump and earnest children tried to go fishing in the river while Monsieur flapped over them like a broody hen in case they were taken by sharks. The other two infants made contact with ours and they all played carefully and politely with each other, each pair trying to conceal their pity and contempt at the other's inability to speak a sensible language that people could understand. That night my wife came out in polka dots and said that she felt ghastly. She looked ghastly too, and was obviously not the sort of sight that could be paraded in front of our guests. They would have started to scratch and wonder about bedbugs.

I was detailed to take over the breakfast which I did with considerable skill although the foreigners made it clear that they did not share my taste for crispy crunchy bacon and instant coffee of a strength that cauterises the ulcers that it creates in the first place by refusing to touch either. It is part of the duty of a bed and breakfast host to make conversation with the guests, or so my wife informed me; and so, after my culinary efforts had been completed, I entered the dining-room rubbing my hands together in an unctuous fashion, ready to make perceptive remarks about the chances of rain. The parents were involved in earnest conversation while their children were playing tiddly-winks with rashers of bacon on the tablecloth.

'What is this spert?' asked Madame.

It was an extremely oblique start to our conversation and one that had me floundering in the search for the conventional response. 'Spert. Ah, no, we call it bacon. It is a little crisp, perhaps.' The rashers were beginning to break up under the strain and the dog was busy hoovering them up as they tumbled from the table. I longed to clip the brats about their ears and tell them to behave but, for all I knew, gross table manners were encouraged on the other side of the Channel.

'No, your child. She say she is spert.' I was damn sure no child of mine had ever declared that she was spert, but it was clearly a point of considerable import as both Monsieur and Madame were staring at me fixedly. 'Your wife,' continued Madame helpfully. A great light dawned. Peter Sellers in *The Pink Panther* had been on television a week or two earlier.

'Spots. My wife has spots.'

'That is what I say to mean,' said Madame beaming at me. I beamed back for a while before I realised that the original mention of spots had been in the form of a question and thus an answer was called for. It was a bit of a dilemma. These charming Frogs represented £40 a day and a sinister plague-like disease creeping round the house would be likely to drive them screaming away to find a safer haven in which to spend their *vacances à Pâques*. On the other hand I could hardly deceive them and thus leave them open to the risk of contracting typhus or whatever was the cause of the sperts.

'Sperts,' I said, my eyes limp with integrity, 'is how we say headache, you know like migraine!'

'Headache! Ah. Migraine. Poor Madame. I too am a sufferer from sperts. Tell her that I feel for her. My husband. He too feels for her.' I knew all about randy Frenchmen, but he was unlikely to want to do much feeling for her in her current state. The family departed for the day to examine the quaint English countryside while the doctor was called in to examine my poxy spouse. The spots were diagnosed as chicken-pox and she stopped feeling ghastly and just felt itchy instead. I gave her all the sympathy of one who had sensibly taken the precaution of having the disease as a child. It was obvious that my wife would have to remain incommunicado for the weekend as I had embarked upon a course on which there was no turning back. So I carried the television up to her bedroom and installed the record-player, bunches of grapes and all the other accoutrements that make for an enjoyable illness.

Madame had other ideas. That evening when the family returned with their day safely tucked away inside their Instamatic, she began to organise me.

'Monsieur, I too am a sufferer from sperts. It is a terrible affliction, *n'est-ce pas?*' I nodded gravely. 'I have purchased this medicine which helps my sperts most agreeably. Now your wife must take this and have no noise and her room must always be dark until the sperts have subsided.'

I passed on the medicine and the advice to my wife but the solicitations of Madame quite ruined her convalescence. The TV and record-player had to remain silent as our guests tiptoed round the house holding their breath and the slightest sound from the sickroom brought frantic French admonitions of dismay. Reading was a dangerous business as well since the bedroom curtains had to remain drawn to keep out the light and Madame patrolled the garden and peered under the door to ensure that her rules were obeyed. My unfortunate wife had to creep downstairs in the early hours of the morning to exercise and feed and passed an uncomfortable half hour in the larder when Monsieur came down to raid the fridge. I considered his behaviour going rather beyond the bounds normally allowable to a guest but, under the circumstances, there was very little that could be done about it.

Easter Sunday was a splendid event. Madame had bought up the stock of the local sweet shop and she and I hid eggs in all the corners of the garden and the children and the dog amused themselves for most of the morning until they had to be sick in the river. The family stayed for four days. Madame took over all the cooking eventually and her culminating evening meal of sauce-smothered veal was a masterpiece of French cuisine. My wife crept downstairs after they had gone to help me count the lovely roll of new notes that they left. There was even a bonus as, for the next few months, the dreaded chore of gardening was enlivened by the frequent event of turning up an Easter egg which I would hurriedly bolt before the children spotted it.

B & B guests provided a rich source of interest. For a week we housed an ancient gentleman who always wore baggy shorts and passed his waking hours dabbling his toes in the river while reading Tolkien at the top of his voice to an interested audience of cattle on the opposite bank. We even had a well-known comedian to stay for a dirty weekend with his floozie. 'Well-known' was actually his description since I have never met anyone who has heard of him, but he arrived in a large American car carefully chosen to ensure his anonymity. He knocked at the door on a Friday afternoon which is a Pavlovian signal to my wife to grab a bottle of bleach and rush upstairs to scrape from the walls any mould that may have appeared since the departure of the last visitor. I answered the door, a chore that was not much fun since I was instructed to ooze charm and salesmanship in vast quantities in order to persuade the callers to stay. The more sensible and reticent visitors tended to recoil in horror in face of my fixed and ghastly grin while others considered me stand-offish.

On this occasion, no great effort was required. To make our guest feel at home, you did not have to say anything. All that was required was a reasonably convincing attempt at hearty laughter whenever he paused sufficiently long in his interminable conversation to suggest that he had reached the punchline of that particular joke. I had better call him Maxie. Maxie was festooned in lovely blond curls that came down to his shoulders. This was his disguise to fool the hordes of fans whom he hoped would be dogging his footsteps. It was apparently the wig he wore when he was playing the most famous of the characters with which he wowed the club audiences of the North. The wig, combined with his enormous belly and his penchant for wearing a red catsuit, made him a remarkable and striking figure which would have stampeded horses wherever he went.

In this gear, he spent the weekend prowling the village looking for fans. He was quite a responsibility. We had a telephone call from the police answering machine which was enquiring whether Maxie was staying with us. He had interpreted the incredulous stares of some of the local citizens as recognition and had cracked outrageously obscene jokes at them from his repertoire until one of them had reported him. Maxie's floozie was equally striking. She was gallantly struggling to remain twenty, a good fifteen years younger than he, and was the epitome of a dumb 1950s American starlet. Blonde, very beautiful except for her bulging gum-chewer's cheek muscles, she tottered after Maxie in plum-coloured boots with stiletto heels that drilled holes in the tarmac as she went.

Maxie and his floozie were such an interesting departure from the human norm that we asked them to dine with us in the evening and even asked some friends round to join us so that we could not be thought to be selfishly keeping to ourselves such rare treasures. Maxie was delighted to perform for us, having been confident that we would be unable to keep the presence of a celebrity such as himself living under our roof to ourselves. During a lull in the stream of dreadful jokes which Maxie inflicted on us after dinner, the floozie managed to get a word in edgeways.

'Martha and I were comparing our bottoms last week. Martha thought hers was prettier than mine. What do you think, Maxie?' As an opening remark, it was quite a conversation-stopper. Maxie paused for thought while the rest of us waited in anticipation for his verdict.

'You can't compare an orchid to a rose, Bernice.'

'Who's Martha?' I asked.

'Martha's Maxie's wife,' replied Bernice. 'I sometimes live with her.'

There was a stunned and respectful silence as we all tried to grapple with the problems that such a relationship would create. Our part of the world was littered with illicit love affairs just like anywhere else, but we did not operate with quite such urban panache. I longed to ask for a detailed exposition but my wife kicked me under the table as I opened my mouth.

We moved through into the sitting-room where Maxie ran through his act for our benefit. It was very droll, too, in a

Northern clubby sort of way. It was Bernice who managed to make the evening truly memorable.

'Do you do any work?' she asked me.

'Sometimes,' I replied.

'Oh good, I do too.'

'Yeah,' said Maxie.

'What do you do?' I asked politely, having a reasonable suspicion that it might not be the sort of work that her grey-haired granny might approve of.

'I'm a writer,' said she.

'Yeah, she's a great writer.' It was a bit like seeing a pig with wings before one's very eyes. One of the basic skills required by a writer is that of penmanship, and I had had to fill out her cheque for her when she had bought up the contents of the local woollen mill that afternoon. She may well have left her glasses behind in Leeds as she had claimed, but I had assumed that was a euphemism for not having completed her degree.

'What sort of things does she write?' asked my wife. Bernice was so obviously a decoration of Maxie that she automatically put the question to him rather than to her.

'Bernice writes novels. Don't you, Bernice?'

Bernice simpered modestly, 'Yes. I'm writing a book about love.'

'Yeah. It's great. You should read the dirty bits,' said Maxie. 'They're about the seamiest stuff I've ever seen. The book's going to sell millions.'

'Yes it is,' said Bernice.

'Mind you,' continued Maxie. 'I still think your best stuff is the things you write about mothers.'

'Mothers?' I prompted faintly.

'Yeah. I'm thinking of getting them made up in enamel so that people can hang them on their walls. They're like mottoes. Give us a sample, Bernice.'

Bernice sat up straight on the sofa with Maxie looking up adoringly at her from the floor where he had spread himself out like a punctured bean-bag. With the reverential air that one might expect a priest to employ at a funeral service, she solemnly intoned:

'Mother dear, mother dear, when I'm with you, I never fear.' She broke the silence that followed this announcement with 'How can I ever love another with you still alive, my old sweet mother.'

Maxie choked back a sob. 'There's nothing you can say after something as beautiful as that. Is there?' He was quite right. None of us could think of anything to say.

Chapter Two

EVERY AUTUMN, the salmon would come up the river to spawn. When they reached our stretch of the river, some of them would turn right and flog their way up the millstream that ran under the house and weave their way through the skeleton of rusting metal that was all that was left of the millwheel that teetered drunkenly at the back of the house. They easily evaded my attempts to catch them with either hook or harpoon and would copulate and then die further upstream after which their decaying but still massive remains would drift down to pile up against the grille that prevented the river in spate from hurling trunks of trees down the millstream and shattering the wheels that had once powered the village.

It must be one of life's sweetest luxuries to be able to amble gently across one's garden of a summer's evening and cast a pensive fly into a good trout and salmon river. Success we never guaranteed. In fact, actually having my fly taken by a trout was such an unusual event that my reaction was usually a mild panic mixed with irritation that the essentially peaceful nature of the pursuit should be interrupted by the inevitably sardine-sized trout that would cover my fingers in slime as I tried to get it to disgorge my hook so that it could be returned to the river.

A few hundred yards downstream, there squatted a large Victorian fishing hotel, all brown walls and faded Persian rugs where geriatric generals and admirals pottered among the stuffed fish and racks of old rods. They spent their days flogging the river pools that had names like the Devil's Cauldron and the Black Hole. It took me a long time to understand how the hotel managed to attract so many fishing visitors since I presumed that their mileage of river must have been about as barren as our yardage. But then I realised that between them and us lay a trout farm from which a continual trickle of fat and stupid fish were washed from the safety of their batteries to be snagged by the barbs that rheumy hands dangled in front of their noses further downstream.

Our stretch of the river was more rigorous water. Only one fat rainbow ever had the initiative to swim upstream rather than allow itself to drift down and it fought with all the enthusiasm of the old gumboot that I had thought I had hooked, until it surrendered at my feet and allowed me to cradle it gently towards the frying pan. The little brown trout, on other other hand, were as streetwise as only fish that inhabit a river that runs through a village can ever hope to be. During the school holidays, the opposite bank to the mill twenty-five yards across the river was lined by small boys with spinning rods. They hurled all manner of piscine delicacies into the river — from maggots to Lymeswold — and any fish without the analytical ability of Einstein and the survivability of Bugs Bunny ended up on a piece of toast for tea before it had had a chance to find out what life was all about.

I had little chance. I was a purist, tossing in a bundle of hair and feathers to compete against all manner of succulent alternatives. My pleasure came from the evening peace, the babble of the river and the satisfaction of being able to place my fly exactly where I wanted to at the end of a dead straight line with hardly a splash. The fish and I grew to know each other. The best of them, which must have weighed a couple of pounds, spent his time swimming at the point where one of our millstreams emerged from under the garden and into the river. It was quite impossible to catch him as a fly or any other sort of lure was snatched away from him by the current as soon as it touched the water above his head. I would sit on the wall above his tunnel exit and we would nod a greeting to each other as I settled down to casting out into the river and he busied himself by feeding on all the goodies that the stream had picked up during its progress through the village. If anyone but me came to the wall and looked down at him, he would cruise cautiously into the tunnel and disappear.

That particular fish became a crusade for Mike Weaver. Mike's profession was that of cowman on a nearby farm and he ran a herd of a hundred cows with supreme competence without ever having bothered to learn more than enough to write his signature or read the figures on his wage-slip. There are a surprising number of country people whose education is just as rudimentary, but it is not the result of incompetent rural teachers or of stupidity on the part of their pupils. It is just that school has to compete with so many more interesting and profitable ways of passing the time. One old farmer of my acquaintance told me proudly that he had had two years of schooling before the pull of the land proved too strong to be resisted. He used to reminisce fondly about his schooldays as if they had been his undergraduate days at Oxford.

'Them were the days. I had to walk five miles across the fields every day to school and then back again in the afternoon. I learned all sorts of interesting things.'

'Like what?'

'Like . . . er . . . Did you know that it would take a horse and cart twenty-five years to go to the moon?'

'Really?'

'It's true. I would never have known that if I had not had the benefit of an education. Times were harder then. You know, all my mother could afford to give me for my dinner was a bit of bread and some pork fat?'

'Is that all?' It sounded lamentably unsatisfactory to me as a late twentieth-century fat-cat. Obviously the farmer decided that I was in danger of getting the wrong impression.

'Mind you,' he added hastily, 'Mother made sure that it was the very best pork fat.'

Mike was a product of the Welfare State which tries to ensure that its sons and daughters reach their full educational potential by keeping them at school until they reach the age of sixteen. But the system had no chance against Mike's passion for poaching. It was embedded deep in his genes by generations of his ancestors who had poached pheasants, used their bows and arrows against the King's deer and probably snatched caribou from under the noses of sabre-toothed tigers.

Mike was a lovely man. On the surface a shy monosyllabic

countryman like so many, but when one tapped into one of his interests or passions, he came alive and communicated it with an enthusiasm and a vividness that painted pictures which lived for his hearers. Mike had really wanted to be a gamekeeper as his knowledge of the countryside was phenomenal, built up over endless warm summers spent lying in the woods on his belly watching the wildlife pass in front of his eyes while his contemporaries were locked in classrooms. He was particularly skilled as a salmon poacher and knew exactly when and where to go to find a migrating fish. He did not even have to look but could go, as I saw him do, to a rock in the river and plunge his homemade trident into the eddy to pull out a wriggling fish.

That was dull work, however. Too much skill and knowledge had taken the uncertainty out of the chase for him. Even the water bailiffs knew that he was too clever to be caught by them and had taken the spice out of his poaching by not bothering to chase him. So my trout was a worthy challenge. 'My' is, perhaps, the wrong word. The fish was very much its own master. The wall above the tunnel entrance was covered in ivy and so Mike first tried to stalk it across the lawn and peer cautiously through the ivy and thrust a spear at it. I could have told him not to waste his time. The creature had no difficulty in spotting him and would disappear under the lawn with a flick of its tail.

He next tried dapping a fly on the water above the fish. It would have worked with most trout. Mike was an expert dapper. He ran through moths, daddy-long-legs, flies, grasshoppers and anything else he could think of or catch, dancing them above the water on a spider strand of nylon filament. But the fish had learned to ignore manna from heaven and to concentrate instead on the jetsam from the village that floated past its nose.

Mike took note of its preferences and started laying his ground bait. At the point where the stream plunged into its tunnel to go under the house, he cast bread upon the waters. The trout could hardly believe its luck. Since I was a regular part of the fish's landscape, Mike had me posted on the wall to observe its reaction as the bread pellets went past. It did not

29

miss any of them and gave me a courteous smile in gratitude for this bounty as I had idly chucked bread and cheese pellets at it in the past. I had not told Mike that the fish was used to being hand fed as he would have tried it with a hook inside one of the pellets which would have spoilt everybody's fun. I was quite happy if he tried it the long way round. He floated some more pellets down the tunnel, the last of which had a hook and line attached. Mike was convinced that he would get the creature. I joined him to see if the fish was ready to be suckered. The bait went down the hole two or three times with no discernible result. I was posted back to the wall to see if it was getting through. It wasn't. The treacherous pellet was getting stuck somewhere in the tunnel.

Mike took off his shoes and socks and went to investigate. The fish was protected by a mesh of branches inside the tunnel around which the line had snagged and, thus, never reached its destination. It was becoming an obsessional contest between Mike and the fish. The trout had retired for the afternoon when Mike had gone down into the tunnel and so he left further developments until the next day. First thing in the morning, he crawled along into the tunnel once more to clear the obstruction. It took real dedication as it was damp, dark and little more than a yard in circumference with a foot of water running along the bottom.

Poor Mike nearly had heart failure. Something about which I had forgotten to warn him was that the tunnel was used as a flight path by a pair of dippers that skimmed through it just above the water and wheeled above the wreck of the millwheel before plunging beneath the house on the other stream where they fed a raucous family of chicks that wheezed and spluttered beneath the joists of our dining-room floor. Never in dipper history had there been an obstruction quite like Mike across their route and the bird's mind was obviously in neutral when it bored its way into the tunnel and flew straight into his face.

The shock and outrage on both sides must have been about equal. The dipper came out looking back over its shoulder as if the hounds of hell were gnawing at its tail feathers and retired to a stone in the middle of the river for an hour until its heart had ceased to palpitate. From Mike came a remarkable flow of fruity language, booming down the tunnel as he splashed his way out at all speed under the impression that he had been attacked by a vampire bat. Mike admitted defeat at that point. A fish that was protected with both entanglements and guided missiles was best left severely alone and the trout is still idly swimming at the tunnel entrance, growing plumper with every passing season.

However peaceful the art of casting could be on a pleasant summer evening as the bats patrolled the air above the water, vying with the rising trout to feed on the swarming mosquitoes and mayflies, it could have become dull if it had not been for the ducks. The stretch of river through the village supported about thirty of them — a horrendous motley crew that were fed by the tourists in summer and moved a few hundred yards upstream when winter came to avoid being put in the pot by the more hard-headed and hard-hearted locals.

They were mostly mallards that had been mongrelised by an assortment of farmyard escapes. In early spring, the drakes would pursue the furiously quacking ducks through houses, gardens and shops all over the village and would usually corner them in the main street where they would copulate feverishly in the middle of the road while the traffic would snarl up behind some tourist too soft hearted to run them over. Later on, the village would suffer a plague of ducklings which were a particular nuisance to us in the mill. A duckling or two a day would become detached from their mother higher up the millstream and, peeping frantically, they would sail down on the current before reaching slack water under the house where they would cheep up and down for an hour or two before giving up and floating out into the main river where they would be eaten with relish by their fathers. One either hardened one's heart to this or spent most of the day chasing ducklings in order to return them to their mothers.

I loathed them, their continual idiot quacking and their penchant for gang rape and cannibalism. The birds were dominated by a couple of muscovy drakes whose relationship and the enthusiasm with which they conducted it put Sodom and Gomorrah in the shade. These two birds regarded the mill garden as their own property and we human inhabitants as trespassers.

Ducks are revoltingly messy creatures and the larger the duck, the more revolting the mess it leaves behind. Muscovies are the jumbo jets of the duck world and they carefully placed their odiferous offerings all over the garden. It was an extremely unpleasant sensation to walk up the garden path after dark and feel oneself sliding from duck turd to duck turd until you eventually cannoned into their source which hissed and flapped its wings and tried to peck chunks out of your leg for interrupting its toilet.

It took a year of chasing them over the wall into the river before it dawned on them that I was not very fond of them and, moreover, was big enough and nasty enough to be able to do something about it. There is only one left now. There was a wonderful afternoon in the height of the summer when, to the delight of the locals and the horror of the tourists, a terrier belonging to a visitor plunged into the river and assaulted one of them by sinking its teeth firmly into its wing. Both growling dog and hissing drake floated off downstream and neither was ever seen again. It was felt that a memorial should be raised to the terrier.

In an environment as aquatic as that of the mill, weather was a topic of peculiar interest. It was not seen as such when we first moved in. Floods? Oh floods. Come to think of it, the house was flooded about forty years ago. It did not seem something worth worrying about although it was disconcerting to discover that the insurance companies took a rather less sanguine view of the matter. The firm that we had used on previous occasions sent out their surveyor who donned his gumboots and disappeared underneath the house with his torch for about an hour. We would have sent down a potholing rescue team to search for him in case he drowned but the flashes of his torch were visible through the perspex panel in the hall and, at intervals, he would fill it with his backside as he ferreted around in the tunnels.

He eventually emerged, pale, cobweb covered but triumphant.

'Are you all right?' I asked.

'Yes, Quite remarkable property this, you know.' He was slightly flushed.

'Did you know that you have not one but two streams running under your house and that the river itself is only forty feet away?'

'Yes, of course I knew.'

'There's also an astonishing colony of rats down there. They're huge, as big as cats. There's one enormous nest and there are all sorts of things in it.'

'What do you mean "all sorts of things"?' My wife was looking a bit uneasy but rats have never done me any harm although I was beginning to go off the man. It has always been obvious to me that the only size to which it is possible for a rat to grow is rat size (adult) and a cat-sized rat is as likely as a rook-sized sparrow or a partridge-sized wasp.

'Well, they've got what looks like a Ford Cortina down there.' Not even a wild surmise entered my brain. The man was obviously a raving nutter.

'A red one?' asked my wife.

'Yes,' replied the surveyor.

'So that's where it went!'

'I'm having a bit of difficulty with this discussion,' I said. 'Do I understand that we have a red Cortina in a rat's nest under the house?'

'Yes. It was in one of the Christmas stockings and got left in the garden and disappeared.'

'A toy car!' I said. This collected a couple of rather puzzled looks so I hurried on. 'Anyway, will you give the house flood cover?'

'Flood cover!' said the surveyor. 'Good heavens no. I couldn't possibly do that. The whole house looks as if it is quite likely to float off its foundations and drift out to sea at any moment. I could tell that the place was uninsurable the moment I arrived. Now fire is quite a different matter. With the amount of damp that you've got in these walls, it would have still been standing after the Great Fire of London.' I had quite definitely gone off him by this stage. He had a large earwig on his tie that looked as if it was going to crawl inside his shirt. I mentally wished it a long and safe journey.

33

'Why were you so long down there if you knew it was uninsurable?'

'It was most exciting. I found three five-pound notes.' He produced three sodden and wormeaten fivers from his pocket of which I promptly relieved him. I was uncertain of the law on this point but he was considerably smaller than I was. Money has a delightful habit of turning up in the bottom of the stream during the summer. How it gets there is a total mystery, but get there it does. The surveyor put up a loud and vigorous protest at my confiscation which only ceased when the ear-wig apparently dug its pincers into his left nipple and I slammed the front door on him leaving him to sort out his problems for himself.

We eventually found an insurance company which was unwary enough not to have asked the 'liable to flooding' question in its proposal form and then we forgot all about such matters. At least we forgot all about them until the autumn monsoons started. The river had its source high on the moors above the village and since moorland is either permanently saturated or else honeycombed by modern field drainage, water ran straight off into the river which had an unsettling habit of rising two or three feet in an hour.

The summer condition of the river was a chuckling pellucid waterway across which it was comparatively simple to walk in nothing more than a pair of gumboots. When it rained on the moor, it became an ugly brown torrent which roared and foamed its way past the garden wall, bearing trees and unwary caravans and general detritus of gargantuan proportions at about twenty miles per hour.

It was one Sunday morning at about 10 am that we heard an apologetic knock at the door. It was Percy. Percy was the local bobby whose boss was the answering machine. He was the most unpolicemanlike policeman that I have ever met. His great problem was that he never had any crime to deal with, and a policeman without any crimes is like a bull without balls; he eventually becomes transformed into another kind of creature. Percy had become a gossip. He had to, really. The average town policeman is rushed off his feet by the amount of business that his urban customers throw at him. Country policemen would never have anything to do at all if they did not gossip, as countrymen close ranks against any outsiders so the policeman has to talk his way gently into a position of trust before he is allowed to be any use. Percy had been at it for twenty-five years and he could gossip anyone under the table.

I had quite recently heard about his crime. Percy had had a real crime over the summer and had got quite excited about it.

'I was called up by Mr Bevis, you know he runs the grocer's shop, and it was old Mrs Masters. She had had her purse taken from her shopping bag. Now Mrs Masters can't afford to lose her purse since her husband died. I helped her to fill in her income tax form last year and she has got very little. Anyway Mrs Masters knew who had done it. I thought it was quite likely to be Richard Southcott, when Mr Bevis phoned, but no, it was one of the young Scotts, she said. Well straight away I knew it must have been young Henry Scott. They're always causing trouble, that family. You remember a year or two back when old man Scott said that Mr Pincombe had taken his shovel? The silly old fool had just left it in his vegetable garden, it turned out. I think he was just trying to cause trouble because he had a fight with Mr Pincombe during the war over that landgirl who worked up on the moor. The one who went off eventually with that American airman.'

You could not stop Percy once he had got going and what citizen in his right mind would ever rebuff a policeman when he was being friendly? It was while he was going on like this that it was wise to pay attention, because, in the same monotonous tone of voice, he would tell you that it had been reported to him that your car, gun or dog licence had run out and that he would have to take action the following week. If you had fallen asleep, the first you would know about it was when Percy turned up with the summons wearing a disapproving look on his face.

'As I was saying, young Henry Scott said that he hadn't taken Mrs Masters' purse and he wouldn't be daft enough to take hers even if he wanted to nick one because everyone knew she was broke. I said that Mrs Masters said that it had been him and he said she was a silly old fool and that he had an alibi anyway.' Percy looked thoughtful 'I'm going to have to keep my eye on young Henry. It looks as if he might be a bit brighter than most of the Scotts, don't you think so?' I agreed while wondering precisely what Percy said about us to everyone else in the village.

'Anyway, young Henry and I went along to see Mrs Masters and do you know what?'

'What?'

Percy began to heave with gentle laughter. 'It wasn't one of the Scotts at all but a Scot.' I must have looked as baffled as Percy did in the original situation. 'You know, a Scot. One of those laddies from north of the Border. There were a bunch of kids from Glasgow camping out by the river over the weekend and it must have been one of them, but they'd all gone by the time I got there.'

However, Percy at 10am was not usual, particularly on a Sunday.

'Good morning, sir.' He always 'sirred' if the conversation was official or if he had some purpose in view. It was the 'sir' that notoriously alerted you to keep your ears open during the subsequent conversation in case someone had reported you for having bald tyres. In the countryside, shop thy neighbour is one of the facets of life that you just have to learn to live with.

'There's a flood warning out.' That was the information that Percy had to pass on. The river was apparently rising dangerously about five miles upstream and it was being fuelled by rain falling on and melting six inches of snow that covered the higher ground. At the bottom of the garden, the river was looking much as it always did during the less tranquil periods of its existence, but it did not stay that way for very long. It began to rise, visibly, and, as the word got around that the river might flood, half the village went up to the bridge to watch the fun from there and it seemed as if the remaining half came, with their bottles of whisky, into our living-room to watch from there, where there was at least a roof over their heads to keep the rain off.

The river rose inexorably. The water was hurtling past capped by great brown rollers littered with dead sheep and entire trees. It became apparent that it was not just the river that needed an eye kept on it. The millstreams were backing

36

up as their exit was impeded by the height of the water and, through the perspex panel in the hall one could watch the still water slowly creeping up the inside of the tunnel. It was an unpleasantly hypnotic sight. We would note the position of a stone in the wall and watch it until it was covered. It was not a steady rise, but one that went in fits and starts so one could always hope that the water might have started to recede. It would stay where it was and then suddenly lurch upwards an inch or two before pausing and perhaps sinking an inch before it rose again.

There was a heated debate going on in the sitting-room as the level in the whisky bottles sank and the water slowly crept up the garden path, swallowing up the duck turds in its advance.

'I think we ought to start moving the furniture upstairs,' I said.

'Don't be daft. It never floods here. Well, only once in forty years.'

'The forty years is up, so it must be about due again.'

There was a chorus of optimism from all the villagers present. I was very grateful for their presence even though it did look like being very expensive in whisky. It was already clear that the most important factor needed to successfully survive a flood was to have plenty of willing furniture humpers around. Although you need to strike a fine balance between providing them with enough alcohol to make them want to stay and giving them too much which makes them incapable of work.

'It's still coming up fast,' I said, keeping a nervous watch on the garden path.

'Don't worry. It's got to rise a couple of feet before it comes in the house.'

'I still think we ought to start moving some of this stuff upstairs,' I said obstinately.

The expert was unmoved. He was Colin, a man of about fifty with a straggling beard who was the water bailiff at the fishing hotel downriver. He had actually been a life insurance salesman in his youth with a beat in the City of London, but he was deeply ashamed of his urban background and the locals were too polite ever to mention it. 'But it would be a complete waste of time if the river started to go down just as we had got everything out of the way and, anyway, who's to say it will stop rising if it comes into this room? What's to stop it keeping going and flooding the next floor and then we'd look proper bloody twits taking all the furniture upstairs.'

'Go on with you,' said another villager. 'It'll never get that deep.'

'How do you know?' asked Colin.

'Well if it did, the water would be coming into my own house.'

'It probably will.' That exchange lost me one of my humpers and so I plied Colin with another whisky in an attempt to stop him spreading fear and despondency among my troops. The major problem was clear. There was an extremely skilful judgement to be made about the precise moment at which we should start to panic. Too soon and the water goes down and you have done all that work for nothing. There again, if the panic button is pressed too late, the water comes in before all the furniture is out of the way and you will feel an even bigger twit for having wasted so much time sitting about when you had plenty of time to shift all the stuff out of the way. An experienced flood victim grows to realise that speed of rise is the all-important factor. A flood that has a lot of growing to do is the one that comes up quickly. On this occasion, our timing was pretty good. What I had got wrong was the precise dosage of whisky that it is safe to inject into the humpers. I had gone slightly over the top and their humping ability was impaired which meant that there was still one small and unimportant room to be cleared as the water rose majestically through the floor, through the doors and through the windows. Once the carpet was wet, it was too late and so we left it.

With most of our furniture upstairs, we could afford to make a general assessment of the situation and so we gathered together our drink-sodden crew and reeled down to the bridge to take a look. It was very impressive. The river normally had about twelve feet of clearance underneath the arches of the bridge, but the water was flowing over the top carrying about twenty times its normal volume. It had spread across the small field on the opposite side of the bank from the mill and had formed a subsidiary river that was flowing through an assortment of back gardens before breaking against our house and rejoining the main stream.

Back at home, the water was still rising. It was about a foot deep throughout the ground floor when I had a sudden flash of genius and turned off the electricity supply just before the sockets went under. There was a distinct flow of water through the house and, the supreme horror, the remaining muscovy drake was paddling happily round in the sitting-room with my wife regarding it balefully from the top of a step-ladder.

Then the cavalry arrived. A large man stuck his head round the sitting-room door and grinned at us from under his sou'wester.

'Afternoon, my dears. Where would you like me to put them?'

He did not seem to be at all fazed to see me splashing round the room trying to clobber the duck with an empty whisky bottle. I paused to hurl the bottle at the bird but it missed and created a splash that soaked a Victorian watercolour of a cow that hung on the wall.

'Where would I like what put?' I asked.

'All the sandbags. We've brought a load of sandbags from the council depot to stop the water coming in.'

'Look about you,' said my wife, paraphrasing Wren's monument. 'What do you see?'

He looked. 'Water, I suppose, and that bloke is chasing a duck.'

'Aha! So you've spotted it.'

'What?'

'The water,' she said.

'Yes, of course, that's why we've brought the sandbags.'

I decided to stop chasing the duck. Every time I got near it, it started to flap its wings to accelerate away from me and it was making me wet.

'What's the point of bringing us sandbags after we're flooded?' I asked. He looked at me in a puzzled fashion, thought about it for a bit and decided that it was probably best if he started again.

'I'm from the Council and we've got a load of sandbags on the truck outside and they're free.' He looked round encouragingly. 'What you do with them is put them in doorways and places like that to stop the water coming in.' I was beginning to wonder if he had been at the whisky with even more enthusiasm than myself.

'What's your name?' I asked.

'Roy.'

'Look, Roy. It's no bloody good putting down sandbags once the water is already in. There's a proverb about it — horses and stable doors.' Roy seemed at last to be near the point of grasping what I was trying to say.

'You mean you don't want the bags because they are too late.' My wife broke into spontaneous applause. She was not feeling in a very tolerant mood since we had run out of wine and she did not like whisky. Besides the duck had made her even wetter than it had made me. Roy was not a man to give up easily. 'But you might need them next time.'

'If all goes according to schedule, next time will be in 2023 by which time we'll be dead or will have sold the house.'

Roy decided to change tactics. 'Look. I've had my instructions to deliver forty-five sandbags here and I've got to do it.' Situations like that put iron in one's soul and I refused to weaken. 'Dump them on someone further up the village who hasn't had the water in yet. Anyway, I'm told the bags are full of red sand which leaves a stain on the wall.'

'Who told you that? It's nonsense.'

'What's on your hands?' I demanded. He looked guiltily down at his meat-plate hands with the tell-tale red stain on them.

'Yeah, well, anyway.'

I could see that the conversation could have gone on for ever and the level of the water had risen to the point where I was having to stand on tiptoe to avoid having my gumboots fill up. There then entered another saviour in the form of the fire brigade. The fireman was actually the local undertaker, the brigade being composed of enthusiastic amateurs who trained furiously and hankered for more dramatic events than the sporadic haybarn fires which was the most that the Lord normally provided for them. They had looked longingly at the fishing hotel, all five storeys of it, ever since they had gone as a party to see *The Towering Inferno* at the cinema. The undertaker had been at the whisky like everyone else and sloshed his way in, wearing thigh boots which sent waves across the room which swamped the ordinary gumboots of both Roy and myself. Instinctively we ganged up against him.

'What the hell do you want, Harry?' asked Roy. 'Got nothing to do because you've wet your matches?'

This was ignored with the lofty disdain of the expert towards the unskilled amateur. 'We were wondering if you would like to borrow a pump.'

Colin pointed through the window at the river which was now half a mile across and looked like the Atlantic Ocean on a stormy day. 'Harry, I don't think your pump is going to do much good against that.' Harry looked out and scratched his head. Colin continued. 'Anyway, where do you reckon you're going to pump the water?'

'From the house, of course.'

'We know that, Harry, but what's the point of pumping it out if the level outside is the same as it is inside? There ain't no point in trying to bail out a boat if it's still under water. By the way, do you know when the tide goes out, Harry?'

'It turns in a couple of hours.'

It always baffled me but the state of the tide was firmly believed by the locals to be a critical factor in the level of the river. The river was tidal for only its last few hundred yards and the sea was ten miles away and five hundred feet lower down. Nevertheless it was firmly believed that the river went down as the tide went out. To me it was a bit like expecting the river above Niagara Falls to drop if the river below them dropped. The trouble was that nobody had ever bothered to discover the truth of this theory by observation. It was just considered to be too obvious to need to be checked.

Harry wandered off to try to rescue someone who might be a bit more appreciative and Colin supped some more of our whisky and went off with me to join the humpers who were now enjoying themselves further up the village in a house that was still a few inches above the flood level. The party was a little too heavy for my taste and I wandered off to join a breakaway group which was slightly more sober. The vicar joined me. He had come along to give succour to those in distress but the Spirit of the Lord had been unable to compete with the spirits of Glen Grant and so he had become one of the humpers. There was an interesting clash of flood cultures at this point. Roy had sneaked into the sixth house to be threatened before anyone else and, when we got there, he had managed to persuade the owner to put her faith in his sandbags rather than the humping team.

The householder was still in complete control. She was a Methodist who could only provide her homebrewed country wines which tasted as disgusting as all such concoctions. Experience had taught me that the best way to consume such creations is to hold your breath and gulp them down in the hope that you can become anaesthetised before the full horror of the taste overwhelms you. Roy had built a mighty rampart of rotproof sandbags in the doorway. Such was the faith of the householder in their efficiency that we had to remove our gumboots before we were allowed in so that we would not mess up the carpets which were still down. We were each given a glass of dandelion wine, uneasily appropriate in both colour and taste to the flower's local name of piss-a-bed, and sat down to wait.

The vicar was finding it all rather exciting. His was a group practice, although I believe that team ministry is the proper trade jargon, and he lived about five miles away so he was an enthusiastically participating spectator in our local crisis rather than drunkenly resigned to it like the rest of us. He was a dog collar and sports jacket type of parson and his gumboots were the authentic country gentleman's green with small ornamental straps at the top.

There is actually a highly precise social gradation in the gumboot and people tend to be very careful in choosing the variety that suits their own station in life. At the top of the ladder was the type that the vicar was wearing. They are rubber and have soles with metal studs on them and are extremely difficult to get on and off as they fit tightly to the leg, trying to ape the old cavalry boot. These are worn by gentlemen and those who would like to be considered gentlemen and are more fashion accessories than working feet covers.

Next down are green plastic boots which are worn by the more superior sort of working farmer who does not feel quite ready to take on full gentry status. The most common sort of boot, made from black plastic, is worn by anyone who wishes to keep their feet dry and warm and does not wish to make a social statement about themselves. At the bottom of the scale is the old fashioned rubber boot with its integral cotton lining. These are now only worn by ancient rustics. Since all the mud and dung that inevitably finds its way into the country boot tends to stick to this lining, these are responsible for the characteristic smell of rotting dung that often heralds the approach of an elderly farmworker. The only disadvantage of the plastic boot as compared with the rubber boot is that they tend to melt on hot days and end up round their wearer's ankles in a series of saggy folds — rather like woollen leg-warmers. Their inestimable advantage is that they can be easily swilled out should something noisome find its way into them.

All the boots were lined up in front of the protective sandbags. By the vicar's green ones stood Roy's. His were black rubber but were saved from ancient rusticity by having protective ribbing on the instep which marked them out as belonging to a specialist of some sort who needed to have his feet protected in case he dropped something on them. My own boots were blandly unclassifiable black plastic. I once considered investing in a pair like Colin's, which have a metal toecap, as I was always stubbing my big toe in the days when I was a dairy farmer. Fortunately I realised that the only reason that I stubbed my toe was because I kicked cows that were misbehaving up the backside or in the ribs and so I remained unprotected to ensure that I could never boot the animals hard enough to do them serious damage.

While I was lost in this reverie about the significance of boots, the others were still bravely knocking back the wine. It was Roy who first noticed and announced in tones of hurt outrage, 'Here, the water is coming in through the sandbags.'

We all turned and looked in dismay at a trickle of water that was seeping through between the two bags at the base of the pile. The seep became a pour as we watched.

'You stupid idiot,' shrieked the householder. 'What's the point of putting down sandbags if you leave a great big gap at the bottom?'

The Church took charge of the crisis. 'Quick everybody, get as much upstairs as we can.' The vicar grabbed a chair and bounded out of the sitting-room. Roy and I grabbed a sofa between us and followed him out with assorted others in pursuit. The furious woman who owned the place was carrying her budgie cage and a cat basket. We all ended up in the kitchen. 'Where are the stairs?' asked the vicar, looking wildly about him.

'The stairs?' replied the owner. 'There aren't any stairs. This is a bungalow.'

That was actually the high point of the flood. They say the tide turned at that point. Whatever the reason, the water receded even faster than it had come up. The humpers went home to try to sober up and we returned to the mill to watch three feet of water drain through the floor and out through the doors like a bath running out. Those who had built the house some centuries earlier had obviously known what they were about as the falls in the house ensured that all the water went away in the same way that urine in a cattle shed always runs out the door or down the drain.

Colin turned up the next day with a couple of blow heaters to dry off the damp patches that remained on the stone floors and we put back the carpets less than twenty-four hours after the flood waters had first come in. We learned from the experience. The most important lesson was that any crisis is best handled by ensuring a plentiful supply of whisky. If that is truly understood, then a flood can be really rather fun. We did not even claim on the insurance. The only damage was to the watercolour cow and the only expense was alcohol and for the latter, we were not covered.

Chapter Three

SHOOTING IS the archetypal country sport and, horrifying
though it may seem to the tender-hearted, the slaughter of
beasts for fur and feather is great fun. It is space invaders
made flesh and there are few country people who would not
grab at the chance of a day's shooting if it was offered to them.

Shooting in our part of the world was not quite like the
shooting that one reads about in the newspapers where
impeccably dressed Royals emotionlessly stroke thousands of
pheasants out of the skies of East Anglia. That school of
shooting reached its apogee at a Sandringham shoot in the
1920s when George V and a peer of the realm were at
adjoining stands when a covey of eight partridges came over.
Bang bang, went His Majesty. Bang bang, replied the peer.
There was a couple of seconds while they exchanged guns
with their respective loaders and they double banged again
and all eight birds were brought down. Each of the two
gentlemen involved instinctively knew which of the birds was
his and, of course, neither of them missed. They had achieved
the same level of skill as the teenager in the amusement arcade
whose spaceship is never gobbled up by the asteroids and, in
both pastimes, the thrill is much the same.

Shooting at that level is an enormously expensive business.
It is estimated that each shot pheasant has cost about £15 to
rear to its point of death. The rough country shooter, which is
the vast majority of us, can afford to rear few of such valuable
creatures. Our local shoot was very rough indeed. We shot
once a fortnight or so during the season over five farms whose
owners had clubbed together to provide a bit of fun for
themselves and their friends.

Our gamekeeper was Mike, when he could get away from his cows. We reared a few birds, or rather Mike did. We all chucked in a couple of fivers and Mike went and bought some pheasant eggs from a friend of his who specialised in the highly profitable trade of supplying day-old pheasant chicks to the smart shoots. These days the only difference between pheasants and broiler chickens is that one gets killed with electricity and the other gets its head blown off — they are both really domestic birds. Mike would obtain his eggs and stick them in an incubator where he would watch them with greater care and concern than their mothers would ever have done. He went away once for the weekend and asked me to take care of them. It was very nearly the end of a beautiful friendship. The eggs were supposed to be turned like toast at regular intervals to make sure that they were evenly cooked on both sides. On his return, I had been forced to admit, under close questioning, that I had been an hour late with their morning gyration because there was a tree down between me and the incubator. Death was the only excuse that he would have accepted and even then I would not have been permitted to go to enjoy my afterlife without first haunting another member of the syndicate to go and turn the eggs.

We had a lousy survival rate for our pheasants. It was not Mike's fault as his skill and dedication were unquestionable, but pheasant chicks have a deathwish that is quite remarkable. If there is the slightest draught in their enclosure, they will take turns at standing in front of it so that they can all catch pneumonia and die. If their keeper foils them by making it draught-free and putting in an infrared bulb to keep them warm, they solve the difficulty of dying by piling themselves up underneath the bulb so that those at the bottom suffocate.

We lost vast numbers of chicks in this way, if any proportion of a hundred could be described as vast. Mike finally sorted out the problem by lowering the heating light so that there was insufficient room for them to build a pyramid underneath it. This resulted in some very odd-looking adult birds that were as bald as the eggs they had come from. The chicks stood beneath the bulb and thrust their heads against it killing off all the head feathers. The practice also probably fried their brains but the creatures were so stupid at the best of times that it was impossible to tell.

Once the young pheasants were strong enough, Mike put them in an outside pen where they were fed up until they were capable of escaping over its fox-proof wire-netting walls and then they were about ready for the slaughter. There was an important factor to be considered before we started shooting. Our farms had the great good fortune to be adjacent to the estate of a country gent who tried to operate an efficient, East Anglian type of operation. So we had to ensure that we did not start until he and his smart friends had already been out because even birds as simple minded as the pheasant have sufficient wisdom to take evasive action when someone is trying to fill their backsides full of lead shot. So when the local aristocrats with their Purdeys and retrievers started to blast away, many of their birds would hop over the hedge and rough it in comparative safety with our own balding bunch.

This propensity for migration can cause much sorrow in the hearts of those who rear pheasants. I know one farmer who was in great need of a cash crop. He put down pheasants and leased out the shooting on a day basis to rich South Americans and Arabs. He should have made it as he farmed an island and the birds had no hedges to hop over into someone else's land. The great day of his first shoot dawned. All the chubby plutocrats lined up in their plus-fours and the drive began down the length of the island. The birds obediently took to the air in front of the guns. Pheasants, as I have said, are not very bright but they had enough intelligence to realise that there were options worth exploring as the guns opened up on them before they were within range. A huge cloud of birds whose numbers darkened the sky, wheeled smartly to port and crossed over the mile or so of the sea to the mainland where they settled on the forecourt of a garage. It was Christmas and birthday rolled into one for the mechanics who stuffed about fifty birds into sacks before the swarm moved off again and was seen no more. The last time I heard, litigation was still in progress.

We never had enough pheasants to know whether they migrated or not. The numbers were so low that a paucity would never have been noticed. Nevertheless, we took our shooting pretty seriously. On a shooting day, we would gather at about 10am which allowed time for the farmers amongst us to have milked and mucked out their cows or hurled the odd bale of hay at their sheep or bullocks. We would all turn up on Ivor's farm which was the most central and fill his yard with rusting motor cars, Land Rovers and hysterical dogs. All those who shoot have a theory that their own miserable hound, which spends most of its time snoring on a hearth rug in front of a fire, is a superb gundog.

I always took along our beast. It is actually some sort of terrier/Alsatian cross that was obtained from Battersea Dogs' Home and hence answers to the name of Battsy. It is extremely endearing as dogs go but has a wetness of disposition that defies description and is thus a great pain to live with. If I did not keep my wits about me, the beast would tiptoe up and attract my attention by thrusting her snout lovingly and painfully into my crotch and it is difficult to scream and kick an animal whose only failing is an excess of love. The creature is locally notorious. I was once walking through the village with the animal dogging my heel when a group of strange children came rushing up and started to fawn over her.

'Be careful, you stupid brats,' screamed a formidable mother. 'Never approach an unknown dog. You can never tell what it will do.'

One of the children, one of those angelic blonde female infants, turned her large eyes, as blue as a mandrill's backside, to her mother, and said, 'This isn't a dog, it's Battsy.'

In terms of being a coarse gundog, Battsy was excellent. The most important attribute in such an animal is to be there in the first place. A dog is considered as vital a part of the day's sport as your waterproof Barbour coat or your gun. The next most important thing is that the animal does what it is told. In this respect Battsy was without peer. There is nothing like a thoroughly miserable puppyhood spent in the back streets of London being stalked by suppliers of Indian restaurants wanting to turn you into meat vindaloo to drum in the virtues of pleasing your master for fear of being sent back to whence you originally came. When you said 'sit' to Battsy, the speed with which her backside hit the ground dented the turf and her nose wore a groove in my heel. Out in the shooting field, the dog stayed by my side like a leech, ignoring pheasants exploding from bushes and rabbits running across her tail. Her obedience was so unnatural that it attracted attention and I have persuaded several shooters that she is a highly bred and trained Hungarian pointer.

As far as the actual business of putting up and retrieving game was concerned, Battsy was, of course, totally useless. But so are ninety-five per cent of all gundogs on coarse shoots. At least Battsy did not actually detract from the purpose of the day. She did no good but she did not do any harm either. Most coarse gundogs do some good when they feel like it, but it is usually entirely outweighed by the damage they cause.

Our shoot was typical. We had Jaspar, a dreadful sort of cross between a foxhound and a coat hanger which spent its day crashing through thickets trying to keep as far away from its master as possible. One could not actually blame the animal for that. Its owner, Pete, was the type of farmer who gives the industry a bad name with a lovely farm going to rack and ruin as posses of RSPCA inspectors struggled to keep his stock alive with batteries of intensive care machinery while he stalked the countryside with his gleaming gun looking for something, anything, to shoot. He was like some character out of a Hammer horror film. I always made it my business to keep as far away from Pete as his dog since his trigger-happy bloodthirstiness was only matched by his total inability to come within a dozen yards of whatever target he had aimed at. He had a bad limp because, in an uncharacteristically merciful gesture, he tried to shoot a dog that had broken its back and blew off half his foot instead.

Ivor, as host of the shoot, had legions of dogs. They all looked the part. One was a fat cocker spaniel, another was an even fatter labrador. Most of the rest were crosses between the two. They were the least popular dogs in the shoot as they were professionals and had their genes well and truly imprinted with the fact that their job was to root out pheasants, but this was combined with a total lack of any obedience and control. At best, they would forage happily about one and a half gunshots away, putting up bird after bird well out of any possible firing range. At worst, they would streak ahead of the guns and plunge into a wood five minutes before we could get there and, after sending birds thrashing out in all directions, they would emerge and trot towards their master each bearing a pheasant in their jaws which they would proceed to eat in full view of the outraged Mike who had not taken all that time and trouble to have his precious charges eaten by dogs.

The most characteristic sound of our shoot was not the ripple of gunfire as the pheasants streamed overhead, but the frantic screams of Ivor as he tried to keep these beasts from performing all the dreadful vandalistic acts of which they were capable.

Another of our regulars was Dennis. He had an elderly retriever that shared many of the characteristics of its master; of considerable age, used to shooting in some of the best parts of the country to great effect before advancing years and the desire for a quiet life had overcome the urge to kill. Both Dennis and his dog liked nothing more than a quiet potter in the countryside with a gun, but neither really wanted any birds to come along to upset their tranquillity. Dennis spent much of his day perched on a shooting stick with his hip-flask cradled in his hands and his dog lying by his side benignly surveying all the sweat and bother that the rest of us went through. Most of us owned rusting Spanish guns festooned with engraved toreadors and mouflons which could be used as fence posts in an emergency. Dennis had a pair of well used Holland and Hollands which had been made for him in 1933 but, if a bird came his way, it was as likely as not to continue unscathed because he rarely remembered or bothered to load the one he had with him. Dennis was even above green gumboots with little straps on them. He preferred beautifully polished and dubbined brown leather brogues which he wore with an ancient set of thorn-proof tweed plus-fours.

Ross was another member of the syndicate. He was our local tycoon who had made millions by scavenging ahead of the advancing tidal wave of public taste. Any craze that swept the country, be it hula hoops, skateboards or things that you stick on the top of your head that wobble and make you look daft, will have had Ross in on the ground floor somewhere and, by the time that they had begun to be talked about in the media, he would have already moved on to the next craze and would be extracting his million pounds or so from it before leaving it for lesser mortals to exploit. How he managed to do this from his Edwardian mansion carpeted throughout in the strident Ross tartan was a mystery that none of us could work out.

Ross had been born in Birmingham some forty years earlier and was busy trying to turn himself into a country gentleman and shooting was part of the impedimenta of the character he was trying to turn himself into. He was very good for the morale of the rest of us for, apart from shelling out three times as much money as the rest of us for pheasants and other expenses, he treated us with a respect that we did not deserve as being people who had cracked the mystery and ethos of shooting and had managed to change what for him was a status-filled way of passing time into something quite normal. I suppose I would share the same sort of feeling if I was invited to play polo in Windsor Great Park. The last thing we would ever tell Ross was that our sort of shooting was not the kind that could be considered smart.

Ross was always beautifully turned out, a bit like Dennis but newer. His tweeds were so country coloured that they stood out in a rather worrying fashion. They camouflaged themselves to the extent that they created a disturbing hole in the landscape. His shooting style was also somewhat odd. The rest of us slouched along until something turned up where-upon, shaking with excitement, we would fire wildly at whatever it was and miss. Ross had spent a lot of money at a shooting school. He would stand stiffly at attention until a target presented itself when he would jerk his gun to his shoulder like an automaton, lean slightly forward with a rigidly extended forearm, counting 'one two three, two two three' under his breath and would then fire and miss like the rest of us.

He also had a black retriever which he had purchased as a

fully trained gundog from a gamekeeper in Norfolk. The creature was so arrogant that it preferred to walk twenty yards behind its owner in case it was associated with him. When the dog first arrived, the rest of us were totally overawed by such a wonderful and superbly expensive shooting accessory but, on its first few outings, it did no more than Battsy. Ross yelled at it as he had been instructed to do, but it took no notice. He complained to the vendor who was as baffled as he, but put him in touch with someone in Yorkshire who had initially had the same trouble with one of his dogs. Ross was told that the dog would only obey if the commands were issued in a thick Norfolk accent. It worked, sometimes. Ross's Norfolk accent was barely adequate and it pained him beyond measure to have to discard his still shaky BBC English in order to communicate with a dog. He gave us up eventually. The last time I saw him, he was perched on the back of a horse dressed in hunting kit, looking like an advertisement for Bristol Cream Sherry. It is a less vocal sport.

How did our shoots work? It almost always poured with rain when it was not snowing. The main covers that were expected to hold pheasants were the hedges, the odd patch of kale and some coniferous woodlands. The kale was always soaking wet and ensured that the knees of everyone's trousers became sodden while the fir trees in the woods surreptitiously deposited their mug-sized drips carefully down the backs of our necks. On the very few occasions when it was not actually raining, there was usually a thick fog. Sometimes we would follow in the footsteps of the dogs watching the rabbits and hares that they flushed disappear into the distance. At other times, the more sedentary members of the party like Dennis would be placed at the end of a wood or hedge and the rest of us would fight through the brambles trying to put up creatures for them to shoot.

An average pheasant bag for our eight guns was about five, but that would be padded by rabbits, the odd snipe or partridge and even duck. Duck were awkward. They lived on a pond in the middle of the shoot and we would crawl up to its edge on our bellies so that we could surprise them and then spring to our feet ready to fire. Unfortunately they usually preferred to come paddling towards us, quacking for bread, rather than show the expected degree of terror and fly away. Even Pete could be too embarrassed to shoot. On our most memorable pheasant day, we shot seventeen birds but that was because the smart shoot was operating just over the hedge from us and we lined up to pinch their stragglers as they tried to escape and many of the birds that came over were already spiralling down with smoke trailing from their engines.

I, like Ross, shot my first pheasant in a situation in which I was totally out of my depth. In the days of my extreme youth, I possessed a shotgun that had twin hammers on it and barrels that looked like a car exhaust pipe after a salty winter. With this lethal implement, I explored the ambivalent depths of the human soul that enables those whose knowledge and love of animals is the greatest to receive such immense pleasure from their destruction.

My first stamping ground was the garden of an old people's home that was infested with rabbits which I would blow to pieces with immense gusto before returning home in time to feed an ancient and much loved white rabbit with which I had grown up. On one occasion I rounded a rhododendron bush in front of the house and came upon a mummy rabbit with her five baby rabbits gambolling on the lawn just below the sitting-room window. Even my cold heart warmed to this vision of family togetherness and I turned away to leave them in peace and, as I did so, I glanced at the window. Inside it was lined with gesticulating geriatrics all pointing at me and the rabbits and raising their crutches to their shoulders. Not quite believing that I understood them, I raised the gun to my shoulder, pointed at the rabbits and gave them an inquiring look. They all nodded furiously. To my shame, I fired and four of the rabbits fell dead. The capering glee from inside the house must have rivalled their celebrations at the relief of Mafeking.

My first visit to a proper pheasant shoot was a total disaster. It was very much the junior section of quite a smart shoot but I was placed next to a contemporary who was a rival in love and he managed to ruin my reputation completely and brought down on my head the frowning contempt of my host by the quite devastating ploy of hurling himself flat on his face whenever I raised my gun and he thought that anyone else was watching. I managed to discourage him with a brisk bout of fisticuffs behind a tree, but he ruined my image of being a safe shot.

After that I was posted well out on the flank by the gnarled old gamekeeper who was one of those people who are so in control of themselves and their job and wield such authority on their own ground that it astonished me to meet his wife and discover that she dared to nag him. Out on the flank, I managed to shoot a woodcock.

Woodcock are considered one of the most difficult birds to hit. They are strange birds at the best of times with their preferred method of alighting being to aim themselves in the general direction of a tree or a bush, then to fold their wings and hurl themselves into it with the unrestrained enthusiasm of a kamikaze pilot. They also have a marked aversion to flying in a straight line. If put up on a shoot, they wander amongst the guns at head height, playing peek-a-boo from behind the trees. This makes them both exceedingly difficult to shoot and also the root cause of a significant number of casualties amongst the shooting fraternity. The aftermath of the appearance of a clever woodcock can resemble that of the gunfight at the OK Corral.

This particular woodcock came loop-the-looping across my bows and I shot it. It probably surprised me more than the bird. I brought my prey to the collecting point at the end of the drive and diffidently proffered it.

'Oh well done!' said the keeper. 'Who shot it?' as his eyes swept round the guns. All the guns except me. Nobody answered.

'I did actually.'

'You!' He and everybody else looked at me in disbelief. My rival in love had succeeded too well.

'Yes, we know you picked it up, but who actually shot it in the first place?'

'Me,' I replied, beginning to feel a little indignant.

'You!' The incredulity was reaching cosmic dimensions. 'Was it wounded?'

'Of course not.'

'Was it flying?' I thought that that was a little below the belt as even I knew that only foreigners would contemplate such a heinous offence.

'Yes, of course it was flying.'

'Well,' he said, rolling his eyes round the rest of them, 'If you say you shot it then I suppose we have to believe you.' It was one of those humiliating moments that still has the power to make me feel pain twenty years later. It was made even worse when the keeper placed me beside him in the next drive and his presence so unnerved me that I missed everything that came my way.

In my last season as a member of our syndicate, the whole nature of the operation suffered a violent change. It stemmed from Julian Shaw. He had spent most of his life in London trying to be a trendy interior decorator and the onset of the recession had neatly coincided with the death of his authentically tweedy aunt who had owned and run the fishing hotel

57

just down the river from the mill. He was as smooth as silk in an interior decoratory sort of way and seemed to be making a first-class job of cosseting the rich old dears who made up the bulk of the clientele he had inherited. He asked himself along as a guest on one of our shooting outings. It was quite surprising as he had come out with us once before and was both a lousy shot and seemed quite terrified of the noise of the guns. Mike had said that he looked like the sort of bloke who could not handle a bang. However, he had brought along a superb lunch for everyone the last time he had come out and so he was very welcome a second time.

He did not turn up at 10am as he should have done, but showed at lunchtime at Ivor's house, complete with his hamper. He distributed the wine and the quail round the table and we all gave thanks and tucked in. It soon became clear that he had an ulterior motive.

'I had an idea that I thought I might put to you,' he said. We quite often were approached by people who wanted to join the syndicate. Ivor, his antennae twitching like a piece of tinsel in a gale, hurriedly broke in. 'I'm awfully sorry, Julian, but we've no room for any more regular members of the syndicate.'

'Good God. You don't think that I would want to go out and spend another miserable day like I did last time. I'm much too busy and anyway, I can think of much more interesting things to do with my spare time. It's a business proposition.'

'Business?' There was a cautious awakening of interest. Business meant money and any of us would rise to the suggestion of money like a trout to a fly.

'Yes. I was wondering if you would mind some of the guests from the hotel coming along to shoot occasionally. Some of my dearest friends from London are going to be coming down and it would be quite fun to be able to offer them a bit of shooting as well as fishing.'

A quick glance round the table confirmed Ivor's opinion that it would take more than wild horses to encourage us to accept Julian's dearest friends. 'No,' he said firmly. 'I've already said that we've no room for extra guns.'

'I'd certainly make it worth your while,' replied Julian. Nobody could have resisted following that up.

'How worth our while?'

'I thought that I might put down a few extra birds.'

'What does a few extra birds mean?' asked Ivor.

'Of course we'd have to negotiate that,' said Julian smoothly.

Mike was looking fairly interested. 'It would need at least fifty to make any difference and we'd need to extend the holding pens and get a bigger incubator. It could be very expensive.'

Peter, too, had been thinking. It was a slow process as coherent thought was not one of his specialities. 'I suppose all these friends would be poofs like you,' he muttered. 'I wouldn't like to go into the woods with a bunch of poofs.'

'My dear fellow,' said Julian, looking at Peter with distaste. 'I can assure you that your virtue would be safe with anyone of either sex that I have ever known.' Peter had not bothered to change the jacket that he had worn while spreading slurry early that morning and chunks of it had stuck to the cloth as well as to his lank and greasy hair and to the beard that never seemed to progress beyond the stage of merely looking unshaven. Peter had to be in the syndicate as his farm had all the best covers in its unkempt acres although the rest of us darkly suspected that he poached our own birds.

Mike was a bit worried about the sexual propensities of Julian's friends as well. 'Would all these friends of yours be homosexuals? I've never known any homosexuals that were shooting men. I thought they were all artists and dancers and things like that.'

Dennis was sitting by the Aga, filling in *The Times* crossword as fast as his fingers would move. 'Edward II,' he said, looking up, 'and William Rufus. Both of them were queer and William was killed while out hunting stags. I don't think that it affects the way they might shoot.'

'Hunting. That's different,' Mike replied. 'I've known some very strange things to go on in the hunting set.'

Julian, fairly newly down from London, had not yet absorbed the full gamey flavour of some of the local characteristics and was looking round in amazement. 'Look,

I've come here to talk about putting down some birds in exchange for a couple of guns for the hotel. I've said nothing about filling the countryside with camp ballet dancers.'

Peter was still gloomily considering the awful prospect of gay times in the hedgerows. 'I hate poofs. Bill Tasker, he was one.'

'Bill Tasker? He who kept that herd of shorthorns up at Withecott? There was nothing queer about him, surely?' said Mike.

'Haven't you heard the story?' asked Peter.

Julian decided that it was time he interrupted. A good tale of juicy scandal might go on for a very long time. 'I thought the hotel might put down a fair number of birds.'

Mike turned from the tale of Bill Tasker and looked at Julian. 'How many is a fair number?'

'But look, old boy,' interrupted Dennis. Julian was lucky that he was not addressed as 'old bean' which was Dennis's more usual expression. 'You couldn't possibly get people to come all the way down from London for some pheasant shooting and offer them this.' He indicated the window beyond which a curtain of grey rain was sweeping across the boggy fields. 'You'd never get away with it.'

'I don't see why not. The sort of people who would come to a hotel shooting weekend are unlikely to know any better. They would have probably only shot clay pigeons before and all they know about shooting birds is what they would have read.'

'That's what I mean,' said Dennis. 'They will be expecting pheasants by the thousand.'

'Well I was thinking of putting down a couple of thousand birds.'

There was a stunned silence. Mike broke it first. 'Two thousand pheasants? Don't be daft. Where would they all go and who would do all the work?'

'Don't worry,' replied Julian. 'We would arrange everything.'

That was how our syndicate changed its character. We became almost a smart shoot in terms of quantity of birds available but both myself and Dennis dropped out as it became just too dangerous. Julian was quite right in his predictions of the sort of clientele that his advertising would attract. Most of them were Londoners who had never shot at live targets before and they expected the birds to come over them with the regularity of clay discs. When they did not, they moaned. They were also extremely dangerous and three of us were peppered with shot when trying to drive birds towards them. Lamentably, it also proved that shooting walking birds was not just a habit of foreigners.

Julian provided an itinerant shooting master whose job it was to impose order on the visitors and arbitrate in the disputes that arose between regulars and guests. It turned out that the guests were incapable of staying put where they were told to and one could never be quite sure that an ill-clad Londoner was not about to erupt from behind a bush with his automatic shotgun blazing.

There was one delightful Saturday when an all-knowing plant-hire contractor was one of our three guests. He reeked of money, drove an expensive German motor car, wore a blue suede jacket and smoked a fat cigar all day. He also told us that he was a major financial contributor to the Conservative party. Colin had become the regular shooting master, having been ordered off his beloved river by Julian, and he had polka-dotted the landscape with numbered stakes to which he tried to verbally tether his charges so that we might have some idea of where they were.

In the middle of the day, I was on the edge of the wood and the blue suede jacket was adjacent to me at a stake about thirty yards away. He was moaning as he had been moaning for most of the morning.

'Bloody cold, isn't it? Isn't it?'

'Yes,' I yelled back.

'Is it always as cold as this?'

'It's usually colder. It's winter, you know.'

'But I'm freezing.'

'Well jump up and down.'

He was jumping up and down when the first pheasant flew over which he missed. There was a lull and another bird came creaming over the trees and he missed that as well. Then there came a succession of birds that flew on the opposite side of the hedge next to which he was standing. The beaters appeared to be about half way through the woods.

'I'm crossing to the other side of the hedge,' he yelled at me.

'I'd stay put, if I were you. That's where the marker is,' I shouted back.

'The marker's in the wrong place. It ought to be on the other side of the hedge.'

'But that is somebody else's land.'

'Who cares? I'm paying through the nose for this and I couldn't give a damn about that.'

'I'd watch your step if I were you and unload your gun.' He did pause to unload his gun before fighting his way through the hedge. I had a wild hope about what might happen but I did not want him to shoot himself before it did. He disappeared and there was a couple of minutes' pause before there was the scream of anguish that I was waiting for. Then the birds started to come over in their squadrons and I was busy missing them for several minutes before Ivor and Colin emerged from the wood.

'Where's he gone?' asked Colin jerking his thumb towards the stake where the blue suede jacket should have been.

'He went through the hedge,' I replied. 'You can probably hear him.'

The ululations of distress had reached a higher pitch now that they were no longer masked by the explosion of the guns.

'Didn't you warn him?' asked Ivor, as we started towards the hedge.

'I did advise him to stay where he was.'

'I'll bet you didn't advise him too strongly.'

'Not too strongly,' I agreed. Colin was looking a bit worried as his charge was now yelling for help in tones of panic. Colin scrambled through the hedge as we climbed to the top and looked over. Ivor started to fill his pipe.

'Could be a bit tricky,' he said conversationally.

'Don't just stand there. Do something,' said the blue suede coat.

Just on the other side of the hedge was a nice flat green area. To an inexperienced eye, it might have looked quite a good place to stand and wait for pheasants, but not to a countryman. Even if I had not known about it, it was very obviously a slurry pit with a thin skim of grass on top of it and the blue suede coat was in it up to his armpits, squealing piteously with his arms outstretched to stop himself sinking in any further and a banana-like cigar lying on top about a foot from his nose.

'I suppose we'd better try to get him out,' said Colin.

'Yes,' replied Ivor, puffing on his pipe. 'But it's not going to be that easy.'

Dennis joined us on top of the hedge. His face lit up. 'Oh! What frightfully bad luck. Are you all right?'

The blue suede coat looked at him balefully. 'Of course I'm not all right. I'm stuck in this bog.'

'I'm afraid it's not a bog, old chap. It's a slurry pit, although I suppose it could be described as a cow's bog.' Dennis seemed to be enjoying himself. So was I.

'Get me out.'

'I'll just go and get a rope,' said Ivor and he and Colin turned and strolled gently off in the direction of the farmhouse which lay a quarter of a mile away across the fields. Dennis carefully placed his shooting stick on top of the hedge bank, sat down and took out his flask. 'You know,' he said, 'you're going to smell absolutely dreadful when you come out. I don't think that pit has been emptied for years.'

The victim was beginning to regain some of his composure although he was not prepared to move a muscle in case he sank any further.

Another of the paying guests eventually stirred himself. 'I'm not paying just to stand here and look at somebody up to his neck in it. Why don't we get on with some shooting?' There was a debate, the upshot being that the rest of the party went off in search of targets while Dennis and I preferred to sit in the hedge. With the numbers reduced, Dennis and I could share his flask quite equably. After about fifteen minutes' further wait, during which time the victim complained bitterly about the cold and Dennis and I extended him our deepest sympathy, Colin and Ivor arrived back across the field with a rope. We threw it the dozen or so feet that the victim had managed to flounder into the pit and pulled.

He took some pulling, particularly since Ivor decided to get the giggles, but eventually we dragged him to the bank where he lay like a stranded salmon. He stank. Oh how he stank. Ancient black slurry coated him in a slick black layer from neck to feet and well-matured slurry which has lain undisturbed for several years has an odour that one can almost touch, such is its appalling power. The victim had not really been aware of it since his body had sealed most of the smell into the pit and the noisome odour of its depths had been neatly corked by his ample stomach. He whimpered in distress as the full horror of the object that he had become came home to him. We all followed him upwind to the river, where he went in and scraped the worst of the muck off.

The hotel lost a customer but we all heard from him again. Julian received a spate of letters from his solicitor and Ivor received a visit from the water authority because the victim reported him for polluting the river in which he had been scrubbed down.

Chapter Four

VILLAGE POLITICS is a minefield for the unwary. The greatest error that a newcomer can make is to look around, decide that a village is dead or dull and that he is the person to make changes. It is not like that. It may seem dull at first but only because the local people do not know you and are waiting to see what kind of creature you are before they decide whether or not to stand aside to make room for you in the community. It has to be done in their time and never in your own.

The Commander was a leader of men through and through who had retired early from the Navy so that he could become a market gardener and make a good living from it with the support of his pension. The village noted his arrival. He was in his early fifties, tall, distinguished looking with a thick head of black hair that made one think suspiciously of the dye bottle. He was very open about his intentions. Since a man of his experience and intellect would obviously not receive a great deal of cultural stimulation in such a community as ours, he intended to start bucking things up and enrich the lives of its inhabitants.

The locality was abuzz with concerned gossip, the distillation of which was 'who the hell does he think he is?' Actually the corporate soul of the village was looking forward to the fray. It knew that the man would inevitably break himself against the immense rock of tradition, inertia and duplicity that its inhabitants would employ. The first preliminary skirmish took place in the local pub. It is a typical village pub, although rather older than most with a reputed origin in the thirteenth century and a reputed ghost, which had recently been introduced to encourage the tourists. It looks very attractive on the outside under its thatch but is nicotine-brown and cathedral gloom within. It is a free house which means that, while the villagers will go there for decade after decade and build up their own carefully structured bar society, the publicans will flit through like transient butterflies. They come from the cities, full of enthusiasm to build up their trade and make the pub a glittering success, and then depart after a couple of years transformed into gloomy alcoholics, broken by the hardness of the work and the difficulty of trying to communicate with a clientele with whom they have nothing in common and who want nothing more than to be left to enjoy their pint in peace.

The Commander came into the pub, ordered a pink gin and sat down in Jimmy's seat. A *frisson* of excitement ran round the room. Nobody in living memory had ever bought a pink gin there. Nobody had ever come in dressed like the Commander — expensively casual with a knotted kerchief at the neck. One either went in working clothes or dressed up in a suit. Above all, nobody ever sat in Jimmy's seat. It was a genuine Jacobean oak chair and it was almost a throne. If you had lived in the village man and boy all your life and not made too many enemies then, in your dotage, you were allowed to use this throne exclusively until it became your turn to pass up the road to one of the humped graves in the churchyard, where your peace would only be disturbed by the copulations of the young who congregated there on summer evenings.

Jimmy had recently attained the throne, its previous incumbent having been buried only a couple of months earlier. It had been touch and go between Jimmy, who was one of the few men left in England who had earned a living all his days as a rabbit catcher, and Bill who was a semi-retired farmer. For a fortnight the occupancy of the throne had oscillated between them until Jimmy had almost killed himself by turning up at opening time for every session for thirty days on the trot and had remained on the throne until last orders. He had drunk far more than was good for him which, admittedly, he had done for most of his life, but he had won the throne and, traditionally, it was left vacant when he was not there to occupy it. And there was the Commander sitting in it as bold as brass at least twenty years before his time even if he had been eligible in the first place.

He smiled round the bar and its inhabitants either averted their eyes or looked stonily back at him. 'Nice weather, isn't it?' he said brightly to Bill.

'Depends,' said Bill.

'Depends on what?' asked the Commander.

'Depends on what you think is nice.'

The Commander was only slightly taken aback. 'Well, you know, sunshine, blue sky, pleasant sailing breeze.'

'If it keeps up the land'll need some moisture.' That came from Kelvin speaking from the depths of his pint with his eyes held straight ahead. The Commander, had he but known it, had made contact with the two most powerful figures in the community. Kelvin was a farmer and leader of the Parish Council, a man of overweening pride and many acres who had browbeaten his unfortunate wife to her grave some five years earlier and had been left with an only daughter whose plainness and legendary sourness of disposition had scared off even the most dedicated of the farmless youths who fancied her chances of inheritance.

Bill Snow was his cousin and reputed to be the richest man in the village. He always looked as if he had been dressed by the Salvation Army and lived in a one-bedroom shack at the top of the village. He was semi-retired and had thus fancied his chances for occupancy of the throne; he had small parcels of land all over the locality and, astonishingly, three flat-racing horses in training at Newmarket. Bill's prowess at making deals was without parallel within a twenty-mile radius.

'May I buy you two gentlemen a drink?' asked the Commander. He bought them both a drink, poor fool. Bill had never bought a drink for anyone in his life and Kelvin had a habit of diving out to the loo whenever it was his round. Being successful means taking care of details. The Commander expanded a bit. 'I suppose you need rain so that your corn will grow?'

'Could do, but I don't,' said Bill.

'I'm not quite with you. Surely you must have rain if your corn is going to grow?'

'No,' said Bill.

'Why not?'

'I don't grow any corn. There's none grown for a dozen miles around.'

The Commander laughed heartily, all by himself while everyone else looked at him. His laugh was very loud and went on for quite a long time. He eventually stopped.

'I'm going in for market gardening down at Meadowacre.'

'Oh, yes?' This was some hard information coming out and people pricked up their ears and prepared to take notice. Hard information meant news and news meant gossip, the staff of life.

'Yes, there's a good south-facing slope there but it's covered in weeds. I've already started to dig them over but I was wondering if any of you farmers could lend me some equipment so that I could clear it a bit faster.'

Bill looked over at him from his elevated position on a bar stool. 'Where have you been digging so far?'

'Down by the hedge.'

'The hedge on the west boundary?'

'That's right. Where all those green ferns were. I had a dickens of a job pulling them out.'

'I bet you did,' said Bill. 'It took Mrs Davis twenty years to get them like that. It was the best asparagus bed in the county.'

'Oh. I see. I was hoping to plant asparagus but I thought it would take too long to get established.'

'Yes, twenty years to get it really good,' said Bill. They lapsed into silence. 'What sort of equipment do you think you would need?' asked Kelvin, looking pointedly at his empty glass. The Commander took the hint. It took another week before he stopped taking it.

'A tractor and a sort of plough I suppose. I've got a Land Race on order and when that comes, I'll be able to use it to cultivate anything I like.'

The pub turned and looked at the Commander with curious eyes. 'A Land Race?' asked Kelvin.

'That's right. I met a frightfully nice chap who said he could get me one very cheap. He said they're much better than a Land Rover and you can sell them very easily for as much as you paid for them.'

'Do you know what a Landrace is, Admiral?'

'It's a little tractor, isn't it?'

'It's a dirty great pig.' The pub exploded in mirth which the Commander did not join.

I felt rather sorry for the Commander. He could not understand how he failed to manage the village like he did the Home Fleet. He organised a village dramatic society and bullied people to turn up to its inaugural meeting. He chaired the occasion and then found that he failed to get a vote when it came to elect a committee to run it. He tried to start up a flower show but could not get anyone interested. A fortnight later, Bill suggested one and it was a howling success. He wrote to the headquarters of the county Conservative Party suggesting that he might start up a village branch and had, instead, an icy interview with the local JP and Master of Foxhounds who was already chairman for the area.

The Commander floundered around for six months spending more and more time in the bar until he finally gave up. He turned up in the pub one evening after spending the day spreading manure on his courgettes. His smell and his appearance were just like everyone else's. He got completely blotto and Bill had to take him home. Now, he is a fully integrated member of the community. He speaks slowly, checks you out before he offers anything and has finally taken over the Flower Show. Only a deep-seated melancholy in his eyes and the occasional longing look that he casts at the gin bottle as he orders his pint reveal that he is anything but a born and bred villager.

It did not need the awful warning provided by the Commander to teach us to tread softly when we moved into the village. We had been away from the city long enough to know that city ways do not work away from the city. There are not enough people around to allow you to be selective about who will be in your social circle. Friends you can choose, but you will know everybody else and they will know you and will want to learn all about you and discover which factions you will join in the complex power struggles that go on inside every community.

The most fundamental struggle that goes on in most rural communities is that between native-born inhabitants and incomers. It was so in ours. We also had clashes between church and pub, Liberal and Conservative, farmers and villagers with the main forum for debate lying within the Parish Council. Its leader was Kelvin and the Clerk was a retired postman whose job had given him an unequalled insight into the lives and scandals of the inhabitants of the area. Our Council fairly accurately represented the population. About half of them were newcomers, the definition of a newcomer being someone who had not been born within the parish. One member was totally senile, one was slightly retarded, two were bores of monumental proportions and about half of them were farmers and half lived in the village.

Kelvin, aided and abetted by the postman, usually had his way by ruthlessly applying those rules of procedure that he thought appropriate. The senile member died about six months after we moved in and I was co-opted onto the Council. This was a very dubious honour which came about because we had so successfully managed to take the opposite course to the Commander that we were all things to all men and each faction thought that it would find an ally in me. Kelvin's secret weapon on the Council was boredom. The meetings were held on the last Thursday of the month and began at eight o'clock and, while the Clerk droned through the minutes of the previous meeting and carefully read through any received correspondence from the watermark on the writing paper to the VAT number at the bottom, the rest of us were all too aware that time was ticking away if we were to be able to fit in our traditional perk of a post-meeting drink before closing time.

Kelvin's most striking characteristics in his position as Chairman of the Council were a refusal to use the English language in a sufficiently logical sequence to make any sense and a fanatic sensitivity to any attempt to usurp the powers that he thought were rightfully his. It was probable that he was born more than a little mad, a Hitler trying to mould his mini-Reich into a realm fit for his leadership. Kelvin's final five-year term was like a Shakespearean tragedy as the events piled up that eventually swept him to destruction. There was the Garagegate scandal when he sneaked through a planning consent for a garage on behalf of his brother-in-law without it going before the full Council. But his worst setback was the Common.

The draining of the Common had been his main plank in the manifesto that had swept him to the pinnacle of power with a fifteen-vote lead over his nearest rival at the last election. The Common was supposed to be the spot where the villagers could stroll, play football and generally enjoy themselves but it was wet, very wet, and Charity Dalby had grazing rights over it. Provided she put her sheep on it at least once a year, the Common could not be altered or approved without her prior consent. The first twelve meetings of the Council that I attended, had the draining of the Common as the most important item on the agenda. After a year, it was finally agreed that myself and Dennis should visit Charity and obtain the necessary permission from her so that we could go ahead with the drainage.

Charity was a farmer, the tenth generation on the same small patch of land in a neighbouring parish and probably the last of her line as she and her husband were into their sixties and had no children or family except Charity's spinster sister who lived with them. Their farm was a remarkable tribute to the resilience of the nineteenth century. They had no mains electricity since the Authority would only run a line to the farm on the receipt of several thousand pounds, so there was an old diesel engine which puttered away in a barn giving them enough power for a few lights.

They raised a few bullocks and pigs and bounced in to the nearest market town once a week on their ancient tractor and trailer to collect vegetable scraps to feed to the animals. Frank Dalby drove the tractor while Charity sat on the flatbed of the trailer gazing straight ahead with her wispy white hair blowing in the fifteen-mile-an-hour slipstream, swathed in a sheet of polythene to protect her from the elements. The queues of impatient traffic that built up behind them were ignored. They kept farm time at Greenwich Mean Time throughout the year. Since they had virtually no contact with anyone else, this eccentricity did not really matter.

I had heard about the Dalbys before being given the duty of visiting them. The farmhouse, roofed in a mixture of thatch and corrugated iron, faced onto a yard littered in decaying farm machinery and nettles among which a few mangy chickens and geese picked their living. The all-pervading impression was one of dampness. Old stone troughs overflowed in several corners of the yard, the ground squelched underfoot as Dennis and I picked our way from his car to the front door across a rivulet that wound its way from a barn that contained her bullocks standing four feet above ground level on a carpet of stinking straw, past the front of the house and out into a reed-filled meadow.

I found the atmosphere of this rural slum extremely depressing but Dennis appeared unaffected. He knocked briskly on the door and, after a couple of minutes, it opened and Charity peered suspiciously out. She was wearing an apron made from an old sack. 'Yes?' she said.

Dennis raised his trilby. 'Good afternoon, Mrs Dalby. We are a deputation from the next door Parish Council. We've come about the Common.' Charity did not appear to be listening. She first of all carefully looked Dennis up and down and then turned to me and subjected me to the same careful scrutiny. It was the sort of examination that made you wonder if your tie was crooked or the zip of your flies was properly done up.

'What are you selling?' asked Charity.

'Selling?' Dennis was mortified. Never in all his life had he been mistaken for a salesman. 'Mrs Dalby, I can assure you that I am not a salesman.'

'Whatever you say, but I'm not buying anything today.' With that she slammed the door in our faces.

'What an extremely odd woman,' said Dennis with charitable understatement as he began to beat on the door again. A large black and white sheepdog sneaked round the corner of the house and nipped me on the ankle. I kicked out at it and it moved half a dozen yards away and settled down to a really thorough chest-clearing bark. We examined my wound which did not appear to be critical and Dennis began to beat on the door again. The knocker came away in his hand. He looked at it in some dismay as the dog began to sidle in to prepare for another attack. 'This place is a dump,' he said and flipped the half pound chunk of iron that was the knocker at the dog. It caught it in mid-bark, right in the chops with an indescribably horrible crunching noise as half a dozen of its teeth snapped. Dennis was aghast. 'Good grief. I'm most frightfully sorry,' he shouted after the animal as it ran yelping towards a barn.

'I have a nasty feeling that you may have made a tactical error,' I said as I saw Mr Dalby coming at us from the far side of the yard. I had only previously seen him seated on the back of his tractor but he was unmistakable. He belonged in the pages of the Brothers Grimm. He was about five feet tall and wore a filthy black suit tied at the waist with baler twine, a flat cap and gumboots. He came squelching through the mud and dung towards us carrying a pitchfork in his right hand. His legs were of a bandiness that seemed to be forcing him to grit his teeth in concentration as he walked to prevent them from taking him off at a tangent to the direction in which he wished to travel.

'I saw that,' he said grimly. 'One of you two threw something at my dog. Which of you was it?'

'Er,' said Dennis rather faintly.

Mr Dalby saw the knocker lying on the ground surrounded by a garland of teeth. 'Who did that? You've knocked out half the dog's teeth.'

'Er,' said Dennis once again.

Mr Dalby fixed him with a piercing eye which even the Ancient Mariner would have envied. 'So it was you was it?' He transferred the fork to his left hand and tacked determinedly towards Dennis who was beginning to look rather alarmed. I wondered if it was my duty to interpose my body between them to prevent violence but decided not to. He stopped a couple of feet away to allow the cloud of miasma that surrounded him to catch up and thrust out his fist at Dennis's midriff. Dennis stepped hurriedly backwards. 'I'd like to shake you by the hand,' said Mr Dalby. Dennis's face cleared as he allowed his hand to be pumped up and down. 'That bloody dog went and bit the Social Security man. I can't have that. Me being disabled —' we looked in sympathy at his bandy legs — 'with my bad arm.' He slapped the arm that was still showing its appreciation to Dennis. 'I don't mind if it bites salesmen, but I'm not having it going around biting the Social Security. They gives me money, not takes it away, and I don't want them frightened off.'

He released Dennis's hand and looked us up and down in the same fashion as his wife. 'What are you selling then? I normally sees salesmen off but since you caught the dog a good 'un and might have taught it a lesson, I might as well hear what you've got to say. Mind you, if you're selling minerals, don't waste my time or yours. If the good Lord had meant stock to eat iron and copper and all the other nonsense that you lot sell, he'd have given them hacksaws instead of teeth.'

Dennis raised his hands placatingly. 'It's all right Mr Dalby. We're really not salesmen, we're a deputation from the Council.'

'The Council!' Mr Dalby's face turned red. 'If there's one thing I hate, it's you bastards from the Council. You lot stole my lambs last year.'

From being full of primitive charm a few moments earlier, he was now quite literally dribbling with rage. It was a fascinating and alarming sight, particularly as he was waving the pitchfork in our direction.

'I think you must be making a mistake,' said Dennis.

'Don't you mistake me, you . . . you frogspawn.' There was something elemental about Mr Dalby. 'Frogspawn', which was obviously the direst insult in his vocabulary, showed a certain originality of mind as it was not a term of opprobrium that readily tripped off the tongue of the locals. 'She's mine and I've had her for thirty years ever since I was married and you've no right to ask me to pay for her and take my lambs away when I won't. She's sweeter than anything you could give me. I love her. It's my right to do what I like with her and you can't make me pay.' His rage was beginning to give way to depression. 'I had three but the smallest one disappeared in the summer. She was the sweetest of all.'

There was something almost surreal about the conversation. Demanding payment for wife or wives in money or even in lambs was an aspect of local government taxation that neither I nor Dennis had yet come across. Dennis wisely decided to distance us from direct involvement in the matter before we pursued the subject further.

'Hang on Mr Dalby, we're from the Parish Council, not from the District Council.'

The old man was looking sadly down at his gumboots, one of which had been repaired with a large red rubber patch. He was obviously lost in a nostalgic reverie about the sweetest one of all. 'She was clean too, always clean and sweet,' he sighed. 'Anyway it ain't no use crying over spilt milk.'

'Parish Council, Mr Dalby. That's where we're from, the Parish Council,' said Dennis encouragingly.

He appeared to get through. 'Oh! You're not from the District Council at all, are you?'

'That's right.'

'Well why the hell did you say you were?'

75

'We didn't actually, but what were you talking about just now?'

'That bloody Council took away my lambs when I refused to pay for her.'

Dennis was as mystified as I, but he persevered. 'Perhaps it was a fine for having more than one?'

'Why shouldn't I have more than one? They're a gift from the Lord. It's not my fault that I had three.'

'Surely you're only meant to have one. It is illegal to have more than one.'

'It's the first I've ever heard of it. I had three for thirty years and my father had about a dozen at one time.'

This was absolutely fascinating. Incest is a recognised problem among isolated rural communities but polygamy on this scale was new to both of us.

'What was it like having three?' asked Dennis.

'What do you mean, what's it like?' asked Dalby.

'Well, I've only got one and I think that most people only have one. Isn't it a bit exhausting with three? You must have to spread yourself round a bit?'

Mr Dalby looked rather puzzled. 'No, it's perfectly straightforward. If one of them gets exhausted, I just put my pipe into another of them.'

We looked at Mr Dalby with considerable admiration. Dennis shook his head to clear his mind of the tremendous ramifications that were conjured up.

'If it's all right by you, Mr Dalby, the one that we'd like to see is Charity.'

'Charity? What do you want to see Charity for?'

'She is the wife that owns the grazing on the Common? I mean it could be embarrassing if we mixed her up with another of your wives.'

'What are you talking about?'

'You know, your three wives.'

'I've got three springs, not three wives, you daft pillock and the Council want me to pay water rates. What do you think I am? Some bloody darkie potentate?'

I looked at the embarrassed Dennis with scorn while Mr Dalby kicked open the door and yelled 'Charity!' into the dark interior of the house. He sploshed off through the mud muttering to himself. I clicked my tongue disapprovingly at Dennis. 'Who's a daft pillock then?'

'I don't think our mission has got off to a particularly good start,' he said. We waited for Charity's arrival with a mixture of trepidation and suppressed hilarity. Charity came shuffling down the passage to the front door.

'Yes?'

'Mrs Dalby?'

'Yes. You'll have to speak up as I'm a bit hard of hearing. What is it that you want to sell?'

I could see Dennis gritting his teeth and counting up to ten. It seemed to be becoming clear why Kelvin had suggested us for this particular expedition rather than coming himself. 'We don't want to sell anything, Mrs Dalby. We're representing the Parish Council and we want to talk to you about the Common.'

'The Common. Oh well, in that case I suppose you'd better come in.'

She preceded us down the passage and opened the door into the kitchen. As she did so, a wall of heat hit us in the face mixed with an appalling smell. It is a curious fact that a hot nasty smell is always much more unpleasant than a cold nasty smell and the smell that lived in Charity's kitchen was just about the hottest and the nastiest that I had ever come across.

The room had a low beamed ceiling, blackened by smoke, with several sinister-looking hooks projecting from various places from which they no doubt hung dead animals or captured local council officials. On one wall was a blazing log fire adjacent to a solid fuel cooker that seemed to be red hot; so much so that the linoleum which covered the floor was charred where it met the edge of the cooker. Both the lino and the walls were the same grey/black/brown colour as the ceiling with decades of dirt and dust obscuring whatever colour they might have been originally. The walls were bare apart from several large photographs of Victorian agricultural personages standing beside much caparisoned carthorses or posing self-consciously beside silver cups. The cups them-selves were there inside a glass-fronted cabinet and a surreptitious look through the grimy panes revealed that most of them were pre-First World War ploughing trophies. There was a large mahogany table on bulbous legs stretching beneath the one window and a battered red plush three-piece suite grouped round the cooker and fire.

The source of the smell was immediately apparent. Stretched out in front of the fire was a heavily bearded billy goat, surrounded by a halo of recumbent cats some of which lay on top of it. These creatures were having their teeth rattled by a continual series of thunderous farts that echoed out of the interior of the goat during the whole time that we were there. As if that was not enough, there was a small calf lying on several sheets of newspaper on top of the sofa. To my expert eye, it looked as if it was in the throes of a terminal case of diarrhoea.

The reek of this assortment of beasts combined with the

heat of the fire and the cooker rendered the atmosphere of the kitchen virtually unbearable even to those like us who thought that their nostrils were used to the worst that the countryside could throw at them. Dennis took a silk handkerchief from his pocket and carefully poured over it some whisky from the flask which, I had heard, he even took to the bath with him, and delicately put it to his nostrils like an eighteenth-century French aristocrat.

Charity looked at him with faintly maternal concern. 'Are you all right, dear?'

'Just a touch of a nosebleed?' he said, his bellow muffled by the gas mask. All I could do was hold my breath. Charity went over to the calf and hauled it off the sofa by its back legs. Its head hit the floor with a solid thud and it twitched feebly. Fortunately it appeared to be unconscious. She dragged it over to the hearth rug beside the billy goat and peeled the disintegrating newspapers off the sofa.

'Have a seat, my dears.'

We apologetically declined and instead perched our backsides on the edge of the large mahogany table. Dennis started to talk as Charity bustled about making us tea from a large iron kettle that stood on the cooking range. We could assume that the boiling water should have been sterile, even in such adverse conditions, but my confidence drained away as she picked up a large red plastic jug that stood beside the fire and decanted some milk from it into two grimy mugs. Even from across the room it was evident that the milk was so full of foreign bodies that it did not pour evenly from the jug but came out instead in a series of gulps.

'We've come about the Common,' said Dennis.

'What did you say dear?'

'We've come about the Common,' I yelled. The billy goat released a mighty explosion in shock that made the cats crouch, fold back their ears and look at me with that expression of implacable loathing that is the speciality of their species.

'I believe you have grazing rights over the Common,' shouted Dennis, sounding, with his smelling spirits jammed to his nose, like a New Englander with laryngitis.

'That's right. I've got grazing rights for sheep on the Common. It's a bit of a nuisance really as me and Frank have to get a few sheep down there once a year otherwise I'd lose the rights. What about it anyway?'

'We want to drain the Common.'

'Do you, dear? And why would you want to do something like that?'

'So that it can be better used for recreational purposes by the villagers.'

'That sounds very nice.'

'I'm glad you think so. We hope to lay out a football pitch. Put down benches so that the old folk have somewhere to sit on warm summer evenings and where the little children can play.' Dennis was waxing eloquent but there appeared to be trouble brewing on the hearthrug where the calf was beginning to thrash its legs about in its death convulsions and was scattering cats all over the room and getting dangerously close to booting the billy goat where no billy goat ought to be booted.

'It's all very interesting, but what's it got to do with me? Just because I've got grazing rights, it doesn't mean I'm going to give you any money towards it,' said Charity.

'Of course not.'

'Good, because I'll never do anything for that village as long as Kelvin lives there.'

We all had a pause for thought. Dennis and I exchanged glances. There was something well worth digging for here. Any dirt on Kelvin could be immensely valuable but our sworn duty as Councillors meant that we had to get the fair Charity's permission to drain the Common and pursuing the matter of Kelvin might well jeopardise our mission.

Dennis's better half won. 'Of course, Kelvin isn't one of us villagers, he farms outside. But we're mainly interested in doing up the Common so that we can improve the quantity and quality of the grass that grows there. Your sheep will have much more feed once the bogs and gorse have been cleared away and it's a sea of waving grass from one end to the other. You'll be able to graze your sheep all the year round.'

'Provided that you fence it,' said Charity.

'Well you can hardly expect us to fence it,' said Dennis.

'Why not?'

'It must be about half a mile in circumference.'

One of the scrabbling feet of the calf found a vital spot in the goat and it leapt to its feet with a bellow of pain.

'Shut up, Kelvin,' shouted Mrs Dalby and the goat, with a disgruntled look at her, lay down again on top of the calf. The cats crept in and covered it like drifting snow and the poor creature was too far gone to be able to do anything about it. It was probably convinced that it had reached hell about ten minutes before it actually did.

'It's all very interesting about the Common, but I don't see that it has anything to do with me. I mean so long as my grazing is all right, it doesn't really affect me.'

'Oh, there's no need to worry about that. We'll make sure that it's even better. There's just one thing —'

Dennis took a deep breath and was forced to wait as Charity went over to pour out the tea. On the way over, she bent down over the pile of animals and, her face reddening from the heat of the fire, she excavated a hole through the cats to prod the calf. It allowed itself to be prodded. She pushed off the goat and, grumbling to herself, she pulled the remains of the calf across the room to a door and thrust it through. Judging by the shelves inside, it was her larder. The goat and cats re-arranged themselves and Charity went to make the tea. I refused the mug that was thrust at me, but Dennis was the chief supplicant and, in the pursuit of diplomacy, he had to accept. It was fascinating to watch him pretend to slurp his tea without removing his handkerchief from his nose.

'As I was saying, Mrs Dalby, there is something we would ask of you.'

A gleam of interest, which had disappeared since she had heard that we were not going to fence the Common for her, was rekindled in her eyes. Her grazing rights were not much use if her sheep could wander off all over the countryside. 'We'd just like to know if it would be all right as far as you are concerned if we drained all the bogs.'

'I see,' she paused meditatively. Dennis made a disgusting sucking noise and smacked his lips appreciatively just to demonstrate how much he was enjoying his tea. 'Would it make any difference if I said I did mind?' Our diplomacy lay in ruins. The woman had gone straight to the jugular of the business. Dennis began to flounder.

'Well, er, no, not really, perhaps, it could do, but it would certainly save all sorts of formalities if you would be prepared to sign a bit of paper saying that you wouldn't mind.'

She paused and thought and an evil grin crossed her face. 'You say that Kelvin Morchard doesn't live in the village.'

'That's perfectly true.'

'You're sure? He has nothing to do with the village at all?'

'Practically nothing.'

'Last I heard he was on your Parish Council.'

'Really?' said Dennis innocently.

'Yes, really. In fact last I heard he was Chairman of your Parish Council.'

'Good Lord. Come to think on it, I believe you are right.'

'I bloody know I am right. You get *him* to come out here to ask me to sign your bits of paper and I might agree. There again I might not.'

I looked at Dennis and Dennis looked at me. It was clear to both of us that we could not leave the situation where it was. 'How do you know Kelvin?' I asked.

'Kelvin bloody Morchard courted me forty years ago. He thought he'd got me in foal and he ran a mile. He hasn't dared to come near me since. I've been wanting to get him beholden to me for a long time.'

One could not help feeling slightly sorry for Kelvin. We reported back to the Council that it required a personal visit from our Chairman before Charity would agree to the drainage of the Common, but he never went to see her and the Common remained a bog. Kelvin sensibly decided that he would not stand at the next election and Dennis and I were too much the gentlemen ever to let on that we knew what had led to his downfall. Unless someone asked us, of course.

Chapter Five

ABOUT A YEAR after we had come to the village, a commune also moved into the area. Its members had previously operated a thriving business near London, running a highly successful cannabis plantation supplying the needs of the Metropolis. Their downfall was a tragedy. It had all begun one pleasant summer evening when the communards were sampling the cream of their season's crop. Picture the scene: eight members of the rich but alternative society seated in the communal living-room in semi-darkness, sprawled out on cushions with aromatic smoke curling towards the ceiling while Bob Dylan whined away proving, as he always does, that however much money you spend on your speakers, you can still never quite understand what made him the great success of the 1960s.

Their tiny minds must have been blowing in the wind along with the song, seeking answers to the meaningless questions that Dylan poses. All in all it must have been a scene fairly characteristic of one aspect of rural Britain in our times, although one that is rarely examined in *The Archers*. A little conversation may have been in progress.

'Great music this.'
'Yeah.'
'Real meaningful, I mean.'
'Yeah.'
'The meaning he gets into the word "friend".'
'Yeah, and those chords.'
'Yeah, great chords.'

But disaster was stalking this peaceful scene. It was Emma who first spotted it. She had decided to stop crossing her eyes

83

so that she could appreciate the subtlety of the curve of her nostrils and examine the ceiling instead. She was making a considerable mental effort to really feel the texture of the plaster round the light fitting — a task which was made particularly difficult since the room was only lit by the fire and one candle — when she saw it. She screamed.

'What's wrong?' came the cry.

She screamed again, her obvious terror beginning to infect the others.

'Look. Up there on top of the wardrobe. Ooh! It's horrible.' The majesty of Dylan's mighty chords forgotten, they looked.

'What is it?' they asked. 'I can't see anything.' This was understandable because in the darkness it was difficult to make out the wardrobe, let alone what was on top of it.

'It's a bear, a huge great huggy bear, and it's about to leap down and attack us.' By God, so it was.

'Christ, look at the brute,' said one.

'How could it have got in here?' asked another.

'What can we do?' asked a third.

'Quick, come away from the wardrobe.' They crouched over by the wall as far away from the wardrobe as they could get. Emma was about to have hysterics.

'Listen!' They listened.

'You can hear it breathing.' They could hear it breathing. Its breathing was heavy and sinister.

'Look at it!' They looked at it. The light from the flickering candle was reflected on its great shiny fangs, blackened by blood and its foul breath.

'What can we do? We've got to do something before it attacks.'

Fortunately leaders of alternative society communes have to have the ability to take command of situations in emergencies and be prepared to take rapid and decisive action. 'I know, somebody telephone the police.' There was a dirty scrum for the door and they all ended up by the telephone in the hall quaking with terror while their leader dialled 999. Two squad cars and a sharp-shooter answered within minutes and a brave communard crept out of the stair cupboard, where they had all taken refuge, in answer to the pounding of the constabulary on the front door. With sharp-shooter to the fore, they crept up to the sitting-room door and one of the policemen put his hand round it and switched on the light. They peered in. There it was on top of the wardrobe. A real, live, ferocious black plastic rubbish bag.

With tears of mirth streaming down their cheeks, the police searched the premises removing illegal substances by the sackload and took most of the members of the commune down to the local nick and comprehensively busted them. It was the end of a beautiful dream. In spite of the fact that the magistrate, prosecutor and police witnesses broke down in helpless laughter when the case came before the court, the pantechnicon-loads of high quality Kent cannabis were too numerous to be overlooked. Most of the growers spent some months at Her Majesty's pleasure and, on their release, they were constantly plagued by giggling policemen raiding their premises in search of bears. So they sold up and moved West. Their palmy days were over even down our way. The local police regularly and hopefully raided them as their fabulous reputation had preceded them. So the commune underwent a metamorphosis.

They set up shop in a large decaying semi-mansion about three miles out of the village that had half a dozen acres of scrubby land surrounding it. They were a hit with the locals right from the start. They wanted to become agriculturally self sufficient and thus provided a ready market for ancient bits of farm machinery and implements that have been redundant for fifty years and litter every farmyard and which are normally unsaleable, even as scrap. They even bought old hens and other forms of livestock that had outlived their useful span.

Their most spectacular item of livestock was a late teenage Jersey cow which one of their number had bought at a farm sale. It could still produce a trickle of milk but had been hardly worth the trouble of slaughtering. Apart from being blind in one eye and blind in two of its teats, its oddest feature was that it was completely hairless.

The communards stuck at playing farmers for a bit and became quite a feature of the pub on a Saturday night when they would entertain the rest of us with local folk songs that nobody had ever heard of before. Then they decided that it was time that they developed and they became explorers of the limits of the human soul and intellect, in an alternative sort of way. Whether they ever got very far was never clear but they provided a priceless source of gossip and amusement for everyone else. It was dangerous to get too close to them as their definition of sanity and normality was very different from that of the norm. It was not usually obvious but during the course of a conversation, one would suddenly become aware of a yawning gulf between their beliefs and those of the rest of us. It was as if they were almost a different species, like hedgehogs that could not curl up or rabbits that preferred to live in trees.

I met one of them limping along the road one morning. Feeling in a beneficent mood, I gave him a lift into the village and enjoyed the usual conversation about weather and crops and whether Miss Pincombe, who had just reached her majority, was as generous with her favours as was rumoured. This was the number one topic in the village at the time. 'What have you done to your leg?' I asked when the subject had been exhausted.

'Oh nothing.'

'But that is quite a nasty limp that you've got.'

'There's nothing that can be done about it. You see I'm an Aquarian.'

'Oh yes?' One got to know when the rabbit was about to shin up its tree.

'Yes. We Aquarians always have weak knees.'

The communards set up an alternative college. They gathered together a number of arboreal rabbit experts and offered courses of instruction to all those who wished to join them in losing their marbles. It was quite frustrating for the villagers, as we were not quite sure what was going on. However, we need not have worried. They took their responsibilities as the intellectual and spiritual shock-troops of the vicinity very seriously and they held a public meeting in the village hall to explain what it was that they were up to and to enrol a few fee-paying pupils.

The hall was packed. They had put up a poster advertising the event in the newsagent's window and nobody wanted to miss the fun. It was a really titillating poster, promising discussion on alternative religion, astrology, ley lines and time travel. The last promised excitement enough but there was also to be a course on massage. The village knew all about massage. A couple of local farmers had gone up to Smithfield the previous winter and had ventured into a massage parlour in Soho. If their stories were anything to go by, the men in the village were all in favour of the practice and most of their wives had come along to make sure that their husbands did not enrol in the promised course.

The alternative religions man was the first to speak. Most of the platform party were experts brought in for the occasion and not regular members of the commune, but this one was. He had seemed a sensible enough fellow called Michael who played a variety of musical instruments rather nicely. He was wearing an orange shirt and trousers. His opening remarks elicited a sigh of pleasure from round the hall. 'I was born in India two years ago and my name is Jogee'. It did not take much insight from those of us present to observe that the speaker was at least thirty and that his accent showed closer affinities to Bermondsey than Bombay. 'I used to be lost, leading a conventional life as a drug addict in Notting Hill where I earned my living as a session musician and by writing poetry, but I went to India to be reborn and to follow the masters, in particular Bhagwan Shree Rajneesh and I now have been called to pass on to others my enlightenment.' He sat down. That appeared to be all that he had to say. People looked uneasily at each other. What did he mean?

'What do you mean when you say that you were reborn?' asked someone from the back of the audience.

He stood up again and smiled seraphically. 'Exactly that. I returned to the womb and began again. Everything that had happened to my previous self ceased to be and I was at one with the infinity again. I was again.'

Kelvin, in his capacity of Chairman of the Parish Council, rightly took on the fearsome task of trying to bridge the serious comprehension gap that seemed to be in danger of opening up. He grabbed hold of the only bit of the speaker's remarks that seemed to make any sense to him, if not sense in the context. At least Kelvin knew about wombs in terms of lambing sheep. 'How did you return to the womb?'

'I regressed through my childhood to the time before I was born.'

'Why?' asked Kelvin. There was a slight rustle of disapproval from the body of the hall. It was generally felt that the question was premature. The audience first of all wanted to know all about the mechanics of returning to the womb which it was not yet entirely clear about, before moving on to the abstract concept of motivation.

'Why?' said Michael/Jogee. 'So that I could re-experience my birth and, by doing that in a peaceful and tranquil manner, it would be possible to avoid the trauma of being born which is at the root cause of most of our problems.'

Kelvin took note of the sleeve tugging and whispering going on round him. 'What was the womb like?' This was more to our taste.

'It is warm and very peaceful, when you are floating in the womb. It is a delightful place and nothing else that we encounter in the rest of our lives can ever match it and we go through life trying to re-experience its peace.'

Kelvin doggedly continued on his search for enlightenment. 'But you can't go back to the womb if you are an adult?'

'Of course you can.'

'But you're too big!'

'But the womb is as big as you need. It is an artificial womb' — There was a disappointed sigh — 'that is used. One floats in the amniotic fluid supported by one's re-birther.' At least the practical difficulties had been disposed of although it all sounded a bit kinky. It is not as though the average countryman is afraid of a little kinkiness but this did not sound as though it would be much fun.

Kelvin moved on. 'You say that all our troubles come from being born?'

'That is right. It is usually a violent and thoroughly unpleasant experience. It certainly was in my own case.'

'You remember being born!'

'Certainly, we all have that memory locked inside ourselves. I was originally born in hospital and I can remember being smacked by the nurse and struggling to get back inside my mother.'

The implications of this remark and the conversation in general were beginning to make one or two of the older members of the audience feel slightly uneasy. One of them was heard to mutter 'How disgusting!'

'However,' continued Jogee, 'the time before that when I

was born was considerably easier. My mother was a shepherdess in Atlantis and I was born in an olive grove.' That was about the point when the villagers decided that if they could not beat them, they might as well join them and we all settled back for a good evening's entertainment. The only exception was the vicar who found the whole thing deeply worrying. After about ten more minutes, during which Jogee revealed that the main perk of being a follower of Bhagwan was to have it off with as many co-religionists as possible and that it was their duty to accommodate him, he sat down to rapturous applause, particularly from the village bucks.

The next speaker was to be the lecturer in ley lines. There was nothing particularly outstanding or unusual about this one. He was wearing an ordinary sports jacket and was rather unpromisingly introduced as Captain Percival. The Captain must have been about sixty and was not a resident of the commune but only a visiting lecturer. We did not expect too much from him.

'Boys and girls,' he started absently. We looked at each other. He corrected himself with a hearty naval/military laugh. It was not clear to which branch of the services he belonged. 'I do apologise but I was a schoolmaster for thirty years and old habits do die hard, what?' He beamed round the hall; after the excitement of Jogee, this one promised to be a real bore. 'What is a ley line? I hear you all ask.' You could hear the deafening uninterested silence. 'Well you lot in particular ought to know!' He said this with a bellow that woke up all those who were thinking that the time was ripe to snatch a quick snooze before someone less boring came along. 'This village is full of ley lines. Dozens of them converge on it. The lines of psychic energy fill the place with force fields that almost put it on a par with places like Glastonbury and Canterbury and Stonehenge. You don't know how lucky you are. The power of the place. Take off your gumboots and the strength of the ley lines almost burns the skin of the soles of your feet. Why, I have a friend with a cottage only a couple of miles away and nobody ever visits him and do you know why? Do you?' His voice at this stage had risen to a shriek that was rattling the window-panes. Thoroughly cowed, the audience, to a man, quavered 'No.'

'Well I'll tell you. Because the ley lines go whizzing straight past his front door and into this village and everyone who tries to call on him is carried along them straight to here. That's why there are so many tourists here in summer. It's obvious, isn't it? They can't help but come.' He made a waving motion with his hands. 'They're wafted down the ley lines. Now, how many of you know what a ley line is?' Nobody answered. We were all mesmerised by the idea of all those tourists wafting down the ley lines to end up with a bump outside the post office.

'The ley lines were first discovered thousands of years ago by our remote ancestors and they are lines of energy that girdle the earth. But, I hear you ask yourself, how do we know where they are? After all I could be some kind of lunatic talking absolute nonsense, couldn't I? You, sir.' He fixed his beady eye on Mike who was about the only member of the gathering who was paying very little attention to what was going on. Mike's interest was purely in the beasts of the field and he had only come to the meeting because it was rumoured that the communards were going to declare their premises an animal sanctuary and police it vigorously, which would cut out one or two rather useful pools on their stretch of the river. 'You sir, how do you think we know where they are?' Mike had obviously not got the least idea of what the man was talking about, but many years of never being able to answer any question posed by school teachers had given him sufficient experience to be able to deal with the situation.

'Dunno.'

'Well I'll tell you. Our ancestors' erections.' An old lady at the back of the hall broke into frantic giggles and had to be helped from the room by her concerned companion. After this hiatus, the rest of us turned back to the speaker, fascinated to discover what was to come next. 'Throughout the country, they buried their dead and erected megalithic tombs and monuments to their gods. Look at the map.' He made a signal to one of his platform companions who unrolled a large map of the British Isles which was criss-crossed by lines, presumably ley. He picked up a billiard cue from the table in front of him and rapped the map firmly. He rapped it just below waist level and the holder, understandably, flinched.

'These lines go through all the primitive sites. Take this one.' He smacked the map again and ran the pointer along one of his lines that brushed past the village. 'It starts here in Cornwall at a standing stone, passes through Avebury and ends up in Kent on a church spire before plunging across the Channel going through Europe, Asia and the Great Wall of China and getting lost somewhere in the Pacific. We have not yet discovered where it crosses the American continent. It's along these lines that the psychic powers that feed the world pass.' He went on tracing his lines with the audience enjoying themselves hugely. He was waving the billiard cue round like a conductor's baton and we were interested to see how much damage he would do with it. The map holder had already been given several painful raps in his nether regions and was now holding it with the wary care that an inexperienced bullfighter would show while holding his cape. His climax was a line which, with a few excusable meanders from the straight and narrow, ran from Land's End down 'here' to John O'Groats up 'there'. On his speedy ascent towards John O'Groats, the cue shot out of his hand and homed in on the next speaker who had been billed as a homeopathic feminist.

That was the end of the lecture. His victim had to be patched up by the local doctor who was seated in the best seats at the front and, while that was going on, the good Captain toured the hall distributing pamphlets on the science of ley lines. The next speaker was a tall striking woman in her forties with long hair, a kaftan and granny glasses. The atmosphere inside the hall was now one of suppressed hysteria with frequent snorts of laughter being hurriedly turned into fits of coughing. There were one or two more conservative members of the audience who were still looking disapproving, but the bulk of us had not enjoyed such a splendid evening since the local dramatic society had put on *The Sound of Music* with the Mistress of Foxhounds, a lady who had been pickled in gin for at least forty of her sixty years, in the role of Maria.

The granny lady was introduced to us as the time traveller. With enormous gravitas, she stood up and announced 'For many years I have been a traveller in time. In the company of others, I have cut across the spiral of time to live in other ages and experience other dimensions. I shall be starting up a group of time voyagers locally and you will all be welcome to join us. Together we will be able to journey to eras that have been and to those that are to come and to those that exist across the fluidity of our consciousness in concrete space in other isms. All you will need to bring is a towel.' It was the towel that broke the dam. There was an extremely ill-mannered but concerted roar of mirth from the entire audience and the meeting broke up in confusion.

That evening raised the reputation of the communards to great heights in the area. Previously there had been some reservations. Some saw them as hippy-type incomers who did little but wander aimlessly around sponging on the State, and country people prize self reliance above all other virtues. The communards had been heralded as a bunch of drug-sodden degenerates and the only kind of drug-sodden degenerate that was socially acceptable were those with a predilection for the bottle. But they had revealed themselves as glorious rip-roaring eccentrics and the pleasure that they had given to the villagers that evening carved them a secure place deep in the hearts of all those present.

It was never clear if the communards really appreciated their role. They demanded that we took them seriously but it was impossible for the locals to do so. Through courtesy, everyone tried, as it obviously mattered a lot to them, but they managed to strike the villagers' funny-bone almost every time they opened their mouths.

The homeopathic feminist took to organising groups of local women for meetings so that she could help them to liberate themselves from the yoke of their undoubtedly chauvinistic menfolk. What she failed to realise was that the women of the countryside were as fixed and traditional in their attitudes as their men and had their husbands on as tight a rein as that which was their own and were damned if they would ever let go. If she had gone about her enlightening slowly and carefully, she might have carried her group with her, but she suffered from the Commander's fault of going too fast too soon and left most of her fellow groupies far behind, sniggering helplessly in her wake. She nailed her flag firmly to the mast one evening in the pub during a conversation with Bill. They were talking about Americans. In particular a fairly local artist.

'I met Lonnie this afternoon,' Bill had said. 'He said he had just come back from New York where he had been asked to do a sculpture for a park and they had paid him $100,000 for it. I think the stupid sod thought I believed him. All his stuff is just blocks of concrete with holes in it.' The rest of those present had growled their agreement, everyone except Sally.

'I think his work is great. It's very subtle.'

'Nonsense,' scoffed Bill. 'It's junk and the Americans aren't stupid enough to pay good money for it.'

'I happen to know that his work is very highly regarded in the States,' replied Sally.

'How would you know that?' asked Bill.

'I was over there a couple of years ago at Christmas.'

'Really?' Bill was not particularly interested. He had only rarely been out of the village like most of the locally-born citizens and, to them, America was little more remote than the Costa Brava. Bill's only foreign excursions were to places like Ascot, Ayr and Chester and then only to the racecourses. 'Do they have Christmas just like us?'

'I would not know,' Sally had devastatingly replied. 'In order to escape the patriarchal aspects of the festive season, I spent time at a farm run for disabled Lesbians.'

In the silence that followed this announcement, Bill inquired, 'Are you a Lesbian?'

'Oh yes, but only as a political statement.' Predictably the pub howled with laughter and Sally huffily retired, never to return.

Chapter Six

FARMERS ARE the key figures in the countryside but, to visitors, they often appear shy and retiring creatures. They can be seen ploughing a lonely furrow in a desolate field. Sometimes you might see one swiftly cross an open meadow and vanish through a hedge on some mysterious agricultural errand that only he can know about. Better sightings can be obtained if you come across one trapped behind a herd of cattle on their way to the milking parlour or behind a flock of sheep on one of their periodic migrations between pastures.

To the visitor to the countryside, the average farmer is shy only in the way that a tiger is shy. He deliberately avoids the company of urban man, not through fear but through choice. If you wish a close sighting, loose your dog in a field of sheep or walk amid his standing corn. He will immediately pop up from behind a hedge and, if you are able, this will give you an opportunity to examine him at leisure.

Ignore, if you can, the red face and foam-flecked lips as the fury in barely comprehensible rural accents issues forth. Ignore, too, the stick or gun which will probably be brandished at you and the cur, which will be skulking or snarling at his feet. Note, instead, the typical scarecrow appearance, the ancient tweed jacket gone at the elbows and fixed round the waist with twine — that twine that provides a thread of continuity throughout the English landscape. It holds together bales of hay and straw, mends gates, repairs hedges and fences, agricultural equipment, tethers horses, cattle, sheep and dogs, as well as holding up countless thousands of pairs of agricultural trousers.

The nether regions of the farmer could be clothed in a pair

of jeans, but more likely in a pair of moleskin or corduroy trousers which are remarkable for their age and bagginess and will disappear into gumboots. If there is the remotest prospect of rain, the whole ensemble will be enveloped in thick black oilskins topped with a woolly hat or a tweed cap with cardboard poking through the brim. This outer layer will be encrusted with mud or dung which will crackle and slough off as he moves.

Our village, like most villages which are not overrun by commuters from the big towns and cities, depended on agriculture and farmers for its living. People mended agricultural equipment, shoed horses, did odd-jobbing round the farms, sold food and clothing to farmers and even the undertaker depended on the surrounding farmsteads for a high proportion of his customers. It was possible to tell fairly precisely who was being buried by the sort of people who attended the funeral. A scattering of middle-aged townspeople would mark the departure of one of their ancestors who had retired to the village to pass his declining years. If he had thrown himself into voluntary work in the manner that was expected, then there would be the addition of official villagers, club secretaries and the like.

If it was a true-born villager being planted, then the turn out would be greater and there would be rather less depression and solemnity. In the countryside, people are not insulated from life and death in the way that they are in the cities and it is treated as just another event, albeit the final event, in one's life. If it was a farmer being orisoned to his final rest, then the fun could be fast and furious. The most distinctive funeral that I can remember was that of a farmer who drank himself to death at the age of fifty-six. Perhaps describing him as a farmer was a misnomer since he had hunted all his days rather than worked on the land. His father had done all the work until he had retired and, by then, the departed's children had been old enough to take over and so he had not done a serious stroke of work in his life.

The village pubs were packed with gnarled brown countrymen off the Moors before the service and, during it, the church was full and they were shoulder to shoulder in the graveyard with the bottle being passed round with the speed of a ball on a roulette wheel. Afterwards a quarter of a mile long motorcade preceded by the hearse wound its way through the lanes on the twenty-five mile journey to the crematorium. The funeral procession had an hour's break at the Fox and Hounds on the way for an address and refreshments since, as the vicar said, the deceased had never passed the pub without stopping in his life, and he could see no reason why he should have to pass it in death.

Characters like him whose families had farmed the same patch of land for hundreds of years, are scarcely touched by the problems that afflict the majority of people who live in this country. Grenville Mowbray was a typical example of this breed. He had no idea and little interest in finding out how long his farm had been in his family, but he had a documented father—son succession going back to the mid-fifteenth century and there was no reason to suppose that their occupancy of the same few acres did not go back long before that. His ancestral holding lay on the edge of the Moor, a permanent denial to all those who believe that if a business stagnates, it dies. The two hundred acres that made up the farm were bordered on three sides by virgin moorland and it seemed a pretty safe bet that an ancestral Mowbray had farmed exactly the same two hundred acres half a millennium earlier.

The Mowbrays had been farmers all their lives. He and his wife were children of farmers and all their friends were farmers. Outside the narrow field of agriculture and its associated interests, the world was a closed book. Politics were of some importance because they could have a direct bearing on their incomes. But only agricultural politics. Both the Mowbrays voted Liberal because, in their part of the world, farmers had always voted Liberal but they only found out which party or candidate won an election if someone should happen to tell them, and that could be weeks later.

The arts had no place in their lives. Nor had any of the sports that can be seen on television, with the one exception of cricket. The farm did not have a television set. They had seen television a few times and had even had one on hire once, but the doings and lives of the inmates of programmes like

Coronation Street and *Dallas* had as much in common with their lives as Australian aboriginals and so they gave it back. Great national events passed them by. Wars, be they Falklands or World in their dimensions, never impinged. The Mowbrays were in the business of producing food, that most reserved of reserved occupations, and the dislocation of normal life that the Second World War meant for most of the population was only marked for them by the occasional visit of a bureaucrat from the War Agricultural Committee. They were not particularly aware of their good fortune because they did not know enough of the lives of others to make a comparison.

There is a remoteness from the mainstream of British culture in the lives of many who live in the countryside that can hardly be conceived by the rest of us. With the addition of a tractor or two, very little has changed over a hundred years. In one way, they are even more isolated. Old agriculture was an immensely social occupation with many of the tasks demanding great gangs of people to perform them with the consequent cross-fertilisation of ideas and information. Now it is one of the loneliest of jobs. The increase of mechanisation and the laws of economics mean that farmers and their families can live for days and weeks without needing to see anybody else.

Grenville was typical of this breed of farmer. He was a short man in his fifties, but immensely strong, who always wore a blue boiler suit. He never appeared to concern himself with anything but the immediate and the practical which could make him seem callous and unfeeling until you saw the tenderness with which he handled one of his sick animals. His one great passion in life outside his farm was hunting and his one great skill lay in handling horses. I used to visit him and his wife quite often. His wife appeared at first glance to be very much under her husband's thumb, but when she raised her voice Grenville listened and trembled and it was she who ran the money and made the business decisions on the farm while Grenville supplied the muscle.

One day I called out to borrow a chain saw from him. He was in his yard sucking his pipe and servicing his tractor. We greeted each other and gently passed the time of day.

'You know old George?' Grenville asked.

'Yes. What about him?'

'The silly old bugger went and hanged himself last week.'

Old George had been a fixture on Grenville's farm all his life. His father had been a ploughman for Grenville's grandfather during the last century and George had eventually inherited the job. He had been a miserable, cantankerous, stupid old devil all his days but he had been part of the farm like the hedges that he had mutilated, and the weeds that he had allowed to grow and so he had always stayed there. When he retired he stayed on, hating everyone and not being much loved in return. It did not surprise me that he had killed himself — it is quite a common cause of mortality in the countryside — but George had annoyed so many people during his life that he had been quite lucky that nobody had ever saved him the trouble of killing himself by doing the job for him.

'The old devil hanged himself in that barn over there.' Grenville indicated the relevant barn with a jerk of his oily thumb. 'I didn't know quite what to do. After all it's not every day that someone hangs themselves in your barn. So I asks the missus and she phones up Kelvin and he says to phone the police, so I phones the police.'

'And?' I prompted.

Grenville pulled himself out of the innards of his tractor and tipped the ever-present cap which warmed his bald head further back. 'Yes, I got the police out. They're a funny lot the police.' He looked reflective. 'Yes, a funny lot.'

'Why?' Some country people never stop talking. Others need the words plucked out of them like feathers from a dead chicken.

'Well, they came out here and I showed them old George, and do you know what they said?'

'What?'

'They asked me why I hadn't cut him down when I'd found him.' He looked at me in amazement that they could have taken such an attitude. 'Strange wasn't it? I mean I wasn't even sure if he was dead. If a fellow wants to hang himself, it's the least you can do to let him get on with it and as far as old

100

George was concerned, if he'd asked me, I'd have tied the bloody twine for him myself. You wouldn't have caught me cutting the old bastard down if I'd've thought there was any chance of him being alive.'

We exhausted the saga of old George and laid him firmly to rest. We moved on to a discussion about whether the hunt ball would be worth going to this year. The ball was one of the main fixtures in the local social round and bore as little relation to the upcountry shindigs as the *Farmers' Weekly* does to *The Tatler*. Conversation is a pleasant way to pass an hour or two. It was mainly gossip, as are most country conversations, since an intimate knowledge of the doings of all one's friends and neighbours is considered to be of prime importance. We carefully savaged the reputation of the new vet.

Vets have degenerated recently. They used to be people born and raised in the country who may not have had too much between their ears but had an instinctive feel for animals and their ailments. They would have grown up with them and college would only put a surface shine on their skill and knowledge. Vets, like artists, used to be born rather than raised. Now veterinary science is the most popular of university courses and thus the most difficult to get into. As a result, the country young are elbowed out by the city-bred students with clutches of 'A' levels who gain honours degrees and move confidently out into the countryside to annoy farmers with their arrogance and total lack of empathy for their patients. The wise vet relies on the farmer — who lives and breathes his animals all his waking hours — for the information that leads him to make his diagnosis. The young and inexperienced vet thinks he knows best. Grenville was just giving me a slanderous blow-by-blow description about how the new vet was killing his ewes because he had not yet realised that his meaty great hand did more harm than good when inserted in a small orifice during lambing when he was interrupted by Lady Country Gent riding past his yard.

Lady Country Gents on horses are a common sight in the countryside and they are best avoided at all costs. Horses are always best avoided at all costs in my opinion. All other forms of domestic livestock ultimately serve a useful purpose by being edible, but horses are just disasters waiting to happen. They either throw those foolish enough to ride them or they cause road accidents.

A feature of Grenville's yard was that the lane that came down to his farm rose up on a ridge twenty feet high and skirted his barns as it led on down to his neighbour's farm. In one of these barns, Grenville stacked his hay in a great cliff that rose up to the level of the lane. The barn was open sided which meant that the hay could be easily stacked up under its domed tin roof from the lane which avoided the necessity of ever having to lift a bale above one's head.

The Lady Country Gent was not someone that either of us knew, which probably meant that she had come down to enjoy some hunting. She looked a very typical specimen of her breed. Her horse was a flashy white-socked chestnut while she herself wore a headscarf and a green sleeveless padded jacket with her face reddened by decades of strong drink and the weathering that gradually turns the skin to leather if you sit on the back of a horse for too long.

'Excuse me,' she shouted down at us. The call of a Female Country Gent is one of the loudest and most penetrating sounds in nature. An irate specimen on the back of a horse, where they spend so much of their time, can stampede a herd of cows half a mile away should she happen to encounter a car filled with tourists on a narrow country lane. This one's voice caused the galvanised water trough next to us to vibrate and cover the surface of the water with tiny ripples. 'Where does this lane come out?'

I left this to Grenville. Female Country Gents always terrified me whilst he had known, in a biblical sense, quite a few in his time. It was one of the fringe benefits of his passion for horses and hunting. 'It's a dead end, missus,' he said back. Said was all he needed to do as she was only twenty yards away although above us on the ridge.

'Why is there no sign to say so then?' she thundered. It is another peculiarity of the Female Country Gent that they are unable to moderate the volume of their calls. Grenville said that it was the same in bed when a whisper from one caused flakes of plaster to drift down from the ceiling.

'I thought the sign that was already up there said enough,' said Grenville.

'Which sign?'

'The one that says "Private".'

She looked at him in total incomprehension. It had honestly never occurred to her that 'Private' could possibly have been meant to apply to her. Both sexes of Country Gent look upon the countryside as their own private fiefs, laid out for their pleasure and amusement. It also drives them insane with fury if the urban masses make the same assumption.

'But for heaven's sake, I am on a horse.' The animal had been getting rather restless. It was used to the volume of noise that normally issued forth from its owner's mouth, but it was being amplified by the curved metal roof of the haybarn and her long and piercing vowel sounds were swooping and wailing round our ears and must have been sheer hell for the animal since it was that much closer to their source. The animal began to prance. Its rider switched her attention from the two rather insolent peasants beneath her and concentrated on the task of controlling her beast. There would normally have been no problem as she could probably ride much better than she could walk, but the lane was rather narrow. On one side was the haybarn with its cliff of bales and on the other was a bank. She backed her animal which was hopping from one foot to the other like something out of the Spanish Riding School, towards the bank and there disaster struck.

Grenville kept cows and there is nothing that a cow likes better than to scratch its head and have a good root around in a nice bank of earth. It does not normally matter but in this case, there was a hedge above the bank and too much bovine activity could cause a landslip and block the lane and so Grenville had taken preventive measures. He had driven fence posts into the bank almost horizontally so that about eighteen inches had been left poking out and, from them, he had strung barbed wire. The horse, with superb accuracy, backed neatly onto one of these posts. The post was at exactly the right height and angle. I could see the animal's expression change. It had been mucking about as much because it had been bored as because of its rider's tannoy tones but, suddenly, the most intimate parts of its person were being invaded by a six-inch diameter chunk of wood. At the right time and in the right place, depending of course on the inclinations of the animal, it might not have minded or could even have enjoyed the experience — but in privacy, not when it was least expecting it with its homunculus upon its back.

The beast emitted a squeal of horror, slammed its tail down across its outraged orifice and leapt forward. It cleared the lane with one bound and landed on top of the hay under the barn roof. It was one of those times when swift action is called for; the beast began to kick and struggle its way towards the edge of the cliff, scattering bales as it went, making its insecure perch even more insecure at every moment and so Grenville and I sprang away from the tractor before we were squashed by half a ton of horse tumbling down from the sky like a gargantuan snowflake. We looked on with concern. The animal had thrashed its way right to the edge of the hay and its two nearside legs were now jerking about in thin air. Its rider was still sitting bolt upright in the saddle, sawing away at the reins, not having realised that the situation had developed beyond the stage where such actions could do any good. Grenville ran towards the bales and scurried up their vertical face like Spiderman. 'Get away,' shouted the rider. 'I can control the animal myself.' Grenville stood back on top of the bales until a particularly galvanic jerk from the horse sent its rider's head crashing into the tin roof of the barn and dislodged one of the corrugated iron sheets. Grenville proceeded to get cross.

'That's it,' he shouted. 'You and your horse can damage each other but I'm not having you knocking my barn to bits in the process.' He hopped across the top of the bales to the horse which paused momentarily in its attempt to work itself up into a panic-stricken lather to give him time to grab its reins. The animal was not prepared to give up that easily. It jerked back its head, snapped the reins and lurched towards the precipice. It should have known better than to tangle with Grenville. He drew back his fist and struck the animal a mighty blow between the eyes. The blow would have felled an ox, but all it had to do was fell a horse. The animal's eyes crossed, it gave a gentle sigh and lapsed into unconsciousness. Its rider, saved from serious injury at the very least, was not a bit grateful as Grenville, with little apparent effort, dragged the slumbering horse off his hay and back to the safety of the lane.

She berated him for striking her mount, frightening the animal and being in possession of dangerous hay bales. Grenville could only bear it for so long. He placed a massive hand on her chest and gave her a gentle shove. She tottered back into the ditch and sat down in the mud. Grenville returned down the hay to his tractor and we continued our conversation about vets as if nothing had interrupted us. Five minutes later, both horse and rider picked themselves up and staggered back up the lane in the direction from which they had originally come.

Both Grenville and his wife were passionate about the hunt. Twice a week during the season they would don their riding kit and go to the Meet. Not I am afraid in the immaculate scarlet coats that one might expect. Grenville in particular looked like something out of the eighteenth century. He wore a black riding coat that was going green at the edges and peppered with holes caused by moths and by contact with blackthorn hedges down the years. His pipe permanently showered his clothes and his immediate vicinity with ash and his clothes and his horse were covered in brown burn spots. He wore a white shirt and a white bow tie as was the convention but the picture that it should have presented was marred by the crushed greyness of shirt and tie as well as their pockmarking of yellow burns. The overwhelming impression that he gave was that of a man comfortable with himself and his situation. He fitted in his saddle as if he had been born there. His faintly ridiculous garb was part of a ritual that had been part of his father's life and his grandfather's before that.

It must be a bit like war, hunting. Long periods of dullness, sitting in the saddle in the winter chill waiting for the hounds to put up the quarry and then, if the hunter is lucky, a few minutes' frantic dash before the hounds lose the scent and the wait begins again. It is a primitive situation, full of primitive feelings and emotions. Most sports are, but in the towns they are enjoyed secondhand from the terracing whilst in the countryside, it is still possible to experience them directly.

Grenville was but one of a dedicated band of hunters. I had wanted to discover what could be the attraction of such an uncomfortable, cold and dangerous business for some time but was prevented from doing so because nothing on earth would persuade me to mount the back of a horse. It was not until Grenville broke his leg when a tractor rolled on top of him that I had my chance.

During his incapacity, Grenville was banned from the saddle and thus from direct mounted participation in the hunt. It did not stop him following the hounds, however, but he was restricted to bouncing after them as best he could from the driving seat of the only automatic-gearboxed Land Rover that I have ever come across. A couple of times, I took my courage in both hands and went with him to be introduced to the mysteries of the sport.

It was an alarming experience with his pipe showering ash over the interior of the vehicle and myself holding doggedly to any available projection as he hurled the thing across ploughed fields and attempted to bulldoze his way through hedges that the average horseman would not have attempted, let alone the average driver. It made him rather unpopular with his fellow hunting *aficionados* on horseback as they were unused to having to watch their front to avoid being carved up by a Land Rover. The usual car follower stuck to the roads somewhere far in the rear where they annoyed other road users rather than bucketed through woods with a plaster covered leg jutting through the window.

We were deep in the middle of a forest one damp morning, with the hounds sniffing about in a desultory fashion without much conviction that there had ever been a fox within fifty miles. There were several mounted hunters round us and we were all waiting for something to happen. Grenville was quietly reminiscing about great hunts of the past and there was a fine drizzle drifting down through the trees to the track where we were waiting. It was, as always, extremely cold.

I was idly watching one of the riders trying to shelter from the biting wind that whistled down the track beside an enormous rhododendron which must have stopped being a bush and become a tree half a century earlier. He was one of the fat city cats who like to come down to follow the hunt for the same sort of motives as our erstwhile shooting companion, Ross. In some of the higher echelons of urban society, hunting is a socially select pastime although most people prefer to be seen in the smarter hunts of the Midlands rather than down our way. However, they are welcomed by the farmers and the rest of the hunt regulars so long as they do not get in the way, because of the revenue that they bring in. This particular one was extremely fat and rather longer in the tooth than most and did not look that happy. He was a merchant banker, I decided.

I turned to Grenville who was waving his arms about to indicate the vast breadth of a river he had once jumped when a horn tooted in the distance and all the horses took off in its direction. The fat-cat's horse did the same but its rider fell off like a sack of potatoes before it had covered half a dozen paces. The horse went on. Grenville snorted in contempt.

'Look at that. These bloody people can't even keep their seats when their horse is virtually stationary.' The fallen rider was lying prone on the leafmould with his nose in a puddle. His friends were in no condition to help him as they were skittering down the track and looked as if they would have been unable to stop even if they had wanted to. Grenville and I looked throught the windscreen at the recumbent figure.

'Do you think we ought to go and see if he is all right?' I asked.

Grenville wound down his window and yelled across at him. 'Are you OK?' Answer was there none. It occurred to me that the position of his nose under six inches of water cannot have been helping his respiration and so I clambered out of the vehicle and went to give him a helping hand. I turned him over. As far as I could tell both his hunting days and his merchant banking days were over, an ex-huntsman if ever I had seen one.

'He looks a bit dead to me,' I observed.

'He was too fat to go hunting anyway,' Grenville replied.

'Let's have a look.' He started the vehicle and drove it the few yards to the fallen figure and peered out at him. 'He's knacker meat all right,' said Grenville.

'What should we do?' I asked as Grenville prodded him in the belly to see if he could get a reaction. He was prevented from replying by the arrival in the clearing of two other riders. To my relief one of them was a local doctor, as fanatic about hunting as Grenville, and the other was the Huntsman who was the administrative chief of the whole affair. The doctor was well over six feet tall and swore like a trooper. He was, therefore, immensely popular with his elderly female patients who kept on bequeathing their houses to him. If they had better stables than he had already, he moved into them. Otherwise he sold them and bought another horse or two. He came cantering up.

'What's wrong with him?' It seemed to be the sort of question that I should have been asking him rather than the other way round.

'He fell off his horse.'

The doctor looked down at the patient. His horse was blowing like Cyril Smith at the end of a marathon. 'Hm! Doesn't look too healthy, does he?'

'No, we think he may be dead,' I replied.

'Wouldn't surprise me a bit. Let's have a look.' He dismounted and examined the patient. 'Yes, he's dead. Probably a heart attack. Bet his horse is grateful.' He remounted his horse and with a wave of his crop, started to move off.

'Shouldn't we do something?' I asked hurriedly.

'You could try some heart massage. It's too late though.' His horse started to move sideways, in response to a kick in the ribs.

'How do you do that?' I asked despairingly.

'You know. Jump up and down on his chest for a bit.'

'Would you show us?'

'Sorry, must rush. It's my day off. Dr Martin is on call. You might give him a ring. But I can assure you, that fellow is dead.' He disappeared off down the track.

'He'd be like that if it was his own son if he was out

hunting,' said Grenville as he lit his pipe and dropped the match on top of the deceased. I thumped the corpse a few times in the ribs. The Huntsman, Ronald, came drifting over. He was an enormously lugubrious man. His was not a job that I would have fancied. He was responsible for ensuring that everyone had a successful and enjoyable day out by finding foxes for the hounds to chase and his employment depended on persuading his highly eccentric and often arrogant members that he was good at it. Huntsmen either have to have the strength of personality to dominate everyone, in which case they are wasted in their jobs and should become charismatic dictators or popes, or else they sink into defensive moroseness and avoid being steamrollered by the hunt followers through being unpredictable. Ronald belonged to the latter category, a small man with sandy hair who looked as if he would never say boo to a goose but prone to loosing off a stream of foul and highly original curses if anyone irritated him sufficiently. People regarded him with wary respect. It was part of Ronald's job to take an interest should any members fall off their horses and so he and a couple of sturdy young farmer acolytes came trotting over to investigate. He tipped his cap at me.

'Arright, Grenville?' 'Arright' was the local greeting. It had taken me several months to work out that it meant 'are you all right?' My slowness was in part due to an ancient neighbour whose 'arright' used to come out sounding rather differently from everyone else's. I eventually asked him about this and it transpired that his 'arright' was actually a slurred version of 'hard sense' which he had used as a greeting all his life for some reason that he was totally unable to explain.

Grenville nodded back. 'Arright, Ronald.'

'What's up with 'e?' He flicked his crop at the prone figure whom I was still thumping on the chest. 'I reckon you can stop hitting him now. It looks as though you've got him beat.'

'I'm not hitting him. I'm trying to give him heart massage. He collapsed.'

'Collapsed has he? Where's his horse?' Ronald, always a man to get his priorities in order, looked round the clearing.

Grenville swung himself out of the Land Rover and rested

his cast on the kneecap of the fallen horseman to keep it out of the mud. He waved his stick in the direction taken by the bolted horse. 'Get after it, Ralph,' said Ronald. One of the farmers nodded and thundered off through the trees. 'Why don't you give him mouth to mouth?' asked Ronald.

I stopped thumping the chest and looked at the face of the deceased. It was a point that I had considered in the past, whether one would tend to be selective about those whom one mouth-to-mouthed. With Bo Derek, for example, there would be no problem. But with Worzel Gummidge? While this character was not Worzel, he was also a long way from Bo Derek. Grenville perceived my difficulty. 'Why don't you try it, Ronald?' he suggested.

'I'm not bloody doing it. I think it's disgusting. Especially with a man and especially if he's dead. How about you?'

'No fear,' said Grenville. 'I couldn't get down to him with this leg anyway.'

That seemed to be the point when we all irrevocably committed the fallen hunter to the hereafter. 'I think we ought to phone for an ambulance,' I suggested.

Ronald looked round the muddy clearing. 'The trouble is that they'd never get an ambulance out here. Anyway there isn't a telephone within ten miles. Is he definitely dead?'

Grenville looked down at the recumbent figure critically. 'Yes,' he said decisively. 'I've been phoning the knacker all my life to bring him out to collect dead animals and I've never got a wrong one yet. He's croaked all right.'

'Had he paid his cap money?' asked Ronald.

'I think so,' replied Grenville.

'Let's have a look,' Ronald got off his horse and strode over. Ronald knelt by the corpse and felt inside his jacket. He pulled a wallet from his pocket and his receipt proved that he had paid for his hunting. Ronald grunted in satisfaction and leafed through the wallet. 'His driving licence gives his name. Does anybody know him?'

'I think he's probably staying at the hotel. There were a bunch of them down from London and his horse was that old screw that Miss Collard hires out to those who don't know any better,' replied Grenville.

'Where are his friends?'

'Dunno.'

Ronald stood and thought for a bit. 'I think the best thing to do would be for you to stick him in the back of your Land Rover and get him out of here.' Ronald, the remaining young farmer and I heaved the deceased into the back of the vehicle with Grenville directing us. He must have weighed a good fifteen stone so it was not surprising that his horse had not come back for a look. Ronald remounted and he and his companion gravely saluted us before cantering off to search for their hounds. I got in beside Grenville who started up the Land Rover and eased off in pursuit.

'Wouldn't it be quicker to go out the way we came in?' I asked since I knew that the track we were following opened out onto the Moor even further from civilisation than we were at the moment. Grenville did not reply for a moment as he was negotiating a pothole at a speed that almost brought the departed over into the front seat beside us.

'No,' said Grenville. 'The hounds are almost certain to go up the river and we can cut them off a couple of miles further up and then there's a likelihood of a damn good run as far as the hanging wood.'

'But aren't you going to take him to hospital?' I asked indicating our passenger who was now leaning against the tailboard and staring stonily at the back of my neck.

'What? And miss the hunting? He's in no hurry. It isn't going to bother him much if we don't get him to his coffin for a few more hours and anyway, he's paid for his day's hunting so he might as well get his money's worth.'

So a-hunting he went. I had to tie him down eventually to prevent him from bouncing over the tailboard as we went over some of the bumps. Whenever we stopped, a few of the other riders would drift over and peer curiously into the back of the vehicle as word had got around that we were carrying a casualty, that he had paid his dues and that there was a small doubt that he was actually dead. By the middle of the day, everyone had satisfied themselves that he was definitely beyond human aid and the rest of the hunt lost interest in him and concentrated on their sport.

At about 3pm, we hit a road and I prevailed upon the grumbling Grenville that we really ought to deliver our patient to hospital. He was beginning to look a little battered by this stage. Grenville and everyone else seemed to find nothing strange or abnormal in the idea of thundering after the hounds carrying a corpse behind us, but I found it very distracting and was unable to concentrate on the finer points of the day's events. We drove the Land Rover, covered in mud, to the local town. Grenville was grumbling like mad because I refused to allow him to take a couple of quid out of the deceased's wallet in order to pay for the petrol that he was being forced to consume in his role as a hearse driver. After all, I argued, in the parable it was the Samaritan who paid for the treatment of the fellow who was mugged, not the other way round.

With our approach to civilisation, I was beginning to feel a little happier. We had a brief debate when we came to the signpost at the entrance to the hospital. What was the appropriate department at which to deposit our cargo? It seemed a bit late to go to Casualty and we both agreed that we had not been faced with a need for Emergency for some time. Grenville was all for Goods whereas I favoured Cardiac since that had been the riding doctor's diagnosis. We asked a passing nurse for advice; she gave us a funny look and directed us towards Casualty.

Grenville parked the Land Rover by the entrance and I went to find someone to advise us on the correct procedure that we should take. There were about twenty people seated in the waiting room who stopped coughing and groaning as I came in and fell silent as I approached the reception desk. There was a powerful looking middle-aged woman in charge — the sort that would have been played by Hattie Jacques in one of the *Carry On* films.

'Excuse me,' I said tentatively.

She looked up at me with little of the spirit of the angel of mercy showing in her eyes. 'Yes?' she snapped.

I looked nervously round at the other patients who were all trying to pretend that they were not listening. 'We've got a body outside in the car.'

'A dead body?' She did not bother to keep her voice down as I had and there was a rustle of horror round the room. Death is the one unmentionable word in a hospital.

'That's right,' I said.

She looked at me carefully. I could see various thoughts like 'nutter' cross her face while I tried to convey sincerity and sanity to avoid the need to go into detailed explanations before our audience. It worked. She rose from her chair. 'Sit down and wait over there,' she said, indicating a vacant chair beside a small boy with his arm in a sling. I sat down. The child's mother gathered her offspring protectively to her bosom while I examined various posters on the wall about venereal disease and pretended that I could ignore the stares to which I was subjected.

After about five minutes, the receptionist re-appeared with a young Asian who, judging from the stethoscope which hung round his neck, was a doctor. She pointed me out and I rose as the doctor came over. 'Where is the er —'

'The er is outside.' I led the way with the doctor and the receptionist in my wake. A couple of the other patients rose to their feet and would have followed but a frown from the formidable eyes of the receptionist turned their legs to jelly and they sank back into their chairs. We went through the swing doors. Grenville had gone.

'Well?' said the receptionist.

'He was over there.' I replied, indicating an ambulance which now occupied the space that had held the Land Rover. The ambulance was disgorging an apparently endless stream of old ladies. I could see the doctor catch the eye of the receptionist and the thought 'nutter' flashed between them again. 'Hang on. I'll go and ask the ambulance driver if he's seen them.'

'Them?' asked the doctor. 'You mean there is more than one body?'

'No. There's only one, but I've got someone else with me who was driving.'

I went over towards the ambulance and discovered that he had shooed Grenville over to the car park because he had been occupying a space reserved for emergency vehicles. The driver was rather curt with me and I could imagine that Grenville had not taken too kindly to the idea of being moved on.

We walked across the tarmac towards the car park, a distance of about a hundred yards. Grenville was leaning against the side of the Land Rover with his muddy cast stretched out in front of him.

'There it is,' I said.

The doctor was muttering under his breath. 'I thought you said that you had a dead body.'

'I did.'

'That chap appears to have nothing more than a broken leg which has already been treated.'

'Oh, he's not the body. It's in the back.'

The receptionist cut in. 'You mean you really have a corpse in the back of that thing?' I could understand her incredulity. The vehicle was filthy with the mud that it had picked up in the ploughed fields that Grenville had forced it across and its windscreen was covered in British Field Sports Society stickers. The doctor said nothing more as Grenville nodded to him. I went round to the back of the Land Rover and peered in. Grenville had done his best to make the deceased look respectable by covering as much of him as possible with a fertiliser bag but there was a great deal of the deceased and only one bag.

'Christ!' said the doctor and he clambered into the back of the vehicle, whipped off the bag and put his stethoscope to the corpse's chest. He turned round to the receptionist. 'Quick. Go and get an attendant and a trolley.' The receptionist sped back across the tarmac like a galleon in full sail while the doctor started heart massage. Grenville and I watched him critically. He then knelt over, wiping off some oil that had attached itself to the deceased's lips, and started to administer mouth-to-mouth. Grenville wrinkled his nose in distaste.

'There's no point in doing that, he's as dead as a door post.'

'Are you qualified to judge?' snapped the doctor, pausing for a second in his work.

'You don't have to wait until somebody's a skeleton before you know that they're dead. That 'un's been dead for hours. He's gone stiff.'

Two attendants came rushing up with a stretcher and trolley and the remains were carefully removed from the back of the Land Rover and placed on it. Grenville placed his hunting cap on top of his belly and he was wheeled away with the doctor still blowing into his lungs.

Grenville turned back to his car and prepared to get in.

'Hadn't we better wait until this is all sorted out?' I asked.

Grenville was sick of the whole business. 'I don't see why. We've dumped the fellow here which was all that we were asked to do and if we hurry we might be back in time for the kill. I've a pretty good idea where the hounds might have gone.'

The last thing I wanted to do was to go back to the hunt. I felt in dire need of a stiff drink and was about to suggest it when we were summoned back into the hospital by a porter. We were seated back in the waiting room under the eye of the receptionist. Grenville looked the part better than I with his plaster-covered leg but it was not a comfortable experience. The corpse had been rushed through a minute or so earlier with the doctor trying to blow it up like a balloon and the other patients were well aware that we were responsible. Grenville took out his pipe but had to return it to his pocket when the receptionist tapped the top of her desk and indicated a 'No Smoking' sign on the wall.

Grenville was beginning to grumble when the telephone on the receptionist's desk buzzed. She picked it up and listened briefly. She replaced the receiver and looked across at us. 'You,' she said. 'Please go through to the second door on the left along the passage.'

We got to our feet and followed the instruction. 'Bloody National Health,' grumbled Grenville as we passed her desk. 'In the old days when we were allowed to pay the bill ourselves instead of through taxes, that cow would have called us "gentlemen" instead of "you". And she would have shown us the way.' He received a frigid look but was quick-witted enough to stick out his tongue at her before he went out of the room.

Behind the second door on the left lay a large office containing the Asian doctor, a desk, a few chairs and two policemen. They stopped talking as we entered and looked at us accusingly.

'The person you brought in is dead,' said one of the policemen, a sergeant, without preamble.

Grenville had long ago lost what little patience he had originally possessed. 'I know,' he replied.

The sergeant pounced. 'How do you know?'

'He's been bouncing about in the back of my Land Rover for hours and he hasn't asked me to stop for a pee once. He'd have to be either dead or have a bladder like an elephant.'

The policeman sighed. His question had obviously failed to catch Grenville off balance and lead to the quick murder confession that he had been after. 'It's not a matter for levity,' he said.

'Sorry,' I said on Grenville's behalf who was looking rather belligerent. The policeman laboriously took our names and addresses before picking up on the interrogation again.

'Now you hit this man with your car.' This was said as a statement rather than a question.

'Certainly not,' replied Grenville indignantly. We had been standing near the door and Grenville hobbled over to grab a chair in front of the desk and sat down. His leg shot out in front of him and the ferrule which the hospital had thoughtfully incorporated into the base of his cast caught the interrogating sergeant a sharp rap on the ankle. 'Sorry,' said Grenville and smiled sunnily.

'If you did not run this man over, how did you come by him?'

'He died of a heart attack,' said Grenville.

'Aha!' said the policeman. 'According to the doctor, he had extensive bruising which is not consistent with having had a heart attack.' He looked at the doctor for confirmation and received a brisk nod in return.

'He fell off his horse, you see,' I said.

'You're changing your story are you? You can't have it both ways. One of you says he had a heart attack and the other says he fell off his horse.'

I have learned down the years that in any dealings with the police, the most important requisite is endless patience and the ability to explain each point several times in words of one syllable before moving on to the next one. 'We think he fell off his horse because he had a heart attack, sergeant, and the fall might account for any bruising.'

'According to the doctor, the body is covered in very extensive bruising.'

'It doesn't surprise me a bit,' put in Grenville. 'As I said, he's been in the back of the Land Rover and we went over some rough ground. We hadn't any cushions and, even if we had, it would have been a bit of a waste to have given them to him under the circumstances.'

'When did this alleged heart attack take place?'

Grenville looked over at me, 'I think it was about half past ten this morning.'

The sergeant looked startled. 'But that was about five hours ago. Why didn't you phone for an ambulance straight away?'

'We couldn't,' said Grenville. 'We were out hunting in the middle of the Moor and there wasn't a phone for miles.'

'But why did you not bring him in straight away?'

'Because we were out hunting. It seemed a pity to break off and it wasn't as if we were in a hurry. It wouldn't have done him any good.'

The sergeant lost his official cool. 'You lot who live on the Moor are bloody barbaric.'

'Get stuffed,' said Grenville.

That was the end of the matter as far as we were concerned. Grenville grumbled about his petrol money for a week or so and was only partly mollified when Ronald gave him the brush of the fox that had been the victim of the day's sport. I gave up hunting and stuck to fishing in future. I found it less traumatic.

Chapter Seven

THERE HAD BEEN vague rumours doing the rounds for some time that 'they' were going to push a road past the village. It was not going to be for our benefit but in order to link a couple of market towns together. They were currently joined by a perfectly adequate road for local purposes but it was blocked for a few weekends each year by lemming-like hordes of tourists on their way to the coast and 'they' had decided that something ought to be done about it.

It was not something that had interested me very much initially. I entertained an ineradicable dislike of all those who plan and build roads since we found that we had been unable to sell a house a decade earlier when the searches done by a prospective buyer had uncovered a musty plan for a bypass and one of the suggested routes had run straight through our sitting-room. The buyer had decided not to go ahead with his purchase as a result.

However, this road did not appear to come within half a mile of the mill and so it had not seemed to concern us until I was buttonholed by Ivor on one of the last shoots of the season. It had been typical of many of our days out since the hotel had joined the syndicate. There had been three guests this time and they had created the average number of problems. They were all Americans. Two were tycoons of some kind and the other was the senior tycoon's bodyguard and flunkey. The senior tycoon was one of those elderly Americans who seem to rattle as they walk, pepped to the eyeballs on vitamins and extract from the testes of unborn monkeys. The sort that one does not dare call wonderful for their age because the illusion that they try to give is that they are still in their prime.

He was given all the best stands and the flunkey stationed himself twenty yards behind him, looking like the sinister mafia heavy that he undoubtedly was. The tycoon would stand still, trembling slightly, until a bird came over whereupon his minder would shout 'Over'. The tycoon then creakily lifted his gun to his shoulder, the sun glinting on his aviator's-style mirror sunglasses and the wind ruffling the roots of his dyed, transplanted hair, and fired into the air. At the same time the minder neatly and economically blew the bird out of the sky and shouted 'Great shot, boss!' Dennis found the process so fascinating that he quite forgot to keep himself topped up from his flask and said that he had enjoyed his first totally sober day for a month.

The other American only came into his own during the lunch break. He was some sort of undertycoon and showed a cringing subservience to the older man. His dress of scarlet sweater and sky blue trousers with gold chains and medallions clanking at his wrists and neck, may have been the very thing for the golf courses round Las Vegas, but it made the pheasants that came towards him stall in the air and flap, croaking with terror, back to the coverts and no amount of persuasion would force them into the air over him again.

The hotel had laid on a Balmoral-style picnic banquet for us and our exotic guests in the middle of the day and we celebrated it in one of Dennis's haybarns. The Americans sat slightly apart from the rest of us with the flunkey cutting up the boss's quail into handy bite-size chunks that would not spoil the shine on his gold and porcelain teeth. There was a certain frigidity in the air since Ivor had insisted that the Americans unload their guns before they came into the barn. We suspected that it had been the first time that the flunkey had been without a loaded gun since he left school.

After the meal, we stood about in the yard again waiting for the junior tycoon who had gone off somewhere mumbling something about a washroom. The phrase obviously had its precise meaning in transatlantic terms but he had been variously directed to the dairy, a water trough and a standpipe while Dennis, always inclined to be rude to those whom he considered to be from the Colonies, had put him on the spot by asking him what on earth he wanted to wash after a meal rather than before it like most civilised people. Ivor was just beginning to become impatient and was about to go and seek him out when there was a volley of yells from round the corner of one of the barns and the American came into view, all glittering bracelets and primary colours. We would have then got on with the shoot except for the fact that he was preceded by forty half-grown pigs.

It transpired, with the characteristic modesty of his race, he had felt it uncouth to urinate in the open where he might have shocked himself if not any passing sparrow, and so he had entered a barn to utilise its comforting darkness. Unfortunately he had not noticed that the chosen barn housed these forty pigs which had taken their chance and escaped while he had been in mid-flow. An embarrassing navy blue patch on the sky blue of his trousers made manifest that he had cut himself off in his prime in an attempt to minimise the disaster, but he had been too late.

Shooting was delayed for an hour while we harvested the livestock. Senior tycoon was permitted to sit on a hay bale and watch, but everyone else had to help. The minder was most reluctant as he felt that his duty lay in protecting his master from any possible attack from marauding porkers but he was overruled. The humiliated junior tycoon was taught by Mike to catch the pigs by selecting a target and running after it and diving at it in a flying rugby tackle to carry it squealing and kicking back to its pen. The method worked quite well for Mike, as he had waterproof plastic trousers that could be hosed down after the event, but the chocolate box American stank like a skunk for the rest of the day although the brown camouflage muted his garments and gave him rather more success in shooting pheasants.

At the end of the day, Ivor buttonholed me. He had been told that this new road would be going right across his farm and he was organising a public meeting to work out opposition plans to the proposals. He had been promised a good turn-out and would be grateful for my presence since I had already had some experience of dealing with the particularly rampant brand of bureaucrat who build roads.

The meeting was to be held in the squire's house the following evening. These days, squires are in decline as a species. Their old authority has been eroded by taxation, the increase in prosperity of their inferiors and their own lack of brainpower as a result of centuries of inbreeding within their own limited class. There are exceptions to the last point, but our own squire was not amongst them. He possessed bags of the misty arrogance that so infuriates those of a socialist persuasion. He did not just think that he was superior to the rest of mankind, he knew it. He also had a Kojak-bald head and a complexion that varied between a healthy pink and the multi-shaded reds and scarlets of an Hawaiian sunset as the waves of his frequent ire washed over him.

In spite of this, he was a much loved figure locally. He represented ancient continuity in the village where his ancestors had done their best to exercise droit de seigneur for so long. His bark was worse than his bite because the modern age had left him virtually toothless and the villagers who were the targets of his wrath would wait patiently for his tirades to end before patting him affectionately on the back and going on their way and recounting the incident in the pub later with all the pride of one telling of the antics of a pet bear.

Unfortunately the squire and I were not good friends. We had had a confrontation shortly after I had moved into the village which had damaged any chance we had of building up a relationship. I had been quietly weeding the garden one evening, an occupation of extraordinary tedium, when bullets had begun to whistle past my ears and ping off the front of the house. It was just like being in some cowboy film. Whimpering with terror, I had hugged the ground and crawled to safety behind a tree where I had sat and listened to the shots and the bullets bumble-beeing by.

After a bit, my fear was augmented by a feeling of outrage. The shots were too random to be aimed specifically at me, I reasoned. Therefore it must have been some tearaway banging away at random and, with a sense of righteous wrath deep in my still quaking bosom, I leopard-crawled my way across the lawn and into the neighbouring field from where the shots seemed to be coming. Actually a healthy sense of self preservation was still coursing through my veins. Young tearaways were something that I treated with great caution. The previous month I had been in charge of 'hurling the weight' at a local fete and it had been won by a Neanderthal fifteen-year-old, as wide as he was tall, clothed in black leather and ear-rings. He had hurled the fifty-six pound weight about five yards further than anyone else and I would no more tangle with someone like that than I would with a bull.

The shots were coming from a small wood at the far side of the field. I tiptoed through the trees, avoiding cracking twigs underfoot and tripping over branches, ready to make a swift exit should the object of my search present a potential danger. It was the squire, of course, although I did not know it at the time. All I saw was a small elderly man with a bald pink head and a Groucho Marx moustache armed with a .22 rifle on whom it looked fairly safe to vent my spleen. I came out from behind a tree — not too far in case I had to duck back behind it. 'You there,' I shouted. 'What the hell do you think you are playing at?' I had clearly caught him by surprise because he jumped.

There is an expression often used of elderly colonels and the like that describes their reaction when they become cross whose imagery I had never really understood until that moment, but he went red in the face and began to gobble like a turkey, real gobble gobble noises. I was entranced. It was like coming across a fully-fledged angel for the first time. One had heard about such creatures but had not necessarily believed that what one had heard was true. This gobbling gunman was trying to work himself up into a rage so that he could take the initiative, but I had started off on the right foot and was not about to let him off the hook. 'You irresponsible hooligan,' I said. 'You were spraying the village with bullets from your silly little gun. Have you got any right to be here? I've got a good mind to call the police. It's people like you that ought to be put away.' I was being ill-mannered but I was enjoying myself and it was a wonderful release to be able to get rid of my terror on someone who was so much smaller than myself. I had always thought that I could have made an excellent bully in my youth if only I had had the courage, but fear can give you courage.

He was still gobbling but did his best to resurrect himself. 'How dare you talk to me like that.'

It was a brave attempt but I ruthlessly beat him down. 'Dare? Dare?' I bellowed. 'You tried to shoot me, sir.'

'I was only shooting rooks,' he replied feebly. That fact was plain to behold as the ground was littered with his victims which had tumbled from the rookery that was set in the tops of the trees. What must have been happening was that some of his shots were bouncing off the branches and ending up in our front garden.

'Well stop it this instant. A man of your age ought to have enough sense to know that you should always be careful of where your stray shots might go. You have no right to have a gun.' He suddenly stopped gobbling. I had hit him in the pit of his metaphorical stomach. The essence of being a country squire lies in being a safe and accurate shot, just as the essence of being a young blood lies in being a devil with the girls and the best driver since Jackie Stewart. By justifiably impugning his shooting, I was hitting at his very manhood. All the bluster went out of him.

'I am most dreadfully sorry.'

'I should hope so too. Do you live round here?'

'Yes.'

'Well, don't you dare come back here again. It's private property as I'm sure you know.' He most certainly did since he owned the place himself, but he allowed himself to be driven out of his wood, leaving me in sole command. I nearly said 'cock a doodle do' and flapped my wings but went back home and poured myself a stiff drink instead to celebrate. I discovered who my potential assassin was the following day and although our paths crossed quite frequently in the following months, neither of us ever mentioned our initial encounter.

The meeting to discuss opposition to the proposed road was billed to start at 8pm. I arrived a quarter of an hour before that and was greeted by the squire at the door. As always, I contented myself with a curt nod while he, as usual, went from pink to mauve through to puce. I went on into the house. It was an enormous pile of a place that was reputed to cost £40 a day to keep warm, which meant that it was always freezingly cold. In the heyday of the squire's family, they had owned several thousand acres, but times were harder now and the estate had shrunk to woodland and a small dairy farm. The squire was a magistrate, on the committee of the Country Landowners' Association and a great friend of Dennis, but none of these activities brought in a great deal of money and so the house was falling down about his ears. He had fathered three daughters who had married well, but the modern breed of young aristocrat who makes his fortune in some shady way in the City, has such expensive tastes that he holds on to his money like grim death and none of it had come the squire's way.

I followed my nose down the corridor lined with wallpaper

and hunting prints that showed tide-marks left by damp down the years. As with the growth rings on a tree, one could work out which were the dry seasons and which were the wet seasons of many years ago from examining them. At the end of the corridor was the ballroom. Ivor had done very well. The room was lit by a dusty chandelier which hung from the centre of the ceiling and it contained about a hundred collapsible chairs, most of which were occupied. I knew only about half the people there by sight and most of those were local farmers whose livelihoods would be directly affected by the new road. Ivor had a problem which I discovered when I went over to Kelvin, our Parish Council Chairman, who put it with his customary finesse.

'Good evening, James. So Ivor's got you to come along as well? You know he should have come to the Council and asked our approval before calling this meeting. I would have been quite happy to chair it if he had asked me. But look at it.' He swept his eyes contemptuously round the room. 'Most of the people here don't even live in the Parish. I think it's a bit of a cheek having all these strangers in on something that ought to be decided amongst ourselves.' Bill was seated beside him and he nodded in solemn agreement. Grenville's wife, Mary, was not having any of it.

'Don't talk nonsense, Kelvin Morchard. This road is going to affect half a dozen parishes apart from this one and Ivor's the only person who's got the gumption to organise a united opposition to it.'

'But if he had brought it up at a Parish Council meeting first, we would have voted against it and that would have stopped the road and saved the trouble of calling this meeting.' Kelvin had a touching faith in the power of local democracy. The chairmanship of the Parish Council was the limit of his own ambition and so he found it difficult to imagine a higher authority. It made him rather vulnerable to the sardonic humour that Bill could sometimes employ against him.

'That's right, Kelvin. We could have written to the Prime Minister and said that we had voted against it and that would have nipped the idea in the bud,' said Bill.

'Absolutely true,' replied Kelvin seriously.

'You're just a damn fool, Kelvin Morchard, and you always have been,' said Mary. Mary could be as forceful as Grenville and, being from a neighbouring parish, she had no need to kowtow to Kelvin. Kelvin's ultimate authority came from his ownership of just about the only level field in our Parish where local sports, fetes and football were held provided Kelvin gave his permission. Some said that Kelvin had machiavellied the failure of the Common drainage scheme so that his power base would not be affected by the parishioners having an alternative venue. The machinations of a Parish Council make the political deviousness of the United Nations look pale in comparison.

The meeting was called to order by Ivor. He was extremely good at that sort of thing. He would have made a first-class diplomat as he was an excellent massager of egos more tender than his own, had a hide impervious to the barbs of others and the patience of a broody hen. His skills were apparent right from the start. 'Ladies and Gentlemen, before we get on with the meeting, I would like to call on the vicar to say a short prayer.'

'Like grace,' whispered Mary and Kelvin frowned her into silence.

The average rural parson might be reduced to rushing between the churches of his group parish dispensing holy wafers like an ice-cream salesman to his few elderly communicants, but he still occupies a ceremonial position on occasions like this.

'Lord,' intoned the vicar, a retired central heating engineer from Dagenham. 'Bless these deliberations and let us not forget that this road is a scandalous waste of money when those, our brothers, in the Third World are still dying in their millions from malnutrition which it is our duty to alleviate.' There was a good deal of coughing and rustling round the hall at this. The vicar had still not learned, after two years in his job, that the locals regarded those in the next county as dirty foreigners for whose wellbeing they felt no responsibility. As for those of different hues on other continents, the sooner they were turned back into slaves to be exploited by true-born

Englishmen, the better off they would be. The vicar sat down and Ivor rose hastily to his feet before the restiveness of the audience translated itself into catcalls or something even worse. He outlined the road proposal, the essence of which was that it would cost some thirty million pounds and comsume the best part of a thousand acres of farmland. The meeting rumbled its disapproval and the communards in the front row hissed.

'I would first like to hear from anyone with ideas and opinions that will help us in our fight against this monstrous violation of our countryside—' there was a mass movement in the room as half those present began to rise to their feet, '—and I would remind you' continued Ivor hastily 'that our most urgent need is for money so that we can effectively fight this proposal and so donations and ways of obtaining donations are what we are most in need of at this moment.' There was a sigh of horror as the import of Ivor's last remark sank in. Talking was one thing but being asked to shell out money was quite another and a gross breach of etiquette. Everyone sat back and looked at their shoes. There was silence until, after some urgent whispering on my left, Kelvin was suddenly catapulted to his feet and stood there looking rather uneasy in his best suit.

'Mr Chairman,' he stared. 'I feel it is my duty to speak out this evening.' Kelvin tucked his thumbs into the pockets of his waistcoat and leaned back expansively, collapsing his chair onto the woman sitting behind him. After the resulting kerfuffle had been sorted out, he continued, 'I feel that it is my duty to bring to the notice of this meeting that the question of this road has not yet been brought before the Parish Council of the Parish in which this meeting is being held and thus, since no vote has been taken, neither myself nor the Chairman of this meeting are authorised to speak on behalf of the aforesaid body.' Kelvin sat down to a rather puzzled silence and I could see Ivor cursing himself for not having foreseen this problem. Kelvin had once read an article in the dentist's waiting room about the collective responsibility of cabinet ministers and had interpreted it to mean that Parish Councillors should not comment on any subject from the

Bomb to the colour of the new barmaid's knickers without a vote having been taken on the matter.

Ivor stood up. 'Thank you, Mr Morchard. I am, of course, aware that the Parish Council of which you are Chairman is unable to express an opinion. However I, like you, am here in my personal capacity—'

Kelvin sprang to his feet, 'On a point of order, Mr Chairman, I am here because I feel it is my duty to take note of any events that take place in this Parish on behalf of my electors. I am here in my official capacity.' The remainder of the audience was beginning to wonder if this was a personal quarrel or whether they might be allowed to join in.

Dennis suddenly popped up from the far side of the room where he was sitting by the fire in one of the few armchairs. 'I would like to make a suggestion, Mr Chairman. Since the details of the road are now well known although they have only become clear since the last Parish Council meeting, and I believe that most if not all the councillors are present this evening, I suggest that we vote now for or against the road and then we will be able to record our views on behalf of this community.' There was a burst of applause from the audience, led by the communards who made up a significant proportion of the electorate. Dennis bowed his appreciation.

Kelvin went into a huddle with the Parish Clerk who was seated two rows behind him and we all waited breathlessly for his response. He rose to his feet. 'Mr Chairman, the suggestion from my friend by the fire brings the dignity of the Council into disrepute and I reject it out of hand. As is very well known to him, we hold our meetings on the last Thursday of each month and that meeting is the only proper place at which such a vote could be taken.'

It looked, for a disappointing moment, as if Kelvin was going to win the day, but the cavalry was riding to the rescue. Another figure rose. There was an excited mutter from around the room. It was the local MP, an unctuous little swine in my opinion, but none the less he was a really big gun for whichever side he should join. He was that breed of Parliamentarian who liked to pretend that he was on Christian name terms with all his constituents and could come embarrassingly unstuck when he got his filing system in a muddle. He was wearing a tweed tie with his usual blue pin-stripe suit to denote that he was out in the countryside.

'Mr Chairman, Kelvin, Dennis,' he beamed at us all. A few beamed back. 'I think I may be able to assist in this matter. The Council may have a meeting wherever it so decides. It depends on what the members wish.' Dennis and Kelvin both leapt to their feet. Ivor selected Dennis.

'In that case, sir, I would like to ask those on the Parish Council to rise and vote upon whether or not they wish to support this road proposal.' Nine out of the ten members stood up. The only one missing was old man Bardsley and he did not really count anyway. He had not attended a regular meeting for a decade but he tottered round the village just before each election saying 'The council is all I have to live for. If I don't get elected, I might as well die.' It was a wonderful vote-winning formula that guaranteed that he came top of the poll every time.

Kelvin shrieked, 'On a point of order Mr Chairman. I would like to remind you that it is my duty to place a motion before members of this Parish Council and nobody else's.' Ivor nodded. 'Therefore with reluctance I would ask those in favour of this road proposal to raise their hands.' Nobody did. 'Those against,' all save Kelvin raised their hands. 'I would like it recorded that the Parish is officially opposed to the Road with one abstention which is myself as Chairman. I would like to—' The rest of Kelvin's speech was drowned by cheers and he sat down to much headshaking from his immediate cronies.

Ivor stood again to more applause. 'Now that the Council has decisively recorded its opinion, I would be grateful for further comments. Perhaps I could ask our Member of Parliament to speak on the subject. I know we are all grateful that he has taken time out of his busy schedule to be with us this evening.'

The Member got up. He had a rather breathless delivery and tended to gabble which added to his general air of shiftiness. His message seemed unequivocal enough. After galloping round the houses for ten minutes giving rise to fears that he was practising the subtle political art of saying nothing at all in the greatest possible number of words, he suddenly stated 'I would like to put it on record that I am totally and utterly opposed to the Department of Transport's proposals for this new road and I will counter it most vigorously in all the arenas that are open to me.' The meeting was turning into a celebration.

The next speaker was an impeccably middle-class matron from one of the conservation bodies who told us that the road was going to go through an area of outstanding natural beauty and would destroy several SSSIs. It sounded a thoroughly wicked thing for it to do so we all clapped again, particularly when she said that her organisation was prepared to handle its share of the financial responsibility for opposing the road.

After her, we had the correspondent for the local newspaper. This was a bit of a surprise as journalists, like small children, are usually seen and not heard on such occasions, but he managed to puncture the euphoria. 'Mr Chairman, I would like to ask our Member of Parliament to clarify his position.' This was puzzling as all of us had thought that the Member had made his position delightfully clear. 'I have here a copy of a letter in which he states that he is in favour of not one, but two new roads and he thinks that the one that skirts the village ought to be upgraded to motorway standard instead of merely being built as a trunk road as is the present intention.'

'Er,' said Ivor. He was a bit out of his depth on this one. The Member appeared to be engrossed in conversation with his neighbour.

The journalist continued, 'He said that he is totally opposed to the proposals for this new road which is true. However, he is opposed to it because he does not think it goes far enough. He is trying to promote an even more damaging change to the environment than the one to which he is opposed.' There was a buzz of talk after he had sat down.

After a little more discussion with his next-door neighbour whom I discovered was his agent, the MP was on his feet once more. It takes a lot more than being found out to faze a politician. 'Mr Chairman, I deeply resent the implications made in the remarks by the last speaker. Whatever the truth of the documents he says that he holds, they are copies of private correspondence written some time ago during a period when we were all exploring the possibilities of improving road communications in this region.' He was off on a broad ranging history of Great Britain with particular reference to its transportation system. Once the audience had become thoroughly confused and was beginning to think about falling asleep, he repeated his ringing declaration. 'I am opposed to this proposal. I shall fight it here. I shall fight it at Westminster. I shall fight it until it is completely withdrawn.' The three-point punchy ending is capable of milking applause out of a shop window full of dummies and he sat down to a ripple of clapping.

The journalist was quite right of course. Not content with sitting on the fence, the MP was trying to be on both sides of it at once, promoting the idea of the road to his urban constituents and opposing it out in the countryside. Not surprisingly, he was a one-term Member.

Apart from that, Ivor's meeting was an unqualified success. We had the county secretary of the National Farmers' Union in a tweed suit and the Country Landowners' secretary in a grey suit and Guards tie, each in the uniform acceptable to his members. We had most of the local environmental organisations represented, who listened uneasily to farmers complain about the road as an interference with their intensive farming methods. There was a sweet man who had us all enthralled with his ideas about bringing back steam engines and filling the countryside with the sound of train whistles and plumes of white smoke along the valleys.

The meeting hog was the secretary of the Ramblers' Association. I had come across him once before. I had been asked by a friend to spray some ragwort for him. It is a very pretty yellow flower that has ruined its chances of becoming as widespread as the dandelion through being poisonous to livestock, so poisonous that it is against the law to allow it to grow on one's land. It is unlikely that you will have the Special Patrol Group paying you a dawn visit if you have the odd plant around, but it is one of the few laws that has the whole-hearted support of country people.

This farmer had a ditch full of the stuff and it would wait until it thought he was not looking before sneaking under the barbed wire fence in an attempt to colonise all the tasty clumps of grass where it could ambush any livestock foolish enough to come too close. It overreached itself one day and I was summoned to eradicate it.

Spraying weeds, particularly weeds as evil as ragwort, is a very pleasant occupation on a summer's day. There is a satisfying feeling of power as you bathe the plant in a fine mist of weedkiller. You know that the plant's initial reaction is one of gratitude that you care sufficiently to water it and you are far away when the realisation dawns that it has entirely misinterpreted your intentions. So I was humming cheerfully to myself when this rambler hove into sight on the footpath that ran alongside the ditch. He was in his fifties with a great bull neck emerging from his yellow anorak on top of which was a grizzled crew-cut head. Like all ramblers, he wore thick leather boots, the like of which no countryman has worn since the Good Lord invented the gumboot. All ramblers are townspeople. A countryman would no more walk the landscape for pleasure than his urban counterpart would tour the local industrial estate. The rambler paused in his dogged progress and scowled at me. I wished him a cheerful good afternoon in return.

'You vandal,' he growled. 'How could you spray God's countryside with your filthy chemicals!'

I considered this remark for a while, chewing over the depth of ignorance and arrogance that it revealed for a few seconds before a wave of pure and beautiful rage swept over me. Words, the like of which I had never used before, flowed from my lips and he hurriedly continued on his way with my curses arrowing into the back of his rucksack.

Apart from the boredom created by the Rambler and the deviousness of our Westminster representative, the meeting went very well. All those present agreed to support the cause and some of them even flashed their cheque books around. The one thing that Ivor forgot to do was form a committee and a couple of days later he telephoned me to tell me that he had decided to make me his policy director as I lived just

133

down the road from him and was thus easily available to ratify any decisions he should feel like making.

The first decision that he took was to go up to London to hire a barrister to represent us at the forthcoming public inquiry and would I come along as well to hold his hand. He also wanted to go to Battersea Dogs' Home to select a replacement for one of his pack of untrained dogs which had been shredded by a forage harvester and, following the success of our dog, he would be grateful for my advice on that matter too. Our first call was to Battersea where, under the *sotto voce* instructions of a kennelmaid, we selected a yellow labrador puppy which was said to have a sweet nature. We deposited it on the back seat of the car and went to call on our barrister.

His chambers were real London-smoothie country with buttoned leather chairs and signed photographs of minor Royals on antique-style side tables. The barrister had gathered together a travelling circus of public inquiry experts to meet us and they coolly talked shop about Inspectors they had known and past defeats in which they had participated. It was rather disconcerting to discover that it was virtually unheard of for an inquiry to go against the government department which had initiated it. Equally worrying to me was the difficulty we had in finding out how much the whole exercise was likely to cost us. These men were professionals and one of the distinguishing marks of any professional is that he likes to adhere to the convention that the fee for his services is of minor importance and the task of extracting the several pounds of flesh that he feels is his due is best left to clerks and debt collectors with whom he pretends he has nothing to do. I broke into a conversation about COBA, apparently something concerning the buildworthiness of a road.

'How much is all this likely to cost?' It was a bit like farting in church. There are some things that are just not done or said. Even Ivor was sufficiently taken in by the atmosphere of elegant intellectual gossip and banter to consider that the question was slightly *infra dig* and looked at me in a pained fashion.

'There was an inquiry up North somewhere that we attended,' said the barrister. He was about forty with his slick blond hair pulled back from his face in a flattened Heseltine. He had about six inches of white silk shirt showing at his cuffs and had one manicured hand resting on the ankle of his crossed leg. His black shoes had a little gold Gucci chain across the instep. Ivor was sitting opposite him in much the same position and the difference in their characters was shown by the soft white hand of the barrister and Ivor's orang-utan farmer's hands with their battered blackened nails, callouses and notched scars.

'Oh yes, Simon, I remember,' said the environmental expert. He wore black brogues to show his country affiliations. 'They did frightfully well in raising money. They had an antique auction, didn't they? They raised something like £10,000 through it.' Ivor and I both blinked a bit. About the only antiques in our neck of the woods were ancient fox masks commemorating great deeds of the past which were as precious to their owners as are shrunken heads to New Guinea tribesmen.

'What about that client of Henry's in Wales? They did jolly well too.'

'Oh yes,' said Simon the Barrister. 'I'd forgotten about that. Some splendid scheme or other. Hang on.' He picked up his telephone and dialled two numbers. 'Henry? I've got a couple of these road chaps with me. Yes, that road. What was it that your Welsh friends did a few years back that raised all that money? A chain letter? How wonderfully simple! How much did it raise? Really? Well worth while then.' He put the phone down and turned to Ivor. 'Just a chain letter within the county. It raised thousands.'

'What's Henry on at the moment?' asked the environmentalist.

The barrister did look slightly discomfited, 'Oh he's on this inquiry too, the department have briefed him.'

'Who's Henry?' I asked.

'He's just down the corridor. We share chambers. Wonderful chap. Quite wonderful.'

The fable of the lawyer and the oyster floated through my head and Ivor himself seemed a little surprised by this incestuous set-up, but I determinedly came back to the unmentionable subject. 'How much is all this going to cost?'

The professionals still looked as if I had released a nasty smell under their noses but Ivor had moved onto my side and was looking interested.

'Impossible to say,' said the barrister, blandly avoiding my eyes and looking instead at a photograph of his wife and two golden children standing in front of their Hampstead house.

'Why?' I asked. Ivor gave me a warning look. This mink-lined shark came highly recommended and we did not want to frighten him off.

'Because nobody can tell how long the inquiry will go on for. The more successful we are, the longer it takes. I told Henry that this could be a long one.'

'Do you think we will win?' asked Ivor eagerly. This was obviously another solecism as they all looked slightly shocked.

'I'm sure we can put up a good case,' said the barrister. 'After all I did turn down the Department's offer to represent them in favour of you.'

'Really,' said Ivor.

'Oh yes. It's much more fun attacking the Department rather than defending it.'

For the first time I warmed to him slightly. Any man who enjoys attacking bureaucrats cannot be all bad. 'Cost?' I asked again.

He gave me a resigned look. 'About three a week when we're all working. I'd have charged the government much more.'

'Three being three thousand,' said Ivor faintly.

'That's right. But don't worry. We'll give you plenty of time to raise the money.'

By the time that we had left the barrister's office — sorry, chambers, the high-powered poker game that the professionals were preparing to play had almost made us forget that we were dealing with people's livelihoods and that life in our part of the country would never be quite the same again if the road went ahead.

We had also forgotten about the puppy. It had decanted its bodily fluids and some part of its bodily solids as well over much of the interior of Ivor's elderly Volvo and was sitting on the driver's seat amid the shambles wagging its tail and much of its body with excitement at our return, still having saved enough urine to copiously water Ivor's seat yet again as he opened the door. Curiously, he did not mind too much, nor did I. It was almost a relief to encounter an agricultural type of problem after the rich diet of the barrister. Clearing up after messy animals was something that was second nature to both of us, although we were more used to cows.

But we had nothing with which to clear up. We sneaked back into the chambers and nicked every roll of lavatory paper from each of the palatial loos and a large pile of *Tatler*s and *Country Life*s from the waiting-room table with which we lined the more irretrievably smelly sections of the car. We returned triumphantly down the motorway, hoping that we might have left a chamber-full of smooth-talking loose-bowelled counsel in a pickle of bother.

Our most urgent need was to raise money. Donations had been flowing in but those who talked the loudest and most belligerently, were often those least willing to excavate the deeper recesses of their pockets. In spite of Kelvin's aggressive apathy, the village had thrown a flower show and a fete for the benefit of the fighting fund and Kelvin grudgingly gave his assent for his field to be used. He managed to make his point, just the same. He had only taken his cattle out the day before the fete and the well-cropped sward was a minefield of un-exploded cowpats, most of which lost their crust as the day wore on.

Being midsummer, the tourists were much in evidence and considerable thought and effort had gone into dressing up methods of parting them from their money. There was a wellie-throwing contest with a £50 prize for the winner. At ten pence a go, it was well worth a try. Macho urban man was well to the fore with their acrylic leisure shirts stretched tight across their swelling stomachs, being egged on by the high-heeled harridans by their sides. That stall made over £100. We had recruited the Young Farmers' wellie-throwing champion of the county to run it and he was under contract to give his winnings to the fund. His was the final throw of the day and he won by a good ten yards, much to the irritation of the

Liverpudlian printer who had stuck around with his family spending money for much of the day in expectation of picking up the prize.

Grenville was in charge of bale tossing on much the same deal. His task was to pitchfork a bale of hay over a high bar which was not so much a matter of muscle as one of skill. Success lay in getting your co-ordination and timing right. The tourists did not know that and spent their money. Unfortunately, the locals did and were just as keen on the prize money as were we. Grenville was just pipped at the bar by the same Neanderthal youth who had won the weight throwing the year before. Grenville was most upset but Ivor had laid him off at highly satisfactory odds with Bill and so the fund benefited more from his failure than it would have done from his success.

About the only contest that we were unable to nobble was the clay pigeon shooting. That went on as it always did at the far end of the field against the hedge. It was a grim incomprehensible business with the same regular participants who banged away at every opportunity throughout the year, operating a league table amongst themselves. Honour was at stake there, and it was unwise to interfere.

Skittling was a cinch. Once again the high rollers turned up to trundle their bowls down the uneven wooden planks that had been laid down across a patch of nettles. They may have been the very devil on the ten-pin bowling alley back home, but they were facing people whose parents and grandparents had spent their evenings in the dank skittle alley that ran behind the pub. It was not legend but fact that in 1910, a farm had changed hands as a result of an evening's duel in the same skittle alley. Against a tradition like that the townsmen had no chance.

In spite of all our fund-raising efforts, we were still massively short the day the inquiry started. It was held in the function room of the local hotel. The Inspector was a very fat legal gentleman who had been imported from Yorkshire, sufficiently far away for him to be uncontaminated by bias. He sat up on a stage at the far end of the room with his secretary beside him. Opposite him, split in much the same way as the relations of bride and groom at a wedding, sat ourselves and the cohorts from the Department.

Behind Ivor and our professionals, sat packed rows of red-faced farmers and environmentalists. Behind Henry sat all the civil servants with their dauntingly large cardboard folders stuffed with enough bumf to keep us there for months. They and their industrial supporters — the makers of plastic pants and brass seaside souvenirs — were ready to say how vital it was that the road should be built and we were all ready to say how vital it was that it should not.

Many of us protesters had been in the hotel a couple of nights earlier at the invitation of the Rotary Club. The chair in which the Inspector was now sitting had then been occupied by a young stripper-cum-contortionist who had done things, balanced naked on her back supported by only one hand, that had had the audience hooting with delight and lust. It was very hard to look at the grave moon-face of the Inspector and keep a serious expression on our faces when we compared it with the pair of gyrating buttocks that had occupied the same cubic foot of airspace forty-eight hours earlier.

The Inspector was very sweet but terrified of losing his dignity and control of the proceedings. He was also brow-beaten by both barristers. They were highly successful. Simon was a QC, but the Inspector, who was also a barrister, had only risen to being the top divorce specialist in a certain suburb of Leeds, but we played it like gentlemen. We were approached by an assortment of funnies who wanted to disrupt the inquiry by sitting on the floor and singing dull songs, but we innocently assumed that our case was good enough and strong enough to triumph without the need for inquirymanship.

The professionals on both sides cantered through their paces first. Their evidence was highly technical, smoothly presented with endless coloured graphs and columns of arid figures which were understood by nobody except their rival professionals on the other side. The Inspector tried to get some of the denser obscurities clarified so that he could understand them but, like the Theory of Relativity, they could only be clarified to the intellectual equivalent of a thick fog. The experts droned on, the soporific bluebottles buzzed against the sun-warmed window-panes and the audience in the back of the hall fell. From those that stayed, the odd snore ripping across the fug was all the reaction they gave. Even the Inspector began to nod.

Then came the amateur witnesses. Our first was a disaster. He was a hotelier, a good financial supporter which is why he was given the honour of opening the proceedings but Henry ate him for breakfast. He said his opening piece, his voice trembling with nerves but he became confused, to put it mildly, under cross-examination. Henry started easily.

'You are obviously against this road, Mr Dickson?'

'Yes,' said Mr Dickson.

'You are in business as a hotelier. Don't you think that a new road such as this would make it easier for your customers to get to you?'

'Yes,' said Mr Dickson. Everyone looked a little surprised at the answer, particularly Henry, while Mr Dickson looked as if he was wondering who it was that had said 'yes'. Henry decided to pursue this line of enquiry.

'Do you not also think that it might bring even more customers to your hotel?'

'Yes,' said Mr Dickson.

'Similarly, do you not think that the road might bring about an improvement in profits and efficiency for industry in the area?'

'Yes.'

'And might even attract new industry?'

'Yes.'

Henry was a bit lost as to where to go next. Mr Dickson had just agreed with the nùb of the Department's case.

'So all in all, Mr Dickson, you consider that the road would be beneficial?'

'Yes.'

Henry sat down and our man, Simon, rose to clean up the mess. Everyone was a bit embarrassed. Even the Inspector was fiddling with his pen. What had happened was that Mr Dickson's brain had seized up with nerves and 'yes' was the only answer he could come up with, no matter what the question. Simon had worked this out.

'Mr Dickson. Can I assume that you are totally and utterly opposed to this road as you had previously stated in your opening written evidence?'

'Yes,' said Mr Dickson gratefully and he scurried from the witness seat.

By the time that our agricultural witnesses were due to appear, Simon the Barrister had begun to take days off in order to save us money and was leaving the responsibility for our defence in the uncertain hands of Ivor, which suited Henry down to the ground. He was being paid by the taxpayer and was perfectly happy to run rings round our supporters for week after week, secure in the knowledge that his fees would be paid.

It was very hard to tell whether the inquiry was going in our favour or not. The elaborate courtesy of those who made their living from appearing at such events smoothed over the emotion and the urgency that many of our supporters wanted to show, but our chief agricultural witness managed to break through some of the complacency. Ivor was looking rather pleased with himself when he called on Dick Hunniford to take the stand. I could not see why. He was a charming man with great bushy white eyebrows and piercing blue eyes which gave him a look of ferocity that totally belied his gentle disposition, but nobody had ever accused Dick of being quick-witted and I could see the sleek Henry could very easily make him look a fool.

Dick strode down the aisle between Them and Us to the witness position, wearing his brown farmer's suit with his evidence on a tatty piece of paper clutched uneasily in his large brown hand. He sat down, took out his spectacles and placed his evidence carefully on the table in front of him. It was just after lunch, the most soporific stage of the day and the Inspector's head was resting wearily on his hand. Nevertheless, he gave his usual advice.

'Take your time, Mr Hunniford. We are most interested to hear what you have to say.'

Dick nodded and cleared his throat.

'AR GOO FLUSH TO ZEE,' bellowed Dick. After the measured Queen's English that we had heard so far, it was as if a verbal rogue elephant had crashed into the proceedings. 'Ar vam ni erea zis ere tu prates, az is goan out bisn.' Dick stared at the Inspector as if he was about to rise and strike him on the nose. The Inspector warily took his hand away from his chin and looked at Dick over the top of his glasses.

'Oo's no ri ou do ar di verm,' said Dick, banging his fist on the table for emphasis, spilling some of the water from the glass as he did so. During the pause while he tried to mop it up with a paisley pattern handkerchief from his pocket, Henry leapt to his feet, scattering papers.

'Sir,' he said to the Inspector, 'I would be grateful if you would instruct the witness to speak more clearly as I am having some difficulty in following his evidence.' The Inspector swivelled his head to the right where, by his side, sat his secretary who was taking shorthand notes to supplement the continually turning reels of the tape recorder. She was looking at Dick with horror, her pencil frozen in her hand. The Inspector turned back to Dick.

'Please Mr Hunniford. It may seem a silly point, but some of us are having difficulty in understanding your quite delightful accent and it would be enormously helpful if you would try to help us by speaking as clearly as you can.'

Dick frowned. 'Do'm baise,' he thundered. He cleared his throat once more and began again, 'AR GOO FLUSH TO ZEE.' It was a spectacular performance. Dick talked for about twenty minutes and most of us had not got the slightest idea what he was talking about. Some of his fellow farmers might have done as they stamped their feet in approval at significant pauses during his speech while Dick glared at the ranks of the civil servants who gazed back at him like mesmerised rabbits. The Inspector tried to hold a whispered conference with his secretary whose despair was pitiful to see, but Dick wiggled his eyebrows at them and they sat back in their chairs. Dick ended on a rising note '—u'll never apin s'loan s ee be yer,' and sat back to allow the applause of his peers to wash over him. The Inspector waited for a bit until Dick turned to look at him.

'Have you finished, Mr Hunniford?'

Dick looked perplexed. He frowned. 'Oi zed oi dee,' he said.

'I see, I see,' said the Inspector hastily. He turned to Henry. 'In that case you may cross-examine.'

Henry rose slowly to his feet. I felt some sympathy for his predicament. The purpose of the inquiry was to allow the general public to have their say, to prove that the average man could influence government and that policy could be changed as a result. Dick was the first of many rural witnesses and it looked as if democracy could be in danger since neither the Department nor the Inspector, the umpire, could understand what the Public was saying. It seemed a bit unfair of the Inspector to hand the responsibility of sorting out this difficulty to Henry, but he had no intention of trying.

'I have no questions to ask of this witness at this stage,' he said and sat down.

The Inspector hurriedly called an adjournment for an early tea break. The civil servants went into a worried huddle to work something out while one of their number sped off to their office in one of the hotel rooms with Dick's own written evidence to have it transcribed. He came rushing back. The typist could not read Dick's handwritng. Dick was enjoying a cup of tea and was being congratulated by his cronies when Henry came over with his evidence in hand.

'Excuse me, Mr Hunniford. We're just about to get your evidence typed up. I wonder if you would mind telling me what that word is?'

Dick did not quite understand the adversarial system and he was rather taken aback by this approach from the enemy. But he was a good-natured man and ignored the lynch-party mutterings coming from his fellow farmers and squinted down at the offending word. 'Ardence,' he said emphatically. 'S'ardence.' Henry smiled feebly and beat a retreat.

The tea break was a specially extended edition. There were heated conversations among the Department's main protagonists while the Inspector and his secretary hunched over the tape recorder with the engineer and played back the tape with worried looks on their faces. The even tenor of the inquiry was totally disrupted and we enjoyed it hugely.

Eventually the Inspector approached Ivor; quite a chummy relationship was developing between the Inspector and our side which was all to the good.

'Ivor, none of us has the faintest idea what Mr Hunniford was talking about. I was wondering if you had any idea about how we might be able to understand your farmers without recourse to an interpreter which seems a little rude and a little drastic.'

Ivor smiled, 'Don't worry. I didn't understand a word either. I doubt if more than two or three people did. He broke his false teeth a couple of weeks ago and I'm told he does not get a new set until Thursday.'

Henry was completely thrown by our witnesses. The next one came to the table with a large basket on his arm and proceeded to unload vast specimens of root vegetables from it to demonstrate the agricultural worth of his land. He named them too. 'That's a mangel. That's swede. That's tater and that there's an aig as big as an ostrich.' The Inspector knew a magnificent 'aig' when he saw one, but it was way beyond Henry. He was obviously a pre-packed supermarket shopper

144

and most of these gargantuan tubers might have been truffles as far as he was concerned. He did try to ask questions, but he did not get very far.

'Mr Trowbridge, how many hectares do you farm?'

'I don't farm any hectares, Mister.'

Poor Henry, he had picked up his papers, balanced the tips of his fingers on the table in front of him and looked the very picture of a thrusting young barrister — a brilliant recovery after his difficulties with Dick, but Mr Trowbridge confused him again. He looked worriedly through his notes.

'You are a farmer?'

'S'right.'

'But you have no land?'

'No, I've got a tidy bit of land.'

'Well why did you say you had none?'

'I didn't. You asked me about hectares and I'll have nothing to do with bloody hectares. Acres was good enough for my father and they're good enough for me.'

'I see,' said Henry patiently, 'I would be enormously grateful, then, if you would tell me how many acres you farm.'

'Why? I don't see that it has anything to do with this damn road.'

'Just answer the question, please Mr Trowbridge,' said the Inspector.

'If you say I must, your worship. I've got 480 acres of which about half is down to corn and roots and the rest is pasture and we run beef and sheep on that. We've got a pig unit and—'

'It's a substantial business then, Mr Trowbridge?' asked Henry.

'It is that and it'll be ruined by this road. It'll go right through the middle of it.' He shot out an arm to illustrate the road going right through the middle of it and half a dozen ostrich-sized eggs fell stickily to the floor along with a swede that rumbled across the floor like a cannonball and came to rest against Henry's table. He bent down, picked it up and returned it to Mr Trowbridge with a long-suffering look on his face. He returned to his papers.

'Could you tell us what your business is worth?'

Quite understandably, Mr Trowbridge objected. 'None of your bloody business, young man. How much my business is worth is a secret between me, my accountant and the tax man.' There were knowing guffaws from the audience at this and Ivor looked embarrassed. He was a tax commissioner and Mr Trowbridge and his barracuda of an accountant appeared before the tribunal with the regularity of returning swallows every year and sent up an impenetrable smokescreen around their activities.

'I am not trying to pry, Mr Trowbridge,' said Henry. 'What I am trying to quantify is the amount of loss that you and farmers like you are likely to suffer as a result of this road being built.' Henry was the voice of sweet reason, but sweet reason has little effect on proudly independent farmers who are never the most reasonable of men.

'Well, I'm not going to tell you.'

'It would be helpful if you could give us some indication,' put in the Inspector mildly.

'I don't mind telling you, your worship, but I'm not telling that . . . that puppy.'

There the matter had to rest. Mr Trowbridge was willing to give a written reply to the Inspector but refused to reveal his worth to everyone else. We lost the inquiry, of course, but we did hold a very successful sale to help raise money to meet the £20,000 bill that the professionals submitted. One of the star items was an immense and billowing pair of jodhpurs that were kindly donated by the Inspector.

Chapter Eight

THE SUMMER OF the inquiry was an eventful one in the village. For a start the publican flipped his lid. They tend to either go mad, die from drink or go bankrupt. This particular publican did most of them at once. The entire village was alerted by a shotgun blast in the small hours of the morning. We all rushed to our windows and peered through the curtains and there was mine host, stark naked, chasing his equally naked wife through the streets. It was a dramatic little incident, only broken up by Percy who took time off from snoozing in the back of the police Land Rover whilst on duty to catch poachers, to come and disarm him.

Kelvin turned out to help as well. He had been a special constable in his prime and his golden moment had come when he had had to disarm his nephew, whom he caught with a gun amid the squire's pheasants. As he frequently said, 'When you look down the barrel of a gun, you soon see what kind of a man you are.' Kelvin had obviously been delighted by what he had seen down them as he homed in like a dog chasing a bitch on heat on any trouble that he heard about ever since then, although he now usually took the precaution of bringing his own gun with him.

Kelvin and his gun had the possibility of becoming quite troublesome in the village. The Commander had been approached by some official from County Hall and asked if he would form and lead an Emergency Committee which was to take over the government in the locality in the aftermath of a nuclear holocaust. The village was divided over the issue. The communards were totally against it, reckoning that any increase in nuclear awareness in the neighbourhood would encourage the Russians to drop the Bomb. On the other hand, Dennis and the squire thought it was a splendid idea and, since they had both been in the army, were very willing to take over the leadership from the Commander who was only a naval man.

Most of the rest of us could not care one way or the other, but Kelvin was incensed. He was the Chairman of the Parish Council and therefore they should have asked him to be leader of the community during its hour of need. He immediately organised all his cronies and set up a rival group with the declared aim of confiscating all the foodstuff when the Bomb dropped and locking it up in the school from where it would be distributed only on his authority. Furthermore he, Kelvin, would guard the door and would not hesitate to shoot any looters who might decide to raid it. The only result of this announcement was that the rest of the Council formed a caucus which appointed Bill to shoot Kelvin as soon as the Bomb dropped to prevent any trouble.

The Emergency Volunteers took themselves pretty seriously to start with. They used to go along to lectures on the delights of the civil collapse that was inevitable after the Holocaust. They were given graphic descriptions of the floods of urban refugees that would come hobbling out from the irradiated cities to die in inconvenient places where they would start epidemics. Then they were told that the Volunteers had to hold an exercise. It was preceded by a week of frantic activity. The Commander delegated Dennis to stand outside the pub on Saturday night with a note-book so that he could write down details of who owned the best cars in the Parish to commandeer when the time came. The Commander himself spent his leisure moments when he could tear himself away from his courgettes, checking round the village to find a suitable Headquarters where he could set up the alternative seat of government when the time came. He really wanted a cellar which would be safe from fall-out and had spent some time confident that the cellars of the pub were his for the asking, complete with beer on tap, until he found out that it had no usable cellar because it flooded every year or two.

In the end, the butcher offered him accommodation in a room above his shop where the snooker club met. The exercise was to be a giant country-wide effort to test the alertness of defences to the Bomb and to find out how the alternative governments would cope with the disaster. As far as the village was concerned, all that was involved was that the telephone in the snooker room had to be manned. That was all there was to it. It had to be manned for twenty-four hours by a team of volunteers. In a foolish moment, the Commander had agreed to provide alcohol for all those who consented to take part and so the pub unanimously agreed that a minimum of four volunteers would be needed at all times. My stint was from 4pm to 6pm. The exercise ran from noon to noon so the mushroom clouds had begun to disperse by the time that I turned up to do my bit to save the nation.

'You're late,' was how I was greeted. 'You can't afford to be late for the end of the world.' The speaker was the district nurse, Lindy, who was idly chalking the end of a billiard cue. Dennis was stretched out across the table trying to achieve a ludicrous pot that looked as if it was more likely to achieve a ripped cloth rather than a sunken ball. The other vigilante was the Commander who was sitting by the telephone reading a battered copy of the doings of Bulldog Drummond which seemed quite appropriate under the circumstances, batting gently at the butcher's Dalmatian, Ramrod, which was a local legend for copulating with anything that moved. It was currently interested in the Commander's leg.

'Help yourself to a drink,' said the Commander. It was country wine, real below the belt stuff. The Commander's was notorious in packing a hangover that reduced its victims to helpless weeping. Judging by his rather foolish expression, the Commander himself looked like being distraught the following morning. Dennis missed his pocket, caught my expression of dismay and passed over his flask. I half filled a glass and Lindy proceeded to pot a red and a black and leave Dennis with a fortuitous snooker. The room did not look much like a headquarters. The walls were bare except for a yellowing Landseer stag having a spot of bother with some hounds.

'What's been happening then?' I asked.

'Not a lot,' replied the Commander. 'Some silly sod phones us up from County Hall every hour or so to make sure we're still here and tells us things. It all seems to be a bit of a waste of time.'

'What sort of things?'

'What was it last time? Oh yes. They said that they were allocating 1500 children to us.'

'And don't you dare tell Kelvin, in case he wants to shoot them' said Lindy.

'What were we supposed to do about it?' I asked.

'I've no idea. I told them that we had given them a room in the pub for the time being and it seemed to satisfy them. I must say if they did dump 1500 brats on us, getting hold of Kelvin might not be such a bad idea. They also told us to organise a chain of CB sets just in case the telephone system should break down.'

'Are they expecting it to break down?'

'I don't think so at the moment, but when the Bombs go off, they say that the telephone engineers will be too busy to come to us out here.'

Once Lindy had beaten Dennis at the snooker table, we started up a game of bridge. Every so often the telephone rang and we were told of raging fires and mountains of corpses near the epicentre of the disaster. It was a very peaceful afternoon until Lindy decided that I had trumped one of her leads when I still could have followed suit.

Lindy was an influential figure in the neighbourhood. She was a very good nurse and handled the cantankerous and frequently difficult patients that she was given with great ease, treating them all as if they were slightly retarded children. She was also the first to find out everyone's dark secrets which, in the countryside, can be very dark indeed. She told me once that she was actually briefed on the prevalence of incest in the county when she became district nurse and it would certainly have driven any genealogist to distraction if one should ever try to unravel the complexities of the relationships between all the aunts, uncles, nieces and cousins. The locals had been interbreeding happily for generations without paying much regard to Leviticus. They bred back their cattle and sheep to retain desirable characteristics and could think of no good reason why they should not try it themselves. Seth Turnbull was one of her patients whom I knew quite well. He hired out his muscles by the hour to anyone who could put them to good use. He was tiny with an ageless nutbrown face and I had put him tentatively in his early fifties before he had told me that he was sixty-eight. He had been a farmworker until an excess of cider had made him drop a concrete block on his foot and he had retired to odd-jobbing to help him with his pension.

Seth's greatest expertise lay in sewers and septic tanks and we used to get him in to trace blockages in the maze of pipes that led out to ours. One of the problems about living at river level was that the falls in the pipes that led to the septic tank were almost imperceptible and any visitor who followed a high fibre diet could easily block the system which necessitated Seth's presence to get the thing flowing smoothly again. The drawback about Seth was that he liked to talk and if he had nobody to talk to, he did not work, so someone would always have to sit on the edge of his hole and listen while he dug. The listening could be startling.

'My daughter is going to have another baby. She suffers from eucalyptic fits.' He tended to string two barely related pieces of information together and leave his listener vainly trying to work out the connection between them.

'Really?' I said, knowing that there was more to come.

'Billy's the father again, I think. He's my younger brother. Billy was the father of her first,' he said, leaning on his shovel and frowning in concentration as he tried to remember it all. 'Her next, he's a fine little lad, she weren't too sure about. It was either her brother, Herbert, or the chap next door.' I hoped it was not Herbert. Herbert was a bad lot. He looked like a young Elvis Presley with black greasy hair and a permanent world-weary pout. He had impregnated so many of the local damsels that the area had become too hot for him and he had emigrated to a town fifty miles away. A friend of mine had once given him a lift and he had ruminated over the follies of the fairer sex. 'I don't know what they sees in me myself,' he said, tilting the driving mirror so that he could comb his hair. He had looked at his reflection critically for a few moments before sighing, 'I suppose it's because I be a handsome bugger.' The little bugger was.

Seth struck it lucky in the end. He was riding along on his moped when he suffered a particularly Seth-type accident. A sheep jumped over a hedge for some unfathomable reason and landed on his back, making him crash. Seth sued the owner of the sheep and won £8000 because he had hurt his foot again. Lindy had kept an eye on him ever since, mainly to prevent him doing himself some more damage and suing whoever he thought might pay up. All this information had come from the garrulous Seth. Lindy was far too discreet.

It was dull, the nuclear war, and so, after a couple of rubbers, we decided to liven it up a bit. Lindy so decided anyway.

'Can we phone up the County HQ if we want to?'

The Commander looked grave. His normally sound game of bridge had gone to pieces due to five hours of continual consumption of his country wine. 'We can, I believe, but only if there is an emergency that we think they ought to know about.'

'Let's give them an emergency,' said Lindy.

'But there isn't an emergency, is there?' said the Commander.

'I don't see why there shouldn't be. They've dumped a mythical 1500 children on us, quite apart from the mythical Bomb, so why don't we give them a mythical emergency to deal with?'

We must all have been feeling a little skittish because even the Commander and Dennis thought it was a good idea. We established that the Duty Officer had no way of knowing who was phoning in so, if we played our cards right, they ought to be unable to blame us and dump another few thousand refugees on us. We started the campaign quietly.

'Duty Officer here.'

Dennis was our spokesman. 'I'm sorry to report that the motorway bridge just west of the city has collapsed. The road is totally blocked for the foreseeable future.'

There was an appalled silence at the other end of the line.

'But you can't do that. We're depending on rescue services to come in from the motorway.'

'Sorry,' said Dennis. 'It was weakened by blast damage and collapsed just as fifteen fire engines were crossing it.'

'But our allocation from the army was only eighteen fire engines. This is dreadful. We won't be able to cope.'

'War is hell,' said Dennis and hung up. We had just poured ourselves another drink and overcome the Commander's objections to further amusement when the phone rang. The Commander picked it up.

'You were to be sent some fire engines to keep in reserve until they were needed but we can no longer spare them. So you no longer need expect them.'

'Oh good. Not that we were expecting them.' He hung up. He looked rather pleased.

'What can we do next?' asked Dennis.

'Epidemics?' I suggested.

'No,' said Lindy. 'It's far too soon.'

'Radiation sickness?'

'They're expecting that and anyway they've probably killed off half the population already. What we want is something that they won't have thought of.'

'Earthquakes?'

'I've got one that ought to set them back a bit,' said the Commander.

He was beginning to enter the spirit of things. He dialled the number. The Duty Officer answered.

'Mayday, mayday,' said the commander.

'What do you mean "mayday"?'

'This is Golf X-ray Charlie, a VC10 of the Queen's Flight containing the entire Royal Family on its way to Canada. We have a problem in our engines and wish to make an emergency landing at the airport.'

'You can't do that.'

'Yes I can, engine failure. Listen. Brm, brm.'

'No, whee, whee,' said Dennis.

'Sorry. Whee, whee. The engine appears to be clogged with blast debris. Her Majesty commands that you do something about it.'

'The Royal Family is supposed to be in a shelter somewhere, I think.'

'Well it's not. It's circling around above your heads.'

'Oh blast you. Hang on.' The Commander hung on, smiling happily.

The Duty Officer came back on the line. 'Try the RAF. You must be a military responsibility. Not ours.'

'The RAF are not the military,' said the Commander. 'Anyway, we're contacting you.'

'Go to Hell,' said the Duty Officer.

'That's no way to treat your Monarch,' said the Commander, but he had been cut off.

'What shall we do next?' asked Lindy. 'I'd better do it to give them a bit of added variety.' We played another rubber of bridge to give the County bunker time to be lulled into a sense of false security. Then they telephoned us. The Duty Officer had been changed.

'Have you been calling us?' the new one asked suspiciously.

'No,' replied the Commander. 'I thought we were not supposed to unless there was an emergency.'

'That's right, but someone has been phoning in with emergencies which have not been fair.'

'Surely all is fair in love and war,' said the Commander.

'It was you wasn't it?' said the Duty Officer.

'Certainly not,' said the Commander.

'I'm not sure that I believe you. Anyway it has been decided that a second strike has landed on top of you, so you are all dead. For you, the war is over.'

'You can't do that.'

'We've done it,' said the Duty Officer. 'You can go home now.' He hung up.

Dennis was incensed. 'The miserable little swine. How dare he kill us all. I'm going to sòrt him out.'

'Leave it for a bit,' suggested the Commander. So we left it for a bit. None of us wanted to leave as the contest had become personal between us and County Headquarters.

Dennis dialled through. He was not messing about this time. 'This is Captain Pissoffski of the Soviet Socialist Republic submarine, *Revolutionary Dawn*. We are anchored just off your coast and will nuke your bunker into tiny bits unless you surrender.'

'I've been warned about you. Contact the War Office or something.'

'We have contacted them. They refused to give in so we blew them to teensy weensy pieces. You have five minutes to give us your answer. We will be in touch.' Dennis hung up and looked round us with a satisfied smile. 'That should sort them out. If they want to play at war, we'll damn well give them a decent game.'

The telephone rang but we ignored it.

'There was a lovely story about a Russian submarine when I was stationed in the Mediterranean,' said the Commander. 'They use it a lot, to and from the Black Sea, and the Americans like us to keep an eye on them. So the Russians wait until nightfall and surface behind a big ship going in the right direction so that their radar echo is masked by the other ship. Anyway, a Russian tried this one behind a Norwegian tanker and he was spotted by the bridge and the captain was called. They tried to contact the sub by radio and by aldis lamp but they refused to answer and so the captain became cross. He rousted the crew on deck and they strung a great big wire hawser across the deck at the stern and tied empty forty gallon oil drums to it. Then they threw it overboard. The hawser got tangled up in the sub's paravanes so that it could not dive, while the drums banged against the sub's hull like a demented steel band. Then they chucked a drum of red lead over the side which smeared a great red moustache over the sail. At dawn they radioed the 6th Fleet and the sub had to clatter its way up to the Bosphorus with an escort of American planes and ships playing "Show me the way to go home" on loudspeakers all the way. The Norwegian captain was advised to avoid Eastern Bloc ports for some time to come.'

The Commander poured us another glass of dandelion wine. Dennis's flask was empty, so we had no alternative.

'What's the Russian for "good afternoon"?' asked Dennis, picking up the phone again.

'Dobri den,' said Lindy.

'Have you just made that up?'

'Certainly not. There was a Russian language course on television and I knew it would come in useful one day.'

Dennis dialled the Bunker. 'Dobri den,' he said.

'What was that?' asked the Duty Officer.

'Dobri den. It's Russian for good afternoon. This is the *Revolutionary Dawn* demanding your surrender.'

'I'm sorry to disappoint you captain, on our instructions, a Sea King helicopter has just dropped a depth charge on your head. You have only a few seconds left.'

'I'm pressing the button now, comrade,' said Dennis hurriedly.

'Your missile will explode before it can get away.'

'You can't do that. You haven't got any Sea Kings.'

'We've got as many Sea Kings as you have got submarines. Listen. Boom. Splash. You're now dead, so you can go to hell.' He hung up.

'It's a bloody silly business anyway,' said Dennis. We continued to play bridge for a bit and then closed down our emergency centre. The Commander resigned his post as war leader shortly afterwards and allowed Kelvin to take over. He built himself a nuclear shelter in an old silage pit which is his pride and joy and the Chief Emergency Officer brings people out to admire it. The trouble is that nobody wants to be part of Kelvin's alternative government and he has to play all by himself.

Chapter Nine

IN THE COUNTRYSIDE, it is almost always a mistake to judge people on first impressions, particularly on first financial impressions. The scruffiest old tramp is likely to be a farmer with land worth half a million pounds to his name. Country people are enormously secretive about financial matters and the last thing they would ever do is to make a conspicuous display of their wealth in case the tax man might be lurking round the corner. The trappings of material success are scorned. Battered old Land Rovers are driven by farmers instead of the Range Rovers they could easily afford. It is said that the difference between a hedgehog and a Range Rover is that the hedgehog has its pricks on the outside.

Some people found it impossible to hide their financial lights under a bushel. Frank Mattock was one of them. Go to any dinner and it would be Frank who would win first, second and third prizes on the tombola. People were originally quite envious of the way that luck seemed to follow him around, but it became such a regular occurrence that we all became used to it and would wonder what he and his wife would win next. Everyone except Kelvin, of course, who nursed a bitter feud with Frank. Something to do with a dispute in ownership over a strayed heifer which Frank had won.

Frank had started off his career as assistant to the local butcher. His was a very immediate business for us. Most farmers sold their stock in the markets or direct to the big abattoirs, but the little individual lots would come to our butcher. He had his holding field next door to the Mill where tame sheep reared on the bottle and juicy amiable steers would wait for a few days until their demise, and amuse themselves meantime by coming up to the fence that kept them off our garden and bellowing or bleating until someone went out to give them a scratch or keep them company for a bit.

Frank would come for these animals at dawn and lead them through the village to the slaughterhouse that operated in a converted garage next to the butcher's shop before the tourists had woken up. Eating out or buying meat locally did not mean being offered legs of lamb or joints of beef, but instead having a slice of Henry's or Mabel's cutlets, 'you know, that dear little heifer that we reared ourselves because it was too small to go to market with the rest of them'. It required a strong stomach.

Frank had his first windfall when he won on the premium bonds. More accurately, his four-year-old daughter won £50,000. He quit his job immediately and bought a small dairy farm on the outskirts of the village above the Mill with the money. Everyone could foresee problems in the future. It was the 'maid's' money, after all, and when she reached her majority, the Mattocks could well find themselves turned out into the snow.

But Frank prospered mightily. He worked all the hours available to him, bought a revoltingly flash BMW every year, erected a startlingly large metal tank to hold his cows' slurry and took an interest in horse-racing. In fact he was the glorious exception to the rule about country people avoiding conspicuous consumption. One of his greater moments came when he went with Bill one day to buy a racehorse. They bought half of it each. Bill was the expert, owning chunks of at least three other animals and he was prepared to offer lots of advice and experience to Frank in a fatherly sort of way. It turned out that Frank needed very little. The animal lost its first two outings miserably and Bill advised selling. Frank wanted to keep it, or rather his wife, Hilda, wanted to keep it because it had a pretty name and so Frank bought Bill out for £800. The inevitable happened. The filly started to win and win and win again. At the end of its first season, Frank sold it for £60,000, payment being made in used notes from a suitcase in Dublin.

Frank and I share a small problem. We had a common water supply. It was spring fed and rose about a quarter of a mile away on land that had recently been bought by a mysterious farmer named Crofton who had come down from deepest Wales, although his accent showed that he was no Welshman. On his land, the water flowed into a lovely concrete-lined reservoir, through a manhole, containing the valves that controlled the supply to ourselves and Frank, and thence on down to Frank's cow buildings and then to us. It was a bit haphazard. Lawyers like to have things tied up forwards, backwards and sideways, but there was no legal document attached to our spring except a licence of abstraction from the local water authority and any unwritten rights that may have been built up in the centuries that the two properties had used the spring. Why the Mill should need the spring with water all round it, was something we never questioned.

Then little problems began to arise. The first was when the water came out of our taps foul smelling and cloudy. We contacted Frank. He came out and together we tramped the fields looking for the source of the contamination. Frank rather fancied himself as a thing of beauty and, although now comfortably in his forties, he did tend to dress rather like a St Tropez beach bum. Farmers build up tans anyway, but Frank's was always a golden rather than a slurry brown. He also went in for shirts which were open to just above his navel, exposing quantities of brown hairy chest and a chunky crucifix that dangled between his pectorals.

The pollution had been caused by Mr Crofton. He had been spraying docks round the spring. We cleaned out the tank, replaced the eel which kept the bugs under control and forgot about the water for a week or two. Then it stopped running altogether. It was not too critical for us as we had the river and streams coming at the house from all directions, but Frank had his cows to keep happy and each needed forty gallons of water a day if they were to give the expected quantities of milk. Frank and I went to visit Mr Crofton. His farmhouse was a couple of prefabs stuck together by a glass-sided porch tacked on the front. Inside there were two slavering Alsatians. Feeling slightly windy at the sight of them, I knocked on the door. The dogs went berserk, hurling themselves at the glass and snapping at the door in their efforts to get at us. Frank and I exchanged uneasy glances.

'If that glass breaks, we're in trouble,' said Frank.

'Yes,' I agreed. Frank went over to one of Crofton's outbuildings and opened the door. 'If the worst comes to the worst, we ought to be able to get in there before the dogs catch us and slam the door on them.'

I knocked again. Crofton must have been deaf not to have heard the noise that his dogs were making. He was certainly in there because his cattle lorry was parked outside. The village tom-toms were not very precise about how he earned his living. He did not seem to farm his land but the lorry trundled through the village a couple of times a week with a load of silent and smelly beasts. Frank knocked once more. 'Perhaps he doesn't want to come to the door,' he hazarded, but he came.

Crofton was a rotund man in his early fifties, with thick spectacles and an infectious crinkly smile. He opened the door and his dogs shot past him. In the nick of time, he put down his hands and neatly hooked each of them by the collar, leaving them snarling at us with their fore feet a yard off the ground. Frank swallowed nervously and I took a step backwards.

'Mr Crofton?'

'Yes.'

'My name is Mattock and we've come about the water. The pipe to my buildings starts off on your land and, at the moment, there is no water coming through. I wonder if we could take a look at the source.' This was the first time that either of us had met Crofton as he had been away when the supply was found to be contaminated last time.

'Certainly,' said Crofton, smiling pleasantly. 'You don't mind if I leave you to it? But we're in the middle of dinner.'

We silently walked through the dockless field towards the reservoir. Crofton's farm was on a ridge above the village and it was laid out at our feet. It was a still day and there was a misty pall of woodsmoke lying over it, trapped by the hills that rose a couple of hundred feet all around. It was so still that we could even hear the noise of children in the school playground as they took their morning break.

'Dinner at eleven in the morning?' said Frank in a puzzled fashion.

Frank pulled up the concrete manhole cover that sealed our stopcock from the defecations of rabbits and sheep and found that it was turned off. He turned it back on again and we walked back down the hill, past the farmhouse and back home.

The next day there was no water. We went through the same business. If anything Mr Crofton's eyes crinkled even deeper in friendly merriment and his dogs were even keener to get at our throats. This time the lid over the stopcock had a padlock on top. We knocked on the farmhouse door on our way down the hill. 'A padlock? How strange. Mother!' he shouted inside the house. 'Somebody's put a padlock on the stopcock to the other water pipe. Do you know anything about it?' There was an indecipherable grunt from inside the house. 'No,' said Mr Crofton, 'Mother knows nothing about it.'

'May I borrow a hacksaw?' asked Frank.

Mr Crofton smiled broadly. 'Very sorry. Haven't got a hacksaw.'

'Oh well, I'll go and get mine and take off the padlock.'

'That's the ticket,' chortled Mr Crofton. We returned ten minutes later with Frank's hacksaw and spent the best part of an hour sawing through the toughened steel of its hasp. Then Frank, the cunning devil, pulled a padlock of his own out of his pocket and clicked it firmly into place. We went home feeling rather pleased with ourselves.

Next morning we had no water. This time Mr Crofton was almost doubled over in merriment and *bonhomie* at the sight of us and he chuckled the harder when one of his dogs slipped past his outstretched hand and tried to bite Frank. The animal had chosen a bad day as Frank was armed with both his hacksaw and a crowbar. The latter gave the Alsatian a brisk swipe across the snout and it scurried back behind its jovial master and contented itself with snarling at us through his legs.

We were early that morning and the dew had not yet evaporated from the grass. We could not miss it. Running from the maison Crofton was a trail of darker green across the field where the moisture had been knocked from the blades, going to the reservoir and back again. If anyone had been at our pipe, it was glaringly obvious that he or she had come from the farmhouse. The padlock was still intact, but the concrete cover had been smashed. Our alkathene pipe had been severed just below the stopcock.

'The man's been doing all this himself,' said Frank.

We spent much of the morning repairing the damage and called in at the house on our way back down. He was out this time, but we got his wife, dogless, to the door. Frank had agreed that it was still the time for diplomacy rather than rage and that I should handle the matter. Mrs Crofton was startlingly different from her husband. She had one of the sourest faces that I had seen and looked rather like a miserable clown under a confection of ash-blonde frizzy hair with a scarlet slash of lipstick across her thin lips.

'Yes?' she said suspiciously, in a voice that was several degrees deeper in pitch than that of her husband.

'I'm sorry to trouble you, Mrs Crofton,' I said, rather uncertainly as this woman was very different from any farmer's wife that I had yet come across. 'But we thought we ought to warn you.'

'Warn me?' she asked in the sort of tones that Lucrezia Borgia might have used when being caught *in flagrante* with a tin of weedkiller in her hand.

'The vandalism that's going on up at the reservoir. We saw tracks on the grass and it looks very much as if they came from this house so I would keep an eye open for anyone suspicious skulking around. It's very odd that your dogs did not give you warning when whoever it was came past.'

She looked at us and we looked at her. She knew that we knew and we knew that she knew that we knew. She sniffed and slammed the door in our faces. The water was off again later in the day. Neither Crofton nor his wife were in attendance. The pipe was severed again and this time our manhole was about two feet deep in dirty sump oil. Frank decided to call it a day and summoned Percy, the policeman. Meantime he went down to the river and collected water for his cows in the large plastic tank he used to store his milk in snowy weather when the tanker from the dairy could not get through to collect it.

Percy called round to see Frank and myself that evening. He looked a shaken man. I offered him a sustaining glass of Scotch as he and Frank came into the kitchen, which he accepted, breaking his usual practice of supping nothing stronger than coffee while he was on duty. He sat down at the kitchen table.

'I'm afraid this is a bit of a nasty business,' he began. 'For a start the Croftons deny that they have been damaging your water pipes. Their version is that you have been doing it yourselves.'

'Us?' asked Frank. 'What possible reason could we have for cutting off our own water supply?'

'They say that you have been taking more than your fair share of the water and leaving them short and, to make even more trouble for them, you've been cutting the pipe so that you can blame it on them.'

'It doesn't sound very likely,' I said.

'No it doesn't,' agreed Percy. 'But that's what they said and I didn't really want to hang around too long.'

'The dogs are a bit alarming, aren't they?' I said sympathetically.

'Not just the dogs,' said Percy cryptically.

'Don't be so cryptic,' I said.

'What does cryptic mean?' asked Percy.

'It means speaking in cipher or code, but what do you mean "not just the dogs"?'

'Well, I'm pleased that it's not me that has fallen out with the Croftons and I hope that you don't ask me to go up and see them again.'

Frank was looking a bit cross. 'Don't be daft, Percy. If they're chopping up our pipes, it's your job to sort them out. It's criminal damage or something. Anyway, what's so awful about the Croftons?'

Percy looked a bit embarrassed. 'He's a warlock.'

'A what?'

'He's a warlock and his wife's a witch. They are the leaders of a coven and he said that he'd made a wax image of the two of you and stuck pins into it. I don't much fancy him going and sticking pins into a wax image of me.'

Many things scare the pants off me. Loud noises, nasty dogs, Liverpudlian comics and VAT forms to name a few, but witches, warlocks and wax images do not feature on the list. As far as the rest of the community was concerned, I was in the minority. There had actually been a private prosecution for witchcraft taken out in Frank's lifetime and he was rather windy about the fate that might befall him.

'That's a bit nasty, Percy. People can't go about making wax

165

images of other people. Can't you get them for threatening behaviour or something?'

'Look Frank,' said Percy with considerable sympathy. 'What do you think would happen if I went to my sergeant and said that I wanted to prosecute someone because they were demons or witches or something. He would think that I'd lost my marbles. It's not against the law to go dancing round bonfires at Hallowe'en, just so long as you don't do it naked in a public place. If I were you, I'd go and make my peace with the Croftons as soon as you can.'

Percy and Frank left while I contacted my solicitor. We could certainly take the Croftons to court for interfering with our water supply but it would be a time-consuming business and our need for water was urgent. So while Frank rushed around trying to avoid black cats and step-ladders, I investigated ways of getting connected to the mains water supply. Frank struck lucky before I did. I was on the telephone trying to sort out the problems of running the pipe from the only available connecting point across a field belonging to an absentee stockbroker who summer-weekended to a cottage from London, across the bed of the river, half of which was owned by Lord Somebodyorother's Settled Estates and the other half owned by the fishing hotel, and then across two fields belonging to separate farmers both of whom scented an opportunity to screw some of Frank's wealth for themselves. Then Frank blew in at the door, just as I was agreeing to hire the farmers' digging machinery at an exorbitant rate in return for a low payment for permission to cross his land with our water pipe.

'Where the hell have you been?' I asked, a bit annoyed at having to do all the telephoning as I was seeking to clear the way for us both.

'I've been out to the commune,' said Frank triumphantly. 'And Margaret has agreed to come round and help us.' Margaret came round the door post. I had met Margaret before. She was the tall time-travelling lady who had so convulsed the Village Hall at the inaugural meeting of the communard's College.

'You poor thing,' she said sweetly. 'Are you all right?'

I had honestly no idea what she was talking about and it must have showed. 'You know — the wax image. Have you felt any effects yet? Frank says that he has got a pain in his back.'

Livestock farmers have two distinguishing characteristics. One is the faint but persistent odour of slurry that always clings to them and the other is a bad back, so the fact that Frank thought he had a pain in his lumbar regions failed to impress me with the efficacy of the graven images.

'No, no, I'm fine but it's very nice to see you. What exactly are you going to do to help?'

'She says that she can protect us from Crofton's spell,' said Frank.

It was a curious fact, but at certain times I used to wonder if I had got the world sussed out completely wrongly, particularly when we met up with the communards. We had been asked out to a party there once and a woman had drifted up to me. 'When's your birthday?' she had asked.

'May,' I replied.

'Oh, hell!' she said, giving me an extremely dirty look. 'I hate Taureans.' And she had turned on her heel and wandered off. I got into similar hot water on the same evening. Yet another woman came up and asked the same question.

'May 20,' I had replied rather warily.

'You're on the cusp,' she replied accusingly.

I glanced down to see if I was squashing the cusp underfoot, but there was nothing on the floor but rush matting. 'What's the cusp?' I asked.

'It's the point where two astrological signs meet and you are under the influence of both.'

'How interesting,' I replied politely. 'But I've never taken astrology too seriously.'

'Heavens,' she had said in a loud and penetrating voice. 'You don't mean to say that you don't believe in it.'

'Well, no, actually.' I had felt rather like a Tory at a meeting of the Militant Tendency as I received pitying looks from all around the room. If all the world about you seems mad, perhaps it is time that you examined yourself to see if it had been you that was mad all along. I could see the same unnerving feeling creeping up on me with Frank and Margaret.

'I thought you were into time travel, Margaret?'

'Oh I used to be, but I felt that it did not give me the freedom to express the real me.'

'Yes, I suppose cutting across the spiral of time to other worlds and other galaxies doesn't give one much of an opportunity to broaden the mind. What do you do now?'

'I'm into witchcraft.'

'It must be more interesting than collecting stamps,' I said politely.

'Oh it's not a hobby,' she replied. 'I hope to make a living as a white witch.'

'Who'd be an accountant?' I replied. All those involved in the commune had skins as thick as a Chieftain tank, so Margaret was completely oblivious to the fact that I might be gently taking the mickey out of her, purely as a defensive measure. Frank shot me a sharp look though. He was prepared to take the idea of a hatpin stuck in his waxen gizzard seriously even if I was not.

'Margaret is going to give us a charm to protect us,' he said.

'Yes,' said Margaret earnestly, sitting down at the table and pulling a paperback book from her large carpet bag. *West Coast Witchcraft* it was called, published by the Occult Foundation of San Francisco. 'Mind you, there is an awful lot to learn and I don't know how good at it I am yet, but it is not nearly so difficult to give protection against a spell as it is to cast one in the first place, so I ought to manage it. It is much easier to be passive in magic rather than active.'

'Really?' I said. 'I'm not altogether sure if the vicar would approve.'

I was almost certainly wrong in that assumption. I had had another of those perhaps-it-is-me experiences with him a few months earlier. I had gone to a christening and had talked to the vicar, flushed with tea and cherry cake, afterwards. Kelvin had been present and the conversation had naturally got on to eccentrics.

'I used to minister to a parish on the Moor,' the vicar had told me. 'And there was an old woman who was reputed to be a witch who lived in a cottage in the middle of nowhere. I thought she was just a lonely old lady, but she told me herself that she was a witch.' I had made some slightly incredulous comment and he had turned and looked at me with a reproving eye. 'No, she really was a witch. I saw her demonstrate her powers once. She and I were standing in her garden. I was just about to go away when a raven flew over just down the valley. She said "I hate ravens" and pointed at it and, would you believe it?, the bird folded its wings and fell dead out of the sky.' That tale did not alter my opinion about witches but it did alter my opinion about vicars, about one in particular anyway.

Frank and I began to discuss the difficulties associated with our new water supply while Margaret prepared her spell. We could not afford to waste much time about it. The pipe came in an enormous great coil and we hoped to have the trench dug and the pipe in place by the following evening ready for the water board to connect up first thing in the morning after. Margaret was not a traditional witch. She made a mishmash of ingredients, following a recipe in *West Coast Witchcraft* that looked disappointingly like the offerings from the spice counter of the local delicatessen, put them all in a filter paper in the coffee percolator and bubbled boiling water through them. There was not an eye of newt or portion of bat's vomit anywhere in sight. The mixture smelt distinctly odd and I felt it was just as well that Percy was not around as the brew would have broken a few hearts in the police laboratory as they tried to analyse it in an effort to determine the legality of the substances contained in it. She then carefully consulted her paperback before deciding that everything was right.

I was terrified that Frank and I were going to be asked to drink this concoction, but all she did was smear some of the residue from the filter paper on the backs of our hands muttering some incantation as she did so. That was all there was to it. We were then pin-proof.

We put in the water main and it made life simpler. I forgot about Mr Crofton but Frank proceeded to grind him through the courts to establish his right to the water. Crofton himself seemed to go gently round the bend. He fell out with the Hunt and with the National Farmers' Union and was reputed to have his bedrooms filled with waxen images of half the Parish. Margaret was kept satisfactorily busy and took to charging £5 for a consultation. She was about to raise her charges to a tenner when the Croftons suddenly disappeared. Their farm was auctioned and Frank bought it. It was a bit of a shame really. They had given the village something to talk about for quite a few months.

Chapter Ten

'WILL YOU BE wicket-keeper?'

'But I haven't played cricket for twenty years and I was certainly never a wicket-keeper.'

'It doesn't matter. I'm sure you'll be jolly good.'

That was how I came to find myself part of that most traditional of rural rituals — village cricket. We were not the sort of team that has regular Saturday fixtures. One never quite knew when and how often we would play each season. It happened by a sort of osmosis. There would be vague talk about the possibility of a match sometime, usually late on in the pub and someone might make a couple of desultory telephone calls and word would get around that we had an opponent and a firm date would eventually emerge. We usually had two or three games a year. One against the neighbouring village which was never taken too seriously, one against a team which came down for a week's tour from London, and the critical match.

The critical match was against a team of estate agents. They all worked for a variety of firms which operated in the nearby market town. There was only one reason why the match was not as relaxed as the other two and that was because their team was captained by the Toad. The Toad took the game seriously. Desperately seriously. He was now very fat and forty but he was the sort of person who must have dreamed about making centuries for England against Australia when he was a schoolboy and he could still reel off half the records in *Wisden* if he ever managed to corner you at a pub or a party. He was also inclined to cheat.

The Toad had challenged the village to a match for the first time when I had been away and, in all innocence, the team had gone off expecting the usual pleasant Saturday out in the sunshine — husbands wielding relaxed bats and lobbing gentle long hops down the pitch while wives and children sat on the boundary feigning admiration at the deeds of derring-do when they bothered to pretend to watch. Instead the team had found themselves immersed in a merciless and ruthless contest.

The Toad had had his troops at net practice for a fortnight and he bullied and cajoled them like a football coach, either from the boundary when they were batting or from his lynch position as wicket-keeper when they were fielding. Our team was traditionally captained by Ivor who may well have been some sort of bat in his prime, but his prime had been covered by a thick layer of years. He had been most upset after he had faced several balls, to have to listen to the Toad exhort his bowler, 'Come on Mark. This batsman should have been out first ball. You've absolutely no excuse. All it will take is one straight delivery.' Although it had been nothing more than a bald statement of fact as the next ball had proved, that, and similar remarks, had upset our team.

We were trounced but the team had not felt that they had been defeated by a better set of players, and when the Toad had accepted a challenge for the next season with the remark 'Well, I suppose we might as well. If you think you could give us a rather better game,' an implacable resolve had built up that next year would prove to be a very different sort of match.

172

Ivor planned the return match with all the thoroughness of a general preparing his campaign. His trouble was that he was unsure of the quality of the troops that he had at his disposal. Grenville, for example, if he ever got his eye in was capable of hoisting ball after ball over the boundary ropes with the regularity of a metronome, but he very rarely managed to stay in long enough to get his eye in. Mike was capable of much the same. But subtlety of play was not their strong point. The Boycott style of innings where the bat comes down like a shutter to protect the wicket was almost unknown. A defensive approach to cricket only existed among the tail-enders — the very old and the very young who were only asked to play so that we would be sure of fielding eleven players on the appointed day.

So Ivor conspired his victory with great care. He needed secret weapons and found two, both from the same source. The first was John. He was a teacher who commuted from the village each day to the nearest comprehensive school, about fifteen miles away. Twenty years earlier, John had been a spin bowler of some repute, of such repute that he had even had a trial with Lancashire, his home county. The passing of the years had seen a severe erosion of both his skill and the aggressive spirit that is so necessary if one is to achieve victory, but the ghost of his genius could still be dimly discerned and there was a chance that it might emerge on the great occasion.

Even more exciting was the information that John had a friend called Tarquin Brownlow. He was getting on a bit, of course, but he was still the opening fast bowler in a team that played in the Lancashire League. None of us actually knew what the Lancashire League was, but John assured us that it was as far removed from the sort of cricket that we played as was Chippendale from G-Plan. In some capacity or other he was even supposed to have played in several matches opposite Wesley Hall who had shattered English bats in test matches against the West Indies not all that long ago. Tarquin should have the same effect on the Toad's team as releasing a tiger into a chicken run and John was persuaded to ask him down for the weekend.

At this stage, I had not even been called in but Ivor could not find a wicket-keeper. It was not surprising. Normally, in the lower echelons of cricket, wicket-keeping is a plum job. If one is fielding out on the boundary, or anywhere else for that matter, one's eyes begin to glaze with boredom as the hours pass and players begin to make daisy chains or discuss quantum physics with spectators on the boundary, but the wicket-keeper is right at the centre of things. Batsmen only rarely connect with the ball so he is always being kept busy fielding balls that the bowlers throw down in a random band six feet on either side of the stumps. Neither the keeper nor the bowler has much idea where the next ball is going to go and it does keep the wicket-keeper on his toes. But on this occasion the word had gone round that we had this terrifying hotshot, who had bowled with Wesley Hall, opening for us. He was reputed to be fast, really fast. While there was nothing that our team would like better than to see the Toad and his attendant tadpoles being set about by scorchers and bouncers, nobody was interested in taking on the potentially lethal responsibility of trying to stop the balls hurtling past the wicket on the way to the boundary. I was not told about him until after I had agreed to keep wicket.

The Saturday of the match dawned bright and clear. Our preparation for the match had been a few telephone calls from Ivor trying to get us out for some practice but the weather had been superb for haymaking and none of our key bats, who were farmers, were willing to miss it. We travelled in a convoy of cars to the pitch. Grenville was the only person who knew where it was and it entailed a three-quarter-hour trip through a maze of tiny lanes. We were the first team to get there.

The pitch, which we had never used before, was very typical of its genre, but it was not what the fiery Tarquin was expecting. The pavilion had its ancestry in a garden shed and the passing of the years had covered its timber in algae; the whole structure was gradually sinking as it rotted on the damp grass from the bottom upwards. It was discernibly a cricket pitch surrounded by a barbed wire fence to keep the cows off, with a cluster of mighty oaks marking the boundary by the pavilion, but the grass had only been cut the previous day and the toppings, eight inches long, covered the outfield although the wicket itself had been raked clear.

Tarquin and John examined the wicket inch by inch and went into a technical discussion about spin, swing, bounce and swerve and whether the bog-like quality of parts of the surface and the scattering of wormcasts would make any difference to the efficacy of their art. Then the Toad and his team arrived in a fleet of shiny new Japanese motor cars. They were all immaculately turned out in whites and cricket boots. Only Tarquin on our team could match them. Most of the rest of us could manage a white shirt but from there we degenerated to jeans, with Walter, who worked for the Council keeping the local roads in order, ending up with a pair of gumboots.

We stood around chatting amongst ourselves and our wives waiting for something to happen while the Toad's team immediately produced bats and started to bowl at each other or hurled around cricket balls with manic force to get their fielding eye in. We watched them, feeling a bit left out until someone managed to unearth a ball from the recesses of the garden shed and we sedately passed it from hand to hand while the two captains went out for the toss. They tossed. We lost. The Toad elected to bat.

My immediate problem was to find some pads and gloves as we relied on our opponents to provide all our kit. I approached one of the least offensive-looking of their team. 'Excuse me. I wonder if I might borrow a set of your pads and gloves?'

He looked at me in a friendly enough fashion for an estate agent but giving such permission was obviously not within his sphere of responsibility. 'I'm afraid you'll have to ask our captain, Frog Foster.'

'Really? Is that what you call him?'

'Frog? Yes. He looks a bit like a frog, don't you think so?'

'There is some resemblance. Either a frog or a toad.'

'Frog, definitely.'

'I lean towards toad. Anyway, I have to ask him?'

''fraid so.'

The Toad was deep in conversation with his fellow opening

bat when I approached him in the shed. They were buckling on pads, obviously discussing tactics and the talk ceased as I came in.

'I wonder if I might borrow a set of your gloves and pads?'

'Oh,' said the Toad aggressively. 'I suppose you're the wicket-keeper? I brought some especially for you. They used to be mine but I bought myself a new set.' One could see why. He removed the gleamingly whitened set of pads that lay on top of his carrying case and produced a split-seamed pair of gloves and a greying set of pads with the stuffing coming out at the edges. 'I suppose you will want to borrow my old protector as well?'

'Protector?'

'You know, my old box.' He indicated the rather nasty piece of flesh-coloured plastic at the bottom of his bag. There were limits about how far I would go in shielding myself from the expected onslaught from the demon Tarquin. Much as caution advised that I should accept his offer, the thought of where the protector had been nestling for most of its life put it beyond those limits.

'Thank you very much, but no.'

'Suit yourself. Now if you would put on your pads outside, then we can get on with discussing our tactics. Ha, ha!'

'Ho, ho!' I replied and backed out of the shed, wondering what on earth there was to talk about. My understanding of the batsman's function in the game was that he should get as many runs as possible whilst avoiding being out. I buckled on my pads and waddled out to the wicket. Ivor was trying to place his field to cater for the demon bowler who was to open. Tarquin was helping. He wanted three slips and had to be taken aside to have the facts of life explained to him. Even against a team as high-powered as the Toad's, three slips was unheard of. It presupposed, firstly, that the slip fielders would be able to catch. Any ball that came off the bat fast enough to need more than one slip to intercept it, would be dropped. Not accidentally, but because it was most unlikely that any of our fielders would be prepared to risk injury by putting out a hand to intercept the ball. It also assumed a certain technical competence at batting.

At our level of cricket, there was one basic shot. It is called the sweep at higher levels or the cowshot at lower ones. The entrapment of a batsman while attempting a shot on the offside is what leads to thick or thin edges. None of us ever attempted shots to the offside. For a game as coarse as ours, what is needed is six fieldsmen strung out in an arc on the leg side; one longstop; one slip so that the wicket-keeper has someone to talk to and from whom to receive moral support; and someone up on the offside near the bowler to fulfil the same function for him.

Ivor and Tarquin compromised on two slips which left the onside dangerously light but the fielder moved was Walter with his gumboots. He was very interested in cricket but was one of those people with spectacularly slow reactions and fell into a complete panic whenever the ball came near him. He was a liability to us but he did at least occupy air space into which the ball occasionally ventured.

The openers walked out onto the field along with two umpires who batted well down in their order. The Toad came to the crease and put his bat down, sticking out his prominent backside. 'Number three', he said to the bowler, Tarquin. Tarquin gave him a scornful look and marched away to pace out his run. 'Number three,' he said again, rather more loudly. Myself and Frank, who was my slip companion, exchanged mystified looks. We thought we knew our cricket but what the Toad was talking about was beyond both of us.

It was his guard and at least his own umpires appeared to understand him. Number three was leg stump, typical of the man, as flash a guard as you can ask for. The average village cricketer asks for centre as it should leave him with a good general indication of the whereabouts of his wicket. He who pretends that he can hit off drives asks for middle and leg but nobody, short of County level, ever asks for leg stump, let alone number three.

The Toad dug a hole in the ground with his bat to mark his guard and then majestically surveyed the field. He really was incorrigible, now pretending that he was capable of steering the ball between fielders towards the boundary instead of falling on his knees in gratitude in the direction of Mecca if he should ever manage to make contact at all. He looked at me, a safe twenty-five yards behind the stumps ready for the demon's first ball, and I could see the contemptuous curl of his lips.

Tarquin commenced his run up. It was an impressive sight. He was very tall and his hair flew all over the place as his skinny legs pounded the ground like a daddy-long-legs desperately trying to beat its rival to a nubile mummy-long-legs. He got within a couple of yards of the bowling crease before the elaborate structure of his delivery came unstuck. His foot skidded on the cut grass that covered the outfield and he cannoned into the stumps, falling flat on his backside. The Toad remained crouched in position, waiting for the ball that never came.

That was the end of our secret weapon. Tarquin's fall had cracked both his nerve and his dignity. From then on he bowled slow measured balls, not risking any run up in case he should do himself an injury and thus damage his effectiveness as the scourge of the North. Number two bat was a fine bad cricketer, looking on all slow bowling as a gift from God and anything within range he tried to slog. Not the Toad. He had watched too much television. He treated each ball, however bad, as if it was a grenade with the pin out. Those outside the line of the stumps were ignored. He stood still with his behind sticking out and glared at the ball as it passed leaving myself or the long stop to scrabble for them. Those that were on target, he also glared at until the last moment when he would suddenly move, describe a complicated arabesque in the air with his bat and bring it down on the ball just as it moved through. Because he left it so late, he had to bring down his bat rather sharply and thus hit the ball with considerable speed and force, accidentally scoring runs.

It was most irritating. What was particularly annoying was that our fielding was so bad. In the first half dozen overs, we missed soft catch after soft catch, infuriating Ivor. The worst of all was when one of the Toad's convulsive jerks sent the ball into the air in a gentle curve a dozen feet over his head straight at my hands. It seemed such an easy catch that I even gave the ball an encouraging clap as it floated down towards my gloves before it bounced off my fingertips and fell to the ground. All that silenced the sound of Ivor's teeth grinding in frustration was him missing a similar dolly a couple of balls later.

We did get them out. Number two fell onto his wicket. Numbers three and four were bowled by John, but the Toad did rather well. Our fielding was so bad that every time he made contact with the ball, he would bellow 'Yes!', put his head down and lumber down the pitch. One of his shots went directly to Mike who stopped it and lobbed it gently back to me. The Toad was already halfway down the pitch while his current companion, Number six, had sensibly not yet moved.

There is a feeling of great power in such situations. There was I standing by the stumps holding the ball while up at the far end of the pitch were the two batsmen looking at me in dismay. I neatly flicked off the bails. There was a problem. Which batsman was out? It should not have been too difficult. It was clearly stated in the rules of cricket that 'Should the batsmen not cross, then a run has not been attempted. Therefore the Toad is undoubtedly stumped as opposed to Number six being run out.' We all agreed, jumping up and down with jubilation. The umpires agreed. Number six agreed. The Toad did not. He did not shout about it but had a few words with Number six who trailed disconsolately off the pitch.

We remonstrated with the umpires — discreetly, as cricket is supposed to be a game for gentlemen — but they pointed out that, however much they might deplore his decision, the Toad was their captain and they had to abide by it. The Toad finally departed to an LBW decision and we tumbled the remaining wickets in time for tea at 4pm.

Tea was one of the high spots of the day. It is a fairly uninteresting meal usually, as meals go, but a cricketing tea has much in its favour. It is not too bad if you have been a member of the batting side and have been able to sit and talk on the boundary, but the fielding side will have spent the past few hours standing around under a boiling sun or, more likely, under a keen wind and will be delighted at the chance of tea, pee and buns. The feeling in our team was one of grim determination. The Toad's team had reached the formidable score of 117 but our resolve stemmed from our dislike of the Toad and his unsporting refusal to depart when he should have done. Even his own side were prepared to join us in a mutinous mutter, but he was a partner in the largest firm of estate agents in town and those who were not actually his employees knew that the day might come when they would want to be and none of them were prepared to come out of the closet and criticise him to his face.

Our openers went out onto the field. I was Number one for much the same reason that I had been wicket-keeper — nobody else wanted the job. The Toad was their wicket-keeper. Unlike myself who stood erect waiting for something to happen, he was the ostentatious squatting kind of keeper who crouched down behind his pads, peering between them, ready to uncoil himself in a panther-like leap to recover the ball. Panther-like, the Toad was not, but he looked quite good.

I played my usual innings. For some reason my usually healthy sense of self preservation flies out of the window when I am faced by a cricket ball. The faster it is bowled, the harder I try to swipe it. The trouble is that I never manage to time the shots quite right. For the first two overs, Ivor's instructions to preserve my wicket were obeyed. It was quite easy to remember, particularly when Ivor was one of the umpires and hissed admonitions to me whenever I came within earshot. By over three, the pusillanimity of trying to do a Boycott caused me to forget caution. It is not easy to try to be a good cricketer when the time is ticking away and all the other batsmen are chomping at the bit in front of the pavilion, wishing that you would hurry up and get out so that they can have a bit of fun for themselves. In over three, I began to hit out. I scored a boundary off the first ball and got the second in the ribs. The third ball was a full toss which I took a massive swipe at and just nicked. The ball pitched just past the off stump and was fielded by the Toad, rolling spectacularly over the ground like a well-padded snowball.

'Howzat!' yelled the Toad.

'Piss off,' I replied. 'First bounce, one hand does not count in this sort of game.'

180

Unfortunately Walter was our umpire and Walter was so impressionable that he was notorious for putting money in the collection box as it passed down the pew and then putting in some more when it came back. He looked stricken, riddled with doubts. The Toad analysed the situation immediately. He glared round at his still silent underlings.

'Howzat!' he shouted again and this time the rest of his team echoed him in a hesitant chorus with the bowler trailing in a limp and apologetic last. Walter crumbled before the force of eleven wills against his own and raised a feeble forefinger. I retired to the pavilion in disgust to be consoled by loads of wives and children who had forsaken conversation as the match had become a vendetta against the Toad for them as well as us.

Once I, the rock of the side, was out, the wickets began to tumble. The Toad appealed for anything and Walter had been browbeaten once and was in no condition to resist. We lost three stalwarts within ten minutes. Ivor attempted a classy forward defensive stroke and was clean bowled. That it served him right for getting ideas above his station was the general opinion of the spectators. Mike fell to a highly dubious LBW. Even from eighty yards at right angles, we could all tell that and sourly booed Walter when he gave it. Frank was stumped. This was quite outrageous. Nobody is ever successfully stumped at our level of cricket. To stump someone you need a wicket-keeper who is brave enough to stand close to his wicket with reactions fast enough to profit by it, as well as a batsman who realises that for some shots, you need to step outside the crease; neither creature exists in coarse cricket.

Our last hope was Grenville and I was sent in as umpire to give him the succour that might prove necessary in his hour of need. Grenville's leg was not that long out of plaster and this precluded him from sneaking quick singles. It did not matter very much as his style meant that each ball was either a boundary or a miss. Grenville's was the key wicket. Once that had gone then the rest of our team could be mopped up in a matter of a couple of overs. At the other end was the grandson of the squire who played in the Third XI at Harrow and cricketers of that calibre are an immovable fixture in our sort of game. Further down were the Walters of this world who barely had the confidence to hold a bat, and right at the bottom were Tarquin and John who were firmly imbued with the old-fashioned idea that the true class of a great bowler is best measured by his total hopelessness when it comes to batting.

The Toad recalled his fastest bowler for Grenville. He ran up, delivered the ball and it whizzed past Grenville, the stumps and the Toad to finish up as four byes. The Toad considered the insurance of a long stop as a confession of weakness. This left us with forty to win with five wickets in hand. The over was not an easy one to live through. Grenville scythed his bat through the air at every ball. The only ball that looked vaguely straight he managed to hit with the bottom edge of the bat and hammered it into the ground just inside his crease where it sat looking like a fried egg. The Toad prized the ball out and squeezed it roughly back into shape.

At the other bowling end was their wizard of spin who bowled a maiden over at the Harrovian. It was enough to make a good bad cricketer weep to see these lovely slow balls curling through the air, just asking to be hit into the oak trees on the boundary, being greeted with a sickeningly straight bat and played carefully back along the ground to the bowler's hand.

Grenville began to connect in the next over. He knew just how much was resting on his shoulders and his frown of concentration was heartening to behold. He missed the first ball, hit the second for a six and the third for a four. He missed the next one and the next but let go of his bat and sent it flying towards Ivor who was back as square leg umpire. He just connected with the last ball which was taken by the Toad with a really brilliant diving catch. If I had not seen it, I would not have believed he was capable of it.

'Howzat!' he roared triumphantly along with all his tadpoles.

'Not out,' I replied and walked firmly to square leg for the next over.

It was not Grenville's most distinguished match performance. He thrashed away at the ball all right but lived very dangerously. The Toad appealed for LBW five times and at least one of them was palpably out, but still the score crept up. The Harrovian fell eventually to a Toad catch. It was Ivor's decision and he should not have been out but his high quality batting was boring the two of us witless and Ivor thought he ought to give our rabbits a chance of swishing their bats.

We won the match by a wicket, but it was a very close-run thing and the Toad very nearly abandoned the game. We had a crisis when we were still about fifteen runs behind. It was one of those balls that one feels is bound to be a winner as soon as it leaves the bowler's hand, straight, good length and with no inadvertent spins or swerves to take if off line. Grenville's shot was lamentably mistimed and it was already completed with the bat over his shoulder on the follow through while the ball was still a couple of feet outside the popping crease, gathering itself for the final swoop towards the middle stump.

However, every crisis breeds a man with the mettle to match it. The solution flashed through my brain.

'No ball!' I shouted just before the stumps were shattered. The howls of protest from the Estate Agents were almost drowned by the roar of appreciation from the boundary which I acknowledged with a modest salute. The Toad did not challenge us again the following season. Nobody really minded.

Chapter Eleven

'WOULD YOU BE interested in being involved in the panto-mime?' asked Frank.

'Certainly not. The only time that I have ever tried to act, all that the critic in the school magazine could think of to say was that I had a good leg in tights.'

'Oh don't worry. I wasn't going to ask you to act. We need a stage manager.'

'I see.' He might at least have given me the opportunity of turning down the starring role. It was winter and traditionally the village intellectuals, who put on amateur dramatics during the rest of the year, vacated the stage in the Village Hall to make way for an extremely bucolic pantomime.

'Why do you want me? I thought that Grenville normally did the managing.'

'He does, but we're doing *Snow White*.'

'So?' I said encouragingly.

'Well, we did *Snow White* about five years ago and all the scenery was stored up at the Colonel's house and Grenville has fallen out with him and we thought that you would not mind getting the scenery out for us.'

'I see. I'm quite happy to go and see the Colonel but I don't really want to be stage manager.'

'Really?' Frank was almost gushing with relief. Any significant role was a matter of great prestige in the village over the next year and if Frank could get me to do the tricky job of approaching the Colonel without reward of the stage managership as payment, then the job would remain within his gift, probably to bribe Bill who was the Village Hall caretaker and tended to moan about its state of tidiness and tried to prevent the stage hands from hammering nails into the fabric of the building to keep their scenery up.

I had never met the Colonel before. He lived about five miles out of the village in an enormous Victorian house that his wife had inherited a decade earlier along with a considerable quantity of good farmland. All I knew was that he was rather ancient and prone to bursts of rage directed at anyone politically left of the National Front. The story was that he had been a brilliant, though outspoken, soldier who had been destined for a Field Marshal's baton. Unfortunately he had attended a lecture given by Montgomery at the Staff College after the War about the campaign in the Western Desert. He had been a major then but had had the temerity to stand up behind the massed ranks of brigadiers and generals and tell Montgomery that he had made several mistakes. Military oblivion had swiftly followed.

I had been told that securing the scenery was an urgent matter and so I went visiting the following day. We were in the frozen aftermath of a blizzard. The roads had been cleared but there were great drifts of snow on the verges and the fields were white with the trees standing out blackly against them. The Colonel's drive had been cleared and I had no difficulty in manoeuvring the car up to the elephantine pile of a house that lay at its end. I rang the bell by pulling a thing like a lavatory chain rather than by pressing a button and the Colonel answered the door.

He was wearing a sleeveless khaki pullover and shirt-sleeves and he was big in every way — well over six feet tall and must have weighed fifteen stone. I explained my mission. 'Oh yes, excellent, excellent. Won't you come in and have a sherry? I think all that scenery stuff was put in the meadow barn. We'll pop down and have a look in a minute. Chilly day, what?'

'Yes, sir.' I was led through to the sitting-room. It must have been about sixty feet by forty and in the grate was a single-bar electric fire. The Colonel's wife was at least wearing a cardigan. She was sitting at a bureau in front of a window, writing a letter, about thirty feet from the fire. The glass in front of her was opaque with a peacock's tail of frost feathers. Our breath preceded us into the room in a puffy cumulus cloud. The Colonel poured me a glass of sherry from a decanter and I felt its icy chill travel down my gullet and spread out in my stomach. The Colonel bumbled on about a tree that had come down across the drive under the weight of snow as I sat with my jaw rigidly locked to prevent my teeth rudely chattering. It is all in the mind, I decided. It is just what you are used to and I was a member of a softer generation.

Our sherry finished, the Colonel led me out of the side of the house and we got into a Land Rover. He had dressed for the climate to the extent of putting on an old tweed jacket and flat cap and had pulled a pair of galoshes over his shoes. He really was rather endearing. 'My wife writes every week to my daughter in South Africa, you know. Got two splendid grandsons, at an age to do National Service — all up on the border shooting natives. Odd sort of business, shooting natives. Not a proper war at all. Not much fun for anyone.' The Colonel chose another driveway from the one that I had come up. He drove fast and inexpertly. The wind came whistling through the vehicle's bodywork and its clattering diesel engine forced him to shout.

'At least the army teaches them something about self discipline, don't you think?' It must have been a rhetorical question. The last thing that a seventy-five-year-old Colonel wants is disagreement with a cherished opinion. The horn on the Land Rover suddenly started to blare. I looked sideways at the Colonel but his hand was nowhere near the button.

'In this part of the world, of course, all the youngsters do is ride around on motor cycles and do *Snow White* in pantomimes. What? No harm in that, I suppose. Probably more fun than shooting natives. Doesn't make a man of you though. Nothing like shitting yourself in terror in war to make a man of you. Don't you think?' The Colonel turned and looked at me for confirmation.

'Colonel, the horn. It appears to be stuck.' A blaring horn is a sound that makes one feel even more edgy than an unanswered telephone.

'The horn? Ah, yes. Don't really notice it now. It just seems to sound off when it feels like it.' He gave the steering column a bang with his hand and the horn shut up. The Colonel looked mildly surprised, 'That doesn't usually work.' We continued down the drive, the Colonel babbling genially on about nothing at all. The heater gradually cleared the frost off the interior of the windscreen.

We came to the road and turned left. On the right was the river with the spray frozen to the branches of the trees that hung over it and the snow piled on the boulders on the river bed. The fir trees blanketed the hill on the opposite bank and the mattress of needles on their branches still supported clumps of white that had been burned off the bare branches of the hedgerow oaks by frost and wind. The Colonel took the road carefully, skating across the icy ruts at twenty miles an hour. After a couple of minutes, an orange mini appeared in front of us, going even more soberly. The Colonel slowed down behind it.

'Had a chap before the Bench last week. Damn flasher. Extraordinary chap, come down from the Midlands or somewhere like that. Asked him if he had anything to say for himself and he exposed himself again right there in the dock. Must have been as mad as a hatter. The only woman there was his solicitor and she wasn't worth flashing at. Built like a damn tank.'

The car in front was going very slowly indeed. It was immaculately clean and showed two white heads in the driver and passenger seats. We were in no hurry. It was a crisp sunny day, making for a pleasant if chilly drive. Then the horn began again. The Colonel hit the wheel absent-mindedly as he talked, but this time it failed to stop. He appeared to ignore it.

He could ignore it, but the occupants of the car in front could not. The Land Rover was right on their tail and the Colonel, with his bristling moustache and the silver stag's head mounted on the bonnet, looked just the sort of chap who would drive them off the road. The horn continued to blare out. In the Alps, it would have started an avalanche. The head in the passenger seat of the mini craned round to look at us, shooting a glance that wavered between fear and anger. It was an elderly lady and she made a vague waving gesture with her hand. If she had been fifty years younger, it would have been two fingers. The Colonel waved absently back. The horn, for him, was part of the background music of his Land Rover along with the roar of the broken exhaust and the whine of a transmission that was on its last legs.

The mini began to swerve from side to side as the activity in its front seat became more frantic. It could no more escape from its pursuer than a Puccara from a locked-on Sidewinder. The Colonel appeared to notice what was happening in front of him for the first time. 'I say. Do you think there's something wrong in front there? Fellow must be drunk.'

'I think it's more likely that he's put off by your horn.'

'Horn? Oh Good Lord. I think you may be right.' The Colonel started to belabour his steering wheel. The passenger was now kneeling on the front seat, looking backwards, and the sight of the Colonel beating his wheel in apparent rage could have done nothing for her equanimity. Nor did the fact that he took his eyes off the road to look at the offending wheel to make sure that he was hitting the right bit and the Land Rover rapidly closed in on the mini. She said something to her driver and he, being a man of decision when it came to the crunch, turned his car and drove straight into a snowdrift at the side of the road.

'Heaven's above!' said the Colonel in alarm and skidded to a halt. I got out of the vehicle and walked towards the mini whose occupants were peering warily through their windows at me like suspicious trogolodytes. The Colonel, all fifteen stone of him, came galumphing after me, shouting vague inarticulate cries of apology. He tripped, cannoned into me with the force of an irate rhinoceros and sent me head first into a snowdrift. It seemed easier to turn over and lie there in peace for a bit and look at the sky while he sorted himself out and calmed the other frightened driver. We got the scenery but I resolved to avoid the Colonel in future. It was both warmer and safer.

In spite of my earnest protestations to the contrary, Frank thought that the very least that he could get away with giving me was the job of doing the programme and I discovered that it was one of the most critically important parts of the production because it was the only form of immortality that the pantomime could provide. Everybody had to be listed. I tried to get away with 'thanks to all those too numerous to mention' after the cast list and those behind stage, but it was not good enough. Everybody with the remotest connection had to be listed and have their names spelt correctly, right down to Christine Tyler who babysat for the wicked stepmother.

There was another exhausting convention associated with the programme. Everyone taking part wished it to be thought that they were modest and self-effacing and were only participating because Frank had pleaded with them to do so and so the last thing that they wanted was that their name should appear in the programme while, in reality, they were absolutely terrified that I would miss them out or spell their names wrong. This unbecoming modesty meant that they would not come to me but I had to go to them. Be it one of the stage-hands or the king, the script tended to be the same.

'Hullo. You're playing the witch's assistant, aren't you?' That would be received with a calm nod of assent. Stars become used to being recognised. 'I just want to make sure I've got your name right for the programme.'

'You surely don't want to put my name in. The last thing I want is any publicity' etc. etc. It could go on for a long time. Frank used his position of power ruthlessly. He had been bullying Francis Kirby for months to come out with his arc welder and mend some gates that needed his attention. He arrived as soon as it was announced that Frank would be the producer of the pantomime and made broad hints that a starring role would not go amiss since his part as a Wise Man in the school nativity tableau in the church hall a couple of decades earlier had given him unparalleled experience as one of the village's leading actors.

Frank had his priorities well worked out. *Snow White* allowed him to fill the stage with dwarves, little furry animals in the forest, ladies-in-waiting to Snow White and battalions of attendants for the King and the Handsome Prince. There were parts for all those who could speak a vaguely intelligible form of English and silent parts for all those who could not. But it all made extra work for me.

'Come on, Tom,' I said to the ironmonger. 'Sneezy is one of the most important parts in the whole pantomime. Everyone is bound to want to know who plays it.'

'But everyone who comes to see it will know it is me anyway,' he pointed out, perfectly correctly. 'Anyway, it is a very small part.' It was that point that obviously smarted with Tom a bit. He had thought himself a Handsome Prince candidate, but it was one of my duties to nip this sort of defeatist spirit in the bud.

'Nonsense. Your sneezing is crucial to achieve the right atmosphere. It proves it is cold and miserable in the Forest and creates an important contrast between Snow White's life at Court and what she is reduced to when she is driven out and has to rough it.'

'No, I don't really think I want my name in the programme.' The minuet could go on for ever. On this occasion I became bored with it.

'Ah, well. If you don't want it, I can't force it. It's a pity though, because it means that your name will be the only one that doesn't appear in the paper.'

Tom glared daggers at me. Getting his name in the paper was what it was all about and now I had departed from the rules of the game and there was a real chance that, unless he humiliated himself and actually asked me, his name might not appear for all to see in Thespian's column in the *Courant*. Either he saved his face with me which meant literary oblivion or he swallowed his pride to ensure that his fame reached a wider audience. He began to crack.

'I suppose if I didn't get my name in, it would look a bit strange with only six dwarves mentioned instead of seven.' What I said next was positively evil. My only excuse was that I was rather out of sorts with Tom as I had had a ballcock for the lavatory on order for three weeks and that is not something that you like to wait around for.

'Actually, I haven't asked any of the other dwarves yet and they might well agree with you. After all, contributing to the success of the pantomime is what it is all about. Even if they were desperate for publicity, I don't suppose it would matter if your name was left out.'

Tom looked at me from implacable black eyes. 'About the ballcock, if you don't mind me changing the subject,' I continued. 'Since there has been such a delay, don't you think you should give a bit of a discount?'

Tom considered. 'We might be able to see our way to giving you a small discount,' he said carefully. It seemed to me that we understood each other.

'That would be very decent of you, Tom. Now, how about spelling your name for the programme?'

'If you really think it might spoil it if my name was left out.'

'It would ruin it. A fiver knocked off?'

'A couple of quid, just. That's Tom Lowe, with an 'e'.'

'Look, Tom. Why don't you write your name yourself to make sure there is no mistake — under dwarves — if you put your name right at the top, it'll mean that your name will be first in the programme. That's right. A fiver?'

'A fiver.'

I often used to wonder if Machiavelli had been brought up in a rural community.

The pantomime slowly began to take shape. Grenville's wife, Mary, had landed the role of being in charge of props because she had a wide circle of friends and the willingness to exploit them and borrow whatever was necessary from them. She was a farmer and came from generations of farmers and such people have a brutal practicality about them. A spade is a spade and life is taken very literally. This quality can create certain difficulties when it is carried through to the subtle and delicate art of illusion which is needed for the stage. The props were props all right and many of the sets would have been passed by the Building Inspector.

The forest scene was typical. It was a short scene — a few fleeting minutes which should have been performed in front of a green backcloth during which a huntsman was due to shoot a robin for some unaccountable reason and where the wicked stepmother transformed herself into a pedlar so that she could con Snow White into eating the poisoned apple.

The first difficulty lay in shooting the robin. The easiest way out would have been to use a cap pistol, but Mary wanted her work to be seen to be good so that people would actively look up the name of the props manager in the programme. She first toyed with the idea of a bow and arrow, but the hunter had never used one before and looked a bit silly. Moreover when a real arrow was tried, the robin almost had her eye poked out as it missed the pillows stuffed in her red breast and whizzed past her ear. A rubber-tipped arrow was insufficiently real.

So the hunter was given a shotgun. Blank cartridges were provided by removing the pellets from an ordinary cartridge and at the first dress rehearsal, the robin was peppered with flaming wadding. The hunter fired at the ceiling next time, but it just looked daft when the robin screamed and clutched its bloody breast in response. Back to the drawing board went Mary. The pianist had to be roped in. He had to play the stalking hunter up to a crescendo and on his cue from the stage of 'Ha! I fire', he had to leave the piano and grab a shotgun and fire it into a bucket while the hunter mimed on stage. The noise was so loud that the robin had no need to feign the shock which was followed by agony and then death accompanied by a heart-rending 'cheep'.

The forest itself was another problem. Frank suggested a piece of painted camouflage netting but that would not have been up to standard. If the script said forest, then forest it would have to be. It was a coniferous forest, a dozen fifteen-foot spruce trees each stuck in its individual oil drum. They were not ideal. When they were on the stage, they left precious little room for anything else and the curses of the wicked stepmother as she threaded her way between their needles in a sleeveless ball gown, were uncomfortably real. A bare oil drum at the base would have been incongruous and so each had to be festooned with yards of precariously attached greenery.

Every solution seemed to create another problem. Where could the forest be stored when it was not needed for the vital scene? The trees were placed in the school playground from where they were carried on wheelbarrows by perspiring stage-hands (names all carefully listed in the programme). At the first dress rehearsal, setting up the forest took eighteen minutes. At the second, they had got it down to sixteen

192

minutes and it averaged around fifteen minutes for the four performances which took place between Christmas and New Year.

We attended the second last performance and it was a truly remarkable theatrical experience. The sets were as impressive as we had been expecting but even they could not disguise the truly atrocious quality of the acting. 'Thespian' was at the back and his snores fought with the frenetic jangling of the out-of-tune piano.

Those on stage would appear quite natural and have whispered conversations with each other until they were called upon to deliver a line. Then a look of terror mixed with concentration would come over their faces and they would face the front at attention to deliver it with all the expression of a depressed Dalek before relaxing when the ordeal was over. Snow White spent most of her time flat on her back inside a macabre and impressive mahogany coffin that dominated the stage once she had expired from eating her apple until the Prince swooped on her like a vampire and kissed her back to life.

The momentous forest scene change was covered by the seven dwarves coming to the front of the curtain, fixing their eyes on the ceiling and going through, four times, an abysmal ditty which involved them going down on their haunches at intervals while making crab-pincer-like movements of their fingers in a weird imitation of birds. Even the children at the front began to cry. The production was saved from disaster by the prompter, as determined not to miss his hour of glory as anybody else, who gave his cues in a Donald Sinden basso profundo that shook the rafters.

We missed the last night by going to Ivor's farm to see the New Year in. On the way home down the valley, we were stopped by a car with a flashing blue light on its roof which signalled for us to pull into the side of the road. It was Percy. On duty. He walked slowly over to the car and tapped on my window. I wound it down. 'Are you entirely sober, sir?'

'No,' I replied.

'Nor am I, sir. I only stopped you to say that I saw Bill Harris going into your garden with his shotgun again. I just thought I had better warn you. Happy New Year.'

Any Fool Can Be A Villager

Chapter One

A COUPLE of times in a decade, the British summer lets go all its inhibitions. It becomes bored with rationing out its sunshine during the short gaps that punctuate the watery march of the stately depressions sweeping in from the Atlantic and decides to have itself a heatwave. They are really quite respectable heatwaves when they come, with the thermometer climbing to levels that would not be considered untoward in places such as Cairo and Khartoum which sit and swelter under a tropical sun.

The Arab inhabitants of such places may be used to such climatic extravagance, but we are not. The fabric of our society starts to crumble in the face of prolonged sunshine. Water supplies run low. Fleet Street newspapers cannot find type large enough to headline the phenomenon. Trains run late as railway lines buckle while office workers copulate in the London parks at lunchtime. If such a heatwave should coincide with a Bank Holiday weekend, then there is a mighty national roar of agony as the British subject their pallid skins to a roasting that leaves them streaky with calamine lotion for a week.

The British landscape and those that dwell therein can stand this climatic extremism no better than its human inhabitants. Great heat takes the competitive edge out of the countryside. It saps the will. Cattle and sheep lie drowsily in the shade of hedgerow trees while farmers turn golden brown as they struggle with sweaty bales of hay. The summer birdsong stops as the land lies and cooks under the unwinking, moisture-sucking gaze of the sun.

They are good times, these. The drought may threaten the crops and the re-growth of grass but country people, like

everyone else, much prefer a good old-fashioned heatwave to
the mingy insipid drizzle that is our summer norm.

Our village lay in a deep valley surrounded by steeply
wooded hillsides. These did an excellent job of funnelling the
storms of winter so that they released their furies on top of us
and an even better job of trapping any drizzly cloud that may
have been wandering past. The heat, for the villagers, was
chiefly remarkable because of the increase in the area of naked
flesh that the tourists felt obliged to reveal.

The men would put on their red nylon shorts with an
effeminate slit up the side to reveal their pasty, office-white
legs supported on open-toed-sandalled feet. There was a clear
sex difference. In women tourists, the more beautiful the
individual, the greater the quantity of unclothed skin she
would reveal and the old patriarchs of the village would totter
into the pub, wild-eyed with lust, full of talk of bulging breasts
and firm nipples sheathed in filmy swathes of silk or cotton
with sleek brown bellies beneath.

Contrarily, the fatter the man, the more he would show and one would see an absurdly thin couple of shanks transporting a great rippling, reddening roll of fat down the street while the owner sucked ice cream and gazed about him with mild incurious tourist eyes. They looked like giant tomatoes with a couple of cocktail sticks thrust into the base.

Curiously, a heatwave did not encourage tourists to paddle in the river which, as it entered the village, settled into a chain of quiet pools. Half a mile below the village lay the Long Pool, an idyllic stretch of water 200 yards long above a weir that had once powered a turbine supplying the first electricity to the settlement. Even on the hottest summer day this pool was usually deserted until the end of the afternoon when the local farmers and shopkeepers tottered across the field between the slumbering bullocks, peeled off their clothes and fell, like logs, into the water where they grampused around, splashing at the biting horseflies while they washed the day's dust and sweat from their bodies.

It would have taken only one weekend visitor or coach driver to light upon the pool and it would have been ruined when the hordes discovered its peace, forcing the owner of the stretch of water to wire it and erect notices to frighten away the trespassers. As long as the pool remained just the playground of the locals, he permitted it to remain as a private village amenity.

What may have helped to discourge the casual visitor was that the field next to the river was populated by a herd of extremely large cattle. The field was owned by the squire, an archetype of the old-fashioned courteous country gentleman, and in it he kept his herd of twenty or so Charolais cattle. They were huge white creatures with great trembling double-muscled buttocks crammed full of expensive and tender steaks. These animals were lorded over by a bull, a truly enormous beast that frightened away everyone who did not get close enough to see the mild contemplative expression in his big brown eyes – mirrors into a nature that possessed the inherent ferocity of a butterfly newly emerged from the chrysalis. You would walk past the whale-like bulk of this creature as he snoozed amid the buttercups and give him an affectionate slap on the backside. A few seconds later, the nerve impulse that the slap had generated might reach the animal's brain and he would open a sleepy eye, fringed by impossibly long eyelashes. It might even set his internal motor into gear and he would sweep his head round with the ponderous precision of the jib of a crane, to look benignly after you while a half-hundredweight of grass came rippling up his throat to be cudded between his enormous jaws.

This animal, appropriately named Snowflake, passed his days in total tranquillity save for the periods that he set aside for copulation. Then, one day, he decided to do something different. The heatwave had climbed to its peak and, deep down in the tortuous depths of Snowflake's brain, he must have become dimly aware that it was hot. He even managed to make the quantum leap in the quality of his thought by deciding that it lay within his competence to do something about it. Having achieved all that, Snowflake went downhill from then on. At some point during the heat of the day, he winched himself to his feet and ambled across the field towards the river.

He must have reached the bank, decided that the water looked cool and managed to find the one beach – about 5 feet in length – where he could wade in without having to brave a dive of a couple of yards down the sheer bank into the water. The weighty beast must have experienced a feeling of elation akin to that discovered by the first hippopotamus that ever ventured into a river when he found that the supermarket freezerful of meat tightly packed round his skeleton was transformed to the equivalent of thistledown by the buoying effect of the water. Snowflake plodded his way to the centre of the river and either waded or floated downstream to the very edge of the weir where the water was a fathom deep and there he rested with his chin laid comfortably on the concrete edge of the weir wall. He put his brain carefully back into neutral and closed his eyes in the blissful cool.

The workers of the village failed to turn up that evening for their usual dip because there was a needle cricket match taking place. This exceedingly coarse tournament between ourselves and the two villages that lay further down the valley was a regular occurrence every second Thursday in June and took precedence over even the hay harvest. Our village came in last as usual, but it meant that Snowflake was left undiscovered for twenty-four hours longer than might have been expected.

I was first down to the pool the following afternoon. Usually there would have been total silence except for the hum of insects and the occasional plop of a trout. On this occasion, the bellyflopping of these fishes was augmented by an eerie moaning noise.

Only those who know bulls can be aware of the remarkably unbull-like sounds that they are capable of making. Unlike in our own species, it is the cow's voice that breaks, while that of the bull tends to climb an octave with every passing year of his life. Snowflake was no dewy-eyed calf; he was a portly mature father of dozens of calves and he could have sung an operatic aria that would have rivalled Callas in her prime. His pure soprano, with just a touch of professional tremolo, was echoing off the water to bounce against the deep midsummer green of the trees. He was standing hock-deep on a ridge of rock by the weir, a long way from his only possible exit. The river at this point was about 25 yards wide and, although the bed was otherwise entirely flat, there was a raised rocky platform, which came to within 18 inches of the surface, that ran down its centre towards the weir. When he saw me coming, Snowflake loosed off another cadenza from his vantage point. There was a moment's hesitation while he tried to decide whether I was a potential saviour or an assassin who might be wielding a pole-axe or even a harpoon, and then he launched himself off his ridge towards me, sending a tsunami-sized wave boring up and down the length of the pool.

Had he been a sheep, or even an average-sized bullock, it would not have been too difficult to lean down the bank to grab a nose, an ear or a tail and given him that extra bit of impetus required to pop him up on to the bank. But he was Snowflake. I entered the water beside him and slapped his backside in the hope that it might encourage him to climb the bank. It was like slapping the boot of a family saloon and had much the same effect, except that the sound was a soggy splat rather than a beer-can 'ting'. I looked at Snowflake and he looked mournfully back at me.

I pulled at his ring and knew what aspiring kings must have felt before Arthur came along to pull out the sword. He shook his head, swinging me off my feet, and released one of his pure siren-like bellows. This was obviously a situation that was beyond my powers to correct and I decided that the squire would be quite interested to hear that a couple of thousand pounds' worth of his favourite bull was in danger of drowning itself.

I put my clothes back on and trudged the half mile or so to the call-box in the village. The squire was not answering his telephone. Following a local fashion the year before, he had dug himself a pond which he had stocked with trout and he tended to spend much of his time sitting in the middle of it in a rowing boat with a fishing line out and his toes dangling in the water to keep cool. I dropped into the post office to brief the post mistress who had the remarkable ability to transmit information, preferably scandalous, to the whole parish within a matter of hours. Some suspected that she used telepathy. Snowflake's popularity ensured that the nucleus of a decent posse was already gathering down by the bridge by the time I re-emerged.

Mary Mowbray had been visiting the saddler to gear herself up for the approaching hunting season. She was the wife of one of the nearby moorland farmers, Grenville, and was one of those thin, tough countrywomen who could have been any age from thirty to sixty. Her conversation was entirely horses, dogs and cattle. She had a couple of teenage children who seemed quite normal, although it was said that her lack of interest in them had meant that they had been unable to talk until they had first gone to school.

Trapped in the front seat of Mary's Land Rover and looking decidedly worried was fellow farmer Dennis. He, poor man, had been flagged down on his way from the big city where he had been visiting his wine merchant. This was a regularly monthly happening, during which he spent a pleasant afternoon trying to decide which brand of peaty malt whisky he should drink the following month. He consumed a case of the stuff every fortnight, so he was allowed a decent tasting session. As a result, it was doubtful whether Dennis would be in a condition to be particularly helpful during Snowflake's crisis.

Mary had also roped in Seth and Ishmael Matravers. They were brothers, now both in their late forties, who farmed in a desultory fashion on the edge of the parish as a cover for their shared passion for hunting. They looked remarkably alike, both being about 6 feet tall and weighing between 17 and 20 stone apiece, which necessitated the ownership of horses that shook the very earth as they passed. Their mother had been widowed early and the brothers had made her life a continual drudgery by leaving her to do all the farm work while they gadded about the moors and the countryside in pursuit of foxes and deer. On her demise, Mother had ensured her revenge with all the cunning of a Renaissance pope. The land she had bequeathed to Seth while the buildings, stock and machinery had gone to Ishmael, causing constant conflict between the weighty pair whose quarrels became legendary in the neighbourhood.

We all headed back down the lane in Mary's Land Rover and across the field to the river for the rescue of Snowflake. Nothing very much had changed since I had seen him last. He had moved across to the far bank and was browsing on the vegetation. As our vehicle bounced to a halt opposite him, he stopped chewing and turned to gaze at us with a sprig of meadowsweet dangling rakishly from the corner of his mouth. The Matravers stood up in the back of the Land Rover and assessed the situation.

'If we get a rope round his neck, we could haul him across and straight up the bank with the Land Rover,' said Seth.

'Don't be bloody silly,' replied Ishmael. 'It's a 5-foot bank and you'd either bugger up the clutch, spin the wheels or pull the beast's head off. The only way to get it out is to drive it back up the river to the beach.'

We disembarked, walked over to the bank and looked across at Snowflake. He gazed hopefully in our direction and sirened his encouragement without dropping his meadow-sweet.

'Won't do the fishing much good, this sort of thing,' said

Dennis, looking rather hot in his tweed suit. 'Whose is it?'

'The squire's of course,' replied Mary, lighting up one of the small cheroots that she carried in the handkerchief of her hacking jacket. She never took it off as she needed it to carry around the sugar lumps and peppermints that she fed to her horses.

'Really? I thought the squire had sold it about ten years ago.'

'It ain't ten years old yet,' replied Mary.

'Not the bull, the fishing.'

'Oh, the fishing. It must belong to the hotel.'

'In that case we'd better get the animal out as soon as possible before some clot of a holiday maker sticks his hook into it and claims it as his catch.' Dennis had a very low opinion of the quality of guest that frequented the nearby hotel to sample the various country sports that it laid on for its clientele. He was a member of a shooting syndicate in which the hotel leased a couple of guns and reckoned that he had been lucky to escape with only half a dozen pellets in his backside and a lightly wounded retriever the previous season. 'I suggest that some of us get into the river.'

'But we'll get wet,' objected Seth.

'That's very true,' said Ishmael and they both looked at me. I resignedly stripped off my outer garments and clambered back into the river with a rope. Under instruction from those on the bank, I waded across to Snowflake and draped it round his neck. I returned with the other end and climbed back on to the bank.

'Now what do we do?' I asked.

'We pull, of course,' said Dennis.

'I doubt if it will do much good.'

We lined up on the rope and, with Seth and Ishmael anchoring us at the back, we pulled. A hurt look crossed Snowflake's face as the rope rose, dripping, from the river and became tense. He tossed his head and the five of us who were pulling were scattered amid the thistles and cowpats.

Dennis regained his feet, swearing. 'I don't think that is going to get us very far. I think we need some more volunteers. Mary, go and see who you can dig up.'

Off went Mary and the rest of us settled on the bank to keep an eye on Snowflake. He shook himself, sending up waves, and turned back to the bank to nibble at some more meadowsweet. Seth and Ishmael each picked a daisy and chewed at the stem.

Colin, the hotel's water bailiff, was next to arrive, attracted by the sight of a vehicle in the field. He lived in terror of poachers stealing the hordes of sardine-sized trout that filled the river. He strode up the bank to where we sat. We placidly returned his gaze. It was rather restful, just sitting in the sunshine.

'What on earth are you lot up to?'

Seth picked a particularly succulent daisy and nodded towards the river. Colin looked and saw. 'Oh hell! I knew that was going to happen some day. Where's the squire?'

'Dunno,' said Seth. 'He's probably on his pond.'

'The old fool should have fenced off the river.'

'I don't see why,' objected Seth. 'You don't expect a beast to go into the water like that.'

'You can expect anything from a beast like that one. It always surprises me that it's got enough sense to impregnate its cows.'

'It's got enough sense to know how to get cool.'

'What's being done about it?' demanded Colin.

'Mary's gone to get some more help.'

We continued to sit in the sun and observe Snowflake. He was having a few problems. By browsing at the edge of the river, he was flushing out the horseflies that lurked beneath the trees for anything worthwhile which came their way, landing on their victim like thistledown before viciously sinking in their proboscises. Snowflake's aquatic environment left him at a grave disadvantage. He could twitch his mighty body in irritation but the highly effective fly swatter that was conveniently attached to his backside could not operate under water and he was forced to retreat to the ridge in the centre of the river, his bellow proving no defence against being bitten.

Mary returned bearing a heavy burden of local citizens. Half the shops in the village must have shut down to supply them. Straggling across the field after her came the first of the tourists who had begun to suspect that something interesting was going on downstream. Judging by the sounds that were issuing from their lips, they were the contents of a Glaswegian coach. They lined up on the bank, parting the willows, and gawped at Snowflake and the prone mounds of the Brothers Matravers.

Ishmael heaved his 18 stone up on his elbows and looked back at them, meditatively picking his nose. Most of the locals were as unselfconscious in front of the tourists as they were in front of their stock. I could never achieve this. I was once shown round a deep-litter chicken house by its proud owner. He had opened the door and walked in with myself following. The 5000 chickens that had been wandering round scratching at their dung had immediately frozen in their tracks and fixed us with their beady little eyes. I had found my hand straying nervously to my flies to make sure that they were properly done up.

Among the latest arrivals was another local farmer, Ivor. He was famous for getting things done and so he straight away took charge of the situation. He rousted us off our backsides.

'Right. I suggest we all get into the water and drive the bull back upstream to the beach where it'll get out by itself.'

There was a general mutter of complaint, but Ivor's assumption of compliance was too powerful to be gainsaid.

Ivor foolishly jumped off the bank while most were more circumspect. Snowflake was standing on his ridge in the middle in about 18 inches of water but, by the bank, the river was at its average depth of 5 feet 6 inches. Ivor was not built of the same mighty thews as the Brothers Matravers and he disappeared beneath the surface to come up, spluttering with indignation, to a round of applause from the gallery which was growing all the time. The local policeman, Percy, had joined the crowd but he was staying well in the background in case he was expected to strip off his uniform and jump in. It was known that his torso was brown – the brown of a policeman who parks his panda behind a convenient bush on a hot afternoon for a sunbathe rather than chase evil-doers and he was rather selfconscious about it.

Ivor positioned his troops on the rope. The Matravers took up their place at the back with myself and half a dozen others taking up the slack. Ivor stationed himself behind Snowflake and pulled his tail up over his back while half a dozen others found convenient handholds round his person. Snowflake did not seem unduly perturbed by this plethora of munchkins that were swarming round him, but he was rolling his eyes a bit at the mob of tourists on the bank. At Ivor's signal, we all took up the strain and heaved. It was one thing to pull the church choir off its feet at the village fete, but quite another to shift a motorcar-sized object with legs instead of wheels, especially whilst we were standing nipple-deep in water. Those in front pulled and those behind pushed while Snowflake, apparently pleased to have some purpose in life again, stood like the Rock of Ages and refused to co-operate.

Ivor paused to re-think his tactics. He untied the rope from Snowflake's neck and attached it to his ring instead. We repositioned ourselves and pulled. This was not quite such fun for the animal. His neck was thick enough to stand up to any force that we cared to apply, but not his comparatively delicate nostrils. He took an uncertain step forward as they stretched like a rubber band, while the audience hissed its disapproval at such wanton cruelty. Then his ring snapped, corroded by a couple of years of bovine snot, and to the delight of the spectators and to despairing cries from the river, all those on the rope disappeared beneath the water.

We all clambered back on to the bank to hold another

conference. The fire brigade turned up to join in the fun. They were a perfectly innocuous bunch of people normally – a mechanic, the cafe owner, an electrician and a couple of farm workers – but, once they put on their uniforms and climbed on to the back of their shiny red wagon, they seemed to think that they were capable of sorting out any problem short of the origin of the universe.

All the while the tourist hordes were thickening. There must have been nearly forty by this time, their customary slack-jawed gape at the passing pageant of life by now being replaced with a certain animation and other signs of humanity, while one or two of them even joined the experts in the water to see if they could help.

Snowflake looked magnificent, standing high on his ridge above the surface of the river with the crowd of mere humans partially submerged below him. Mick, ace tractor repairer and fire chief, stripped to his Y-fronts and took to the water to explore the river bed with his toes while Ivor went off to find another ring. To show his authority and station in life, Mick kept on his white helmet and it was this that seemed, for the first time, to stir some emotion in Snowflake's broad breast.

As the helmet approached, he lowered his head and snorted with alarm before launching himself off his ridge and paddling down towards the weir. He had become well practised in aquatic locomotion in this depth of water and he moved surprisingly fast in a most unbovine series of undulating bounds. The multitude of rescuers, bathers and sightseers who by this time populated the river scattered before him like dinghies before the majestic advance of the royal yacht. Some failed to make it and were swamped by his bow wave, but most of them popped up again after he had passed and had come to rest about 30 yards further downstream with only his head now showing above water.

Colin, mindful of his fish, stood on the bank and wrung his hands. Mick joined him while a couple of tourist children on a plastic inflatable whale parked their vessel on Snowflake's back and he wriggled his appreciation as they leaned out and scratched him. Percy came to join the worried group of would-be rescuers.

'That bull doesn't look as if it wants to come out, if you ask me,' he said.

'Well, we didn't ask you, so shut up,' replied Colin.

Chapter Two

MATTERS IN the rescue of Snowflake had now reached a bit of a crisis. Ivor had decided not to go to look for a new ring in case something interesting happened while he was away and he was afraid that Mick might take over his position as *de facto* leader of events. He was prepared to consult, however.

'Have you any advice, Mick?' he asked.

Mick, still in his helmet and pants, gave the matter due thought. 'It's a bit of a problem. We can't haul him up the bank because it's too steep and it would need a vertical lift which we can't achieve. We can't get a winch into the river further up so that we could drag him back all the way to the beach, because there's no chance of getting the fire engine into the field, let alone into the river, and the brute is so strong that we can't drive him. Could we knock a hole in the weir and lead him through that?'

'No,' said Colin firmly. 'You'd muck up the flow of water to the trout hatchery and end up with half a million dead fish. In this heat they need all the water and all the oxygen they can get.'

'So that's out. How about getting a JCB to dig out the bank here to give him a way out?'

'It wouldn't work,' replied Ivor. 'There's solid rock only a foot beneath the surface. It would take dynamite to shift it.'

'Could we get a crane in?' suggested Seth.

Mick gave him a scornful look. 'We can't get our fire engine in without knocking down half a mile of hedge along the lane and the same would apply to a crane.'

There was an interested semi-circle of tourists listening-in to the discussion. One of them, a plump middle-aged lady in thick-lensed spectacles, tried to join in. 'Excuse me,' she said.

Mick looked at her in irritation. Civilians should be seen but not heard. Percy the policeman came into his own and began to wave his arms about as if he were driving chickens.

'Stand back. Would you please clear the bank. Come on, madam. Please step back.' He shooed them all back by about 10 yards to leave a clear demarcation space between the locals who thought they knew what they were doing and the tourists who had just come to watch. The experts continued their council of war.

'You know what I think?' said Mick.

'What?'

'I think that the only way we're going to get him out is to have him winched out from above.'

There was a stir of excitement from the rest of us.

'You don't mean . . . ?' queried Percy.

'He does mean,' said Seth.

'It's the only way,' said Mick firmly. 'We're going to have to call in the Brylcreem Boys.'

'Of course,' said Dennis, the residue of his tasting session making his brain work rather slower than the rest of us, 'a helicopter.'

The RAF is very much a part of last-resort agriculture, pelting blizzard-bound sheep with bales of hay, dropping toilet rolls on cut-off villages and doing all sorts of similar good works. If it did not issue such enormous bills for its services along with its bounty, it would have been used much more frequently. The glamour of ordering up a helicopter and its laconic crew of Biggles look-alikes appealed greatly to everybody and here was a situation where we could all enjoy the fun without being landed with the bill.

'What do you think, Ivor?' asked Mick.

'I think it's the only thing to do,' said Percy, interrupting the experts in his enthusiasm.

'Shut up, Percy,' said Mick.

'I think we'd better get in touch with the squire,' said Ivor. 'It could cost him a tidy penny or two, if they agree to come out.'

'Tell them that you'll sue them for disturbing your hens or something if they don't co-operate. Their bloody jets are always tooling round the spire of the church like a flock of bloody jackdaws,' said Ishmael.

This was an aspect of life in the valley to which newcomers took some time to grow accustomed. The valley, with the village and its church at the head, must have had a similar topography to one of the bombing runs to the Kremlin as young pilots, their acne clearly visible to observers on the ground, were continually hot-rodding up and down over the village. It was only disconcerting if one was in a car or on a tractor, when the sudden increase in engine noise as a jet scraped its belly along the top of the roof made one think that the vehicle was about to blow up.

'Talk of the devil,' said Dennis, as the squire's four-wheel-drive Subaru bounced through the gateway into the field and roared across the grass towards us, scattering tourists before it. He came to a stop and skidded in a cowpat as he emerged. The mirth from the tourists did nothing to improve his temper. He was wearing open-toed sandals underneath his Eighth Army-pattern khaki shorts.

'What the hell's this all about?' he snapped.

Ivor quickly apprised him of the situation and he strode to the edge of the bank to take stock. Snowflake was still up to his neck in water down by the weir and was licking a blue and white plastic dinghy containing a little girl who was squealing with delight.

'Hm. I see the difficulty. Can't we winch him upstream?'

'It would need a rope several hundred yards long to get him back to that little break in the bank and it would probably injure him,' replied Ivor.

'We certainly can't have that. I've just agreed to sell vast quantities of his semen. I had a chap out the other day who thought he was one of the best Charolais bulls in the country and the last thing I can afford is that any harm should come to him. Damned animal! He would go and get himself stuck now.'

Percy, his eyes gleaming with anticipation, chose his moment to sidle up. 'I think there's a way to get him out safely, Squire. It'll probably cost a bit, though.'

'Well, come out with it, man,' said the squire impatiently. 'I can't let the beast stay there all day. He's liable to exhaust himself and then drown.'

'The RAF.'

The squire turned pale. 'O God!' he said faintly. 'Has it come to that?'

'I'm afraid so,' replied Ivor.

The squire sighed heavily. 'If you're sure there's no other way, I suppose I'd better go and telephone them.'

'I'll come too,' said Dennis.

'So will I,' I offered.

'And me,' said Ivor.

'I'll keep the crowds back and clear a space for the helicopter,' announced Percy.

'We'll help,' said the Brothers Matravers.

'Excuse me,' said the plump lady in thick spectacles.

'I'm sorry, madam,' said Percy. 'You'll have to keep well back. We've got a helicopter coming in.'

Mary, who had been sitting on the bonnet of her Land Rover sucking peppermints and smoking her cheroots, suddenly came to life. 'What you could do, Squire, is charge some of these people who are coming along to watch. It might help to defray the cost of the operation.'

'That's a jolly good idea,' replied the squire, brightening up a little. 'Percy, would you mind handling that?'

The policeman looked justifiably outraged. 'I can't do that sort of thing. I'm a constable in uniform and it would be completely against the rules if I went round this lot with a hat.'

'I'll do it for 25 per cent of the take,' offered Seth.

'I'll do it for 20 per cent,' countered Ishmael.

'I'll do it for nothing, provided you give your usual Christmas party for me and the lads,' declared Mick. 'And you order the booze through me,' he added.

'How very kind of you,' said the squire. 'What I would suggest is that you charge ... er ... let's say 50p for adults and 25p for children. That sounds about right, wouldn't you agree?'

Leaving Mick and Percy in charge of matters by the river, the telephone party returned through the village in the

squire's car to the manor. The house was beginning to show
evidence of a century's neglect but, on a hot summer day, the
Virginia creeper and clematis that climbed all over the walls
covered its blemishes and the interior no longer had the icy
dankness that spoke of attempts to save on heating bills, but
instead oozed a luxurious coolness.

The squire's wife was pottering in the garden like a
character in an Edwardian play. She stopped deadheading the
roses as we swept up the drive to park in front of the columned
porch of the house and crossed over the lawn towards us,
stripping off her gardening gloves as she approached. She
wore a blue blouse and skirt with matching rope-soled
sandals, the shade of which she had been crafty enough to
match exactly with the vivid blue of her eyes that beaconed
out of her tanned face. She was in late middle age and still

stunningly beautiful; how the squire had won her was a bit of a mystery. She was even reputed to be rich.

'What's all the excitement about, dear?' she asked, as her husband leapt out of the car, galloped across the gravel and disappeared into the house.

'It's Snowflake. He's gone and got himself stuck in the river,' replied Dennis.

'Oh dear, the poor little chap.'

'We're going to phone for a helicopter to come and rescue him.'

'That sounds like a sensible idea. I do hope he won't be too frightened.'

'No,' said Dennis. 'I'm sure he will be all right.'

'Good,' she said. 'I must get back to the roses.' She drifted off as we turned towards the house, calling back over her shoulder, 'Make sure they don't put their wires too close to his balls.'

'I'll tell them to be careful,' said Dennis.

The squire was in the library whose shelves were filled with ancient bound copies of *Punch* and thrillers by Sapper and Dornford Yates, most of which had a fine white mould growing over them. The RAF took some time to reply after he had dialled the number: at least half the four-minute warning passed before he spoke.

'Hullo . . . good . . . I'd like to order a helicopter, please . . . I know you're not a minicab firm. You see, we have a crisis . . . No, we're not the coastguard. I'm a farmer. My bull is stuck in the river . . . No, I don't think it's a job for the navy . . . Yes, it was very droll.' The squire lifted his eyes to the ceiling. 'Oh good! How very kind. We can expect you in about three quarters of an hour, then. Thank you so much.' He hung up. 'They're coming out.'

'I think you forgot something,' said Ivor.

'Really? What?'

'You didn't tell them where to come.'

'Oh, good heavens! Nor I did.' He picked up the telephone and dialled through once more. 'Hullo . . . Yes, it's me again. I forgot to tell you where to come. Now the easiest way is to follow the motorway until you hit the A3321, then take the second left and carry on until you cross the river, then right for a dozen miles and you can't miss it . . . Map reference? I've no idea. Just follow my directions . . .' He gave an embarrassed whinny of laughter. 'Oh, I'm so sorry, I forgot you wouldn't be coming by road. Let me see now. I think the best thing to do would be for us to mark the spot and you just follow the river upstream until you see it . . . Weight of the bull? I suppose that is a good point. I haven't put him on the scales recently. At least a ton, I should think . . .'

'A ton and a half,' murmured Ivor.

'. . . Perhaps even a ton and a half. Can you manage that? . . . Good . . . er . . . One final thing. How much do you think it will cost? . . . Oh, I see. Goodbye, then.' He put down the receiver.

'How much did he say that it would cost?' I asked.

'He said it wasn't his department.'

'Not to worry,' comforted Ivor. 'It's probably covered by your insurance.'

Dennis, on his way out through the door, suddenly stopped and turned, his eyes lighting up like fairy lights. 'I've just had a marvellous idea. Why don't we get on to the television people and get them to come out. You could charge them a whacking great fee. Imagine the pretty pictures they would get of a huge white bull hauled out of the river by a rope dangling from a helicopter. It would appear on the national news. They could sell it in America. They'd make a fortune.'

'That's not bad,' said the squire. He gnawed at his Groucho Marx moustache for a couple of seconds. 'You don't think it might make me look a little silly? It is my bull and some might say that it was actually my fault that it got into the river in the first place.'

'Who cares?' said Dennis. 'Think of the money.'

The squire thought of the money. 'Right. You get back on the phone while the rest of us get back to the river and prepare things for the helicopter.'

We went back through the village which was strangely silent, considering that it was the height of the season. The shops were all shut and the coaches which were normally surrounded by milling tourists, terrified to venture too far away in case their bus left without them, stood empty and lonely in the car park. Their passengers were toiling in unaccustomed fashion down the hot, dusty lane towards the river between the high hedge banks lined with campion and willow herb.

The squire ploughed through the stragglers, his horn tooting importantly as befitted the owner of the centre of the attraction. There must have been nearly a hundred people standing amongst the thistles by this time. Most were lined up on the river bank, having broken down the lower branches on some of the trees so that they might have a better view. Snowflake was back on the ridge, placidly chewing his cud, with only a few children in the water to keep him company.

Percy shooed the crowd away from the centre of the field and a couple of lines of discarded shirts were laid out in the shape of a cross which he had had the initiative to place as a guide for the helicopter. Snowflake's harem was lying on the grass right at the far end of the field, content to keep well away from the excitement.

We hung around and waited. Mick's wife, Beryl, who owned the cafe, had turned up with several cartons of ice cream which had a ready sale amid the spectators. Then Dennis returned from his efforts to attract television coverage. He was not looking particularly happy.

'I can't understand it,' he reported. 'They didn't sound all that interested. They said they already had the story covered. But how on earth could that be, since we were the only ones who knew about it?' He was most apologetic about his failure and passed his ever-present flask of whisky round which, in the late afternoon heat, was not as welcome as Beryl's ice cream.

In another half-hour, the helicopter came clattering down the valley. The tourists 'oohed' and 'aahed' with excitement but the local inhabitants, both animal and human, showed little interest. We'd had the lot over the village – Tornadoes, Sikorskys, Gnats, Phantoms, Harriers and even the Hercules, thundering low enough to shake the fillings in your teeth. The best of them had been the old Vulcan bomber. However many times we had seen it, it was still an event when its enormous triangular slab-shape slipped over the top of a hill and rumbled down the valley, spraying burnt kerosene out of its backside.

The helicopter chuntered up the river, stopped to examine Snowflake in a rather predatory fashion from 100 feet or so while he continued his cudding and then came over the field, causing the tourists to shriek with excitement, and settled on the grass, blowing all the shirts into the hedgerow. The blades slowly whumped to a stop and a door in its side opened. The crowd pressed forward. One almost expected a creature with a dozen tentacles to emerge and say, 'Take me to your leader.'

The behelmeted aristocrats who stepped out in its stead had a glamour that no extra-terrestrial could possess, however. These were not the spotty passers-by in the jet trainers, but the heroes who plucked bulls from rivers and small children off inflatables that were blown out to sea while their parents were copulating in the sand dunes. Their leader took off his helmet and came over to Percy who was standing beside the squire and other leaders of the community: 'That's the cow you want hauled out, is it?'

Mary sighed in appreciation. His hair was fair, his eyes were blue, his chin was firm, his nose was chiselled with a delicate flare to his nostrils and a scraggy blond moustache squatted on his upper lip. His accent was pure Scouse. 'My name is McKenna, Flight-Lieutenant McKenna.'

'Good afternoon, Flight-Lieutenant,' said the squire. 'Yes, that is the . . . er . . . bull . . . er . . .'

Dennis took over the socializing. 'Would you like a whisky?' he asked, proffering his flask. Then: 'Perhaps you'd prefer an ice cream,' he continued hurriedly as he received a basilisk stare from the pilot.

'Is your bull in any immediate danger?'

'No,' replied the squire. 'It's just that we can't get him out.'

'In that case, have you got a strawberry split? I do like a nice strawberry split.'

'Beryl! Have you got any strawberry splits?'

Beryl, a large lady, waddled over with her ice creams. 'Only one, Squire.'

'Not to worry,' said the pilot. 'I'll take that and I'll have a couple of chocolate flake cones for the lads.'

The crowd watched with grave interest as Beryl handed out the ice creams while looking expectantly at the squire. He sighed and fumbled in the pocket of his shorts, producing a crumpled fiver which she took and carefully counted out three notes in change.

'Is that all I get?' asked the squire.

Beryl looked hurt. 'I had the extra expense of transporting the ice cream from the village and putting it in the cold box. We've got to make a living.'

'Have you paid for the ice-cream concession in this field?' asked Dennis.

'A very good point,' said the squire and snatched another pound note from Beryl's grasp. We stood and watched the three-man crew as they sat in the shade of their machine, supping their ice creams. They finished them and showed little inclination to do anything else. The tourists moved in and started to poke the large yellow helicopter with 'RAF RESCUE' painted prominently on its side.

'When do you think they're going to do something?' asked Mary from the bonnet of her Land Rover. 'I can't sit here all day. I've got horses to feed.'

'When they're ready, I suppose,' replied Dennis.

'Do you think they charge by the hour?' she asked.

'Heavens!' said the squire. 'What a ghastly thought! Perhaps I'd better go and find out.' He advanced to the helicopter and had a short exchange of views with the flight-lieutenant. He returned to the Land Rover. 'He says they shouldn't be long now.'

We waited for another ten minutes.

'Look!' said Dennis suddenly. 'The rotten swine!'

A couple of Volvo estate cars had drawn up in the gateway of the field and a posse of people was coming through. It was a television crew. The RAF had spotted it as well and stood up and stretched. One of the TV people pushed his way through the tourists, went up to the pilot and shook his hand.

'Afternoon, Allan. Good of you to wait for us. This looks like being quite a goody. Let's have a look at the cow.' They went over to the river bank with the tourists trailing after them.

'Oh yes, this should make the network all right. Lovely creamy-white cow.'

'Bull,' snorted the squire, who was pushing his way through the mob after them.

'Bull, even better, dangling on the end of a cable. You'll have to pull it up slowly to make sure that we get some decent shots.'

The squire finally managed to make his presence felt. 'Here, we phoned you up and you said that you weren't interested.'

'It's all right, mate. We'd already been tipped off by the RAF.'

'What a damned cheek! It's my bull.'

'Is it? Oh well, we'll take an interview with you later. But it's great stuff for the RAF. Lovely PR. The taxpayers will think they're marvellous.'

The squire had an extremely short fuse at the best of times and a tidal wave of blood swept up his cheeks. 'This is nothing short of outrageous. I'm going to get a damn great bill while you people are going to make money out of it.'

'No need to get your knickers in a twist, my son. Remember that freedom of the Press is the corner-stone of our liberty.'

'I do not consider that a bunch of bloody nancy-boys with television cameras have anything to do with Press freedom.' Before the squire let the conditioning of a century of democracy fall away from him and grabbed Mary's horse-whip, Dennis took hold of his arm and whispered in his ear. The squire brightened. 'Good point, Dennis.' He turned to the director. 'Excuse me. Have you been given permission to film in this field?'

The director looked furtive. 'Don't need it.'

'I'm afraid you do.'

'All right, then, who do I ask?'

'Me.'

'Oh, I see. Well, may I have permission, then?'

'Certainly,' replied the squire with relish. 'It'll cost you . . . er . . .' Dennis whispered in his ear. '. . . £150.'

'£150! Bloody hell. We're News, not Features. That sort of

money would cover me for a week. How about a tenner?'

'I'm sorry,' said the squire firmly. 'If you want to film, it's £150 or nothing.'

The flight-lieutenant was fiddling uneasily with his helmet. The director looked appealingly at him, but he shrugged. This was not the sort of thing that had been covered during lectures at Cranwell.

'Come on, mate. We've driven a hell of a long way for this. It'll make you famous. Be a pal. Make it twenty quid,' pleaded the media man.

'£150,' said the squire.

The director took a deep breath. 'Right. Be like that. Charlie!' The cameraman, to whom this call was addressed, appeared to be totally uninterested in the outcome of the negotiations: he was much keener on exploiting his televisual glamour by allowing the most attractive female tourist in the field to peer through the viewfinder of his camera while he clasped her and it in his great hairy arms. 'Charlie! Do you think you could climb on to the top of the car and get decent pictures from the next field?' The next field was only 100 yards away but there was the lane and the two 6-foot hedges bordering it in between.

Charlie raised his eyes from the tourist's cleavage and looked over at the hedges. 'Yeah, Ray. No problem.'

'Right then,' said Ray. 'We'll do that.'

'Excuse me,' said the squire. 'Have you got permission to use that field?'

'Don't tell me. You own that damned field as well.'

'That's right.'

Ray sighed heavily. 'Why are you being so difficult? Most people like to see themselves on TV.'

'For a start, Sir, I do not possess a television receiver and, in the second place, I am trying to offset the expense of that machine.' He flapped his hand in the direction of the helicopter.

'I suppose that's reasonable. Look. What I'll do is go and phone the editor and see if he will authorize £150.'

Meanwhile the tourists pressed closer to the helicopter and peered into its interior. Beryl re-appeared with a fresh load of ice cream and did a roaring trade. The Brothers Matravers tried to persuade the helicopter pilot to give them a joy-ride over their farm. Snowflake was, for the moment, ignored, while his cows, with the middle-aged female tourist amongst them, cropped their way up the river bank past him, most of them taking no notice of his plaintive cries of indignation.

Eventually Ray returned bearing good news. He prised the cameraman away from the brown-bellied nymph, who was now being taught the delights of zoom, pan and tilt, and came over to the squire: 'OK, you can have your money. But you'll have to send in an invoice for it. I can't produce that sort of amount from petty cash.'

His announcement was greeted by a ripple of applause from the tourists who had been afraid that they were about to be cheated of their spectacle and a chance of appearing on TV. A circle was formed round the protagonists in the drama about to unfold so that none of its nuances would be lost.

There was, however, a problem.

'Where's the bloody cow?' asked Ray, scanning the water.

'He hasn't drowned, has he?' asked the squire anxiously.

Snowflake hadn't drowned. He was 200 yards upriver and, as we watched in dismay, he pulled himself out of the water via the beach and mounted one of his harem.

'I thought that would happen,' said the middle-aged lady tourist. 'I saw that one of the cows was on heat and I drove her down the bank so that he could get a sniff of her and he followed like a lamb.'

The squire refused an additional £100 to push Snowflake back in. The RAF clattered away muttering about large bills and wasting their time but, as Dennis remarked, it was their own fault for hanging about when they first came. Beryl bought Snowflake a new ring out of her ice-cream profits and, for the first time in ten years, the TV station refused to announce the village fete on their future events programme. As the squire said, none of their employees was a gentleman, so we were not surprised.

Chapter Three

'TOURISTS,' SAID Arthur firmly. 'That's what I'm after. It's ridiculous to farm in an area like this and not make full use of the natural resources. Tourists are an annual cash crop like any other, and I'm going too make sure that I get my share of the harvest.'

Arthur, in the opinion of the locals, could hardly be said to farm in the area. He was a foreigner, having only lived in the vicinity for twenty years, and had come down from 'up country', a legendary region that took in all the land surface of the United Kingdom lying east and north of the county boundary. Arthur had begun his career as a relief milker, a locum for dairy farmers who had finally cracked under the strain of milking cows twice a day for year after year and had taken their wives for a fortnight's holiday to wander the sea front at Torquay at 5.00 am, worrying themselves to ulcers about what might be going wrong back home.

Arthur was quite good at his job and had been given a lot of work, but a *frisson* of horror had passed through the community when, after five years, he had gone out and bought a 50-acre farm. The farmers who had employed him all counted their cows, checked their silver spoons and did their inventories, but no discrepancies could be found. It was a baffling problem. Arthur, when approached directly about the source of his wealth, tapped the side of his long nose and winked. It was a gesture which looked impressive but was not very informative.

Percy's predecessor was even stirred sufficiently to make a few enquiries, but Arthur sent him off with a flea in his ear. Eventually it was agreed that Arthur was the son of a rich northern landowner and had had the money passed to him by his parent. This was totally imaginary but, by that stage, nobody cared. Every problem has to have its solution and any solution, however unlikely, was better than none.

Arthur's 50 acres were pretty useless. His financial cornucopia seemed to have stopped cornucoping before he was able to invest the large sum needed to drain and re-seed the muddy, rushy hilltop that he had purchased. It was the bogs that were his main problem. The water seemed to defy both logic and gravity by ignoring all the valleys that surrounded his farm belonging to other people and settled on the top of his mountain, refusing to move. Serious farming was not possible and he was forced into the ultimate agricultural cop-out of covering his land with sheep.

With his status raised from that of agricultural odd-job man to farmer, if only a sheep farmer, Arthur could no longer work for other people and so he built up a very reasonable business selling the sort of knick-knacks that farmers always need – concoctions to pour down animals' throats to drown worms, curious tools to help build barbed-wire fences and subtly curved knives with which to pare cows' toenails. But it niggled. There he was, a fully-fledged farmer, messing about with a few bone-headed sheep that needed gumboots if they were to thrive. Even all those cabinet ministers with their farms in the home counties kept beef as well as sheep.

'Tourists. It's got to be tourists,' he reiterated to the evening assembly in the pub. Of the two bars in the thatched building, the one with the nicotine-coloured walls and dung from muddy boots covering the carpet in a protective layer was used almost entirely by local inhabitants. Tourists used the lounge bar, complete with juke box and padded benches. Even though Arthur was a foreigner, he used the locals' bar.

'Tourists are supposed to like unspoilt countryside and nobody could call my land spoiled.'

'Well, I don't know about that,' said Bill. 'It's pretty spoilt-looking to me with all those weeds and rushes all over it.'

'No, you daft old pillock. That's unspoilt. The more useless and like a rubbish tip the land is, the more unspoilt it's supposed to be if you are a townsman. They all love weeds and nothing upsets them more if you go and turn a bit of barren land into a decent field of grass or corn. They've got laws against that sort of thing these days.'

'They're all potty if you ask me. They've no right to interfere with what a man does with his own land,' said Bill.

There were jeers from round the bar.

'Where the hell have you been for the last thirty years?' asked Arthur. 'Anyone would think you thought we still lived in a free country.'

'It's still not right,' grumbled Bill. 'They ought to stop people in towns digging up their vegetable gardens or mowing their lawns rather than come out and interfere with us farmers trying to make an honest living.'

That was rich coming from Bill. He was a farmer – or certainly had been – but he had not felt the need of restricting himself to making an honest living during any of his sixty-five years. It was not his fault that his bullocks always seemed to escape and find their way back home after he had sold them, or that his sheep spent most of their lives eating his neighbours' grass, or even if the driver of the milk tanker always seemed to be his wife's cousin which meant that the reading of the contents of Bill's bulk milk tank was always more than generous. It may not have been his fault, but it all helped to keep him in beer, baccy and racehorses.

Bill had been as bald as a mushroom for thirty years, but few people knew it as he never took off his trilby. It was rumoured that he kept a fighting fund of £20 notes inside, in case a sudden deal should come his way, but this theory was discounted by the more knowledgeable villagers because we knew, however sweet the deal, Bill would never remove his hat. I had once walked with him under an overhanging branch which had momentarily dislodged his head cover. Bill's sight of my startled look at the colour contrast between the smooth white toadbelly of his scalp and his gnarled, sun-beaten face, had made him blush deeply.

'Anyway,' continued Bill, 'not even the tourists would find any reason to visit your farm, Arthur. Why should they?'

'Bed and breakfast?'

'Bed and breakfast,' repeated Bill derisively. 'You won't

catch any tourists coming if they have to queue up for your outside khasi.'

'Oh, I don't know. It's the only double-seater in working order in the parish. It'd give them the authentic feel of country living.'

'Sure. An arse full of splinters.'

'You're an ignorant pig, Bill Hockridge,' broke in Arthur's wife, Annie. 'The seats are polished smooth by generations of backsides. You'd never get a splinter from them.'

'It's a hell of a thought, really,' said the commander, who ran a market garden on the edge of the village. Its profits, combined with his pension, just managed to keep pace with his alcohol consumption. 'Those seats must have cradled more than a century of bums. They must have watched little ones perch precariously on their edge as nippers, seen them grow into adolescence and get spotty before changing into the fighting trim of maturity, the flabbiness of middle age and then shrinking again as they move towards senescence. They could tell a tale or two about the frailty of human hopes and ambitions, those bog seats.'

The commander sometimes got like this with a few drinks under his belt.

'That's true enough,' said Bill. 'They've seen some important backsides too. The minister of agriculture's, for one.'

'The present one?' asked Arthur.

'No, during the war. A whole bunch of bigwigs came down with a newsreel team to make a film about how important farmers were to the war effort. The old squire gave them a meal in the manor and the whole lot of them got the trots. They went round to your place and they were bloody grateful that it was a double-seater. They didn't have to queue so long.'

There was a rapid series of clicks from a chair at the side of the bar which meant that Jimmy, the village's oldest inhabitant, was loosening his false teeth in order to make a pronouncement. We turned in anticipation.

'That privy must have known Maisie Appleyard,' he said. There was a reverent silence round the bar.

'Who's Maisie Appleyard?' I asked.

229

Bill answered, 'She was the most beautiful girl that was ever bred in the parish —'

'— and a real hard worker,' broke in Jimmy.

'She was that, too,' agreed Bill. 'She married a Yank during the war when she got pregnant. She was the only one who managed it. To marry a Yank.'

'Well, I suppose she had to if she got pregnant,' said Arthur.

'What do you mean, "had to"?' said Bill scornfully. 'I should think half the people in the parish have got an American parent or grandparent if they only knew it. All the girls were after one of those Yanks who were stationed in the house the commune's got now. They said they were training to be commandos but it turned out they were all casualties from what they called battle fatigue. We called the place the chicken house, and they sure behaved like roosters when they got the chance.'

'But they spent money in the village and we were grateful enough for that,' said Jimmy. 'All the shopkeepers changed the price tickets when they heard the American jeeps coming down the valley.'

'It sounds as if they were a bit like today's tourists,' said Arthur.

'They weren't the same at all,' answered Bill. 'The tourists just come down in their caravans and sit on the sites cooking up tins of baked beans they bought in Birmingham before they set out. They don't spend anything at all.'

'A caravan site!' said Arthur. 'That's what I'll do. We'll start up a caravan site.'

And he did. He made a grand job of it in one of his less boggy fields. He put down lorry-loads of quarry waste to make hard stands, dug a pit in which they could empty their chemical loos, put in a water standpipe – spring-fed from a bog in the field above – and erected a large sign by his front gate which announced that he was now open for business. It was even rumoured that he had applied for planning permission.

All the same, Arthur did not look a particularly happy man when he came into the pub a couple of months later. He ordered his usual pint, specifying a glass with a handle, which was one of those little foreign habits that he still retained, and gazed rather sadly down into his beer. Arthur, looking as if life was a bit of a desert drear, was an unusual and interesting sight and he was soon surrounded by a commiserating group of villagers trying to get him to talk. He was well into his second pint before he was willing to unburden himself.

'Bastards! That's what they are. A miserable crowd of bastards. I go and spend hundreds of pounds on a really lovely caravan site and nobody turns up. It's a waste of bloody time.'

'You know what's wrong with it, don't you?' said Bill. 'It's got no shelter. Sitting on top of your blooming hill, even the caravanners have got enough sense to know that they'd be blown into the next county if they went and parked there.'

'It's got views, magnificent views, for miles. That's what makes it special,' replied Arthur defensively. 'And you can't have both views and shelter. Either you're down in a valley or boxed in by trees where the weather can't get at you, or you're out in the open where it's windy and you can see a long way. Anyway, tourists are supposed to come out here to get lots of clean country air.'

'Not as much air as you're offering, Arthur. What are you going to do?'

'I don't know.'

'You ought to advertise,' said the commander. 'It's not as if you're on the beaten track.'

'I can't afford to. I spent all my money on preparing the site.'

'How about a bit of public relations, then?'

'What do you mean?'

'It's pretty much the same as advertising, but it doesn't cost you anything. You get newspapers to print stories about you and your caravan site,' replied the commander.

'Why should they want to do that?'

'You make the stories interesting.'

Arthur thought for a few seconds. 'How many interesting stories can you think of about a caravan site?'

'Well . . . I see what you mean. Can't you have a vicar in

a love nest with a verger's wife? That would get you mentioned in the mucky papers for a start.'

'It would, but I haven't had any caravans yet and, even if one did turn up, it would be highly unlikely to contain a vicar and a verger's wife.'

'You don't understand,' replied the commander patiently. 'In public relations you make up the stories. They don't have to be true. And, for heaven's sake, you don't expect to read true stories in the mucky papers.'

'I suppose not . . . You mean I can make up anything I like?'

'That's right.'

'Like what?'

'Well, let's think about it.'

And think about it we did. The campaign to put Arthur's caravan site firmly on the map was born that evening. If Arthur himself had known what he was getting into, the campaign would have probably been still-born, but he could have only reached that conclusion with the advantage of hindsight. We came up with the outline of a plan which was approved by all those present in the pub and we were all sworn to secrecy.

The following day, Bill, myself and Bill's elderly and extremely fat labrador went out to see Arthur and inspect the terrain. His farm was pretty bleak even when it was not too windy, though the house itself nestled into a bank which gave it some protection against the elements. Photographed from a distance, in soft focus, through a filter, it could have sold calendars by the thousand – white-washed under a thatched roof with a pond at its front and a stream running alongside. Close to, the illusion lost its potency. The pond was muddy and had once been described by a visitor from the water authority as being 'dangerously feculent', which was probably the fault of the ducks. There were a few fertilizer bags floating in the cocoa-coloured water and the long-dead corpse of a sheep.

Arthur's house was beginning to revert to the earth whence it had sprung, which became evident when we were asked in for a cup of coffee. Our host was one of that common breed of countrymen who begrudge spending any money on themselves or their dwellings and, less commonly, his wife appeared to be of the same persuasion. It is this habit which makes it so difficult for urban man to gauge the wealth of a countryman with any hope of accuracy. Some of the dingiest and least prepossessing individuals are those before whom the Stock Exchange would do well to tremble.

The farmhouse was dark with no windows on its bank side and small square portholes piercing the thick cob walls on to the duckpond. It was not possible to see through them, the glass being distorted by the passing of the years and obscured by a layer of grime and fly droppings. At one end of the house was the sitting room, the end wall of which was taken up by a cavernous fireplace still containing the original crucks on which the cooking pots would have been suspended a century earlier. The walls, whatever their original colour may have been, were grey – the dense grey formed by decades of smoke trying to force its way up through a chimney jammed with old jackdaws' nests before giving up to wreathe miserably round the room and settle there unfulfilled.

The dwelling had that unique, still, dead cold that can only be found in an unheated thatched building where the superb insulating qualities of the roof retain all the mould, must and damp from year to year. Arthur's thatch had actually passed the point of no return as much of it had decayed to slime and was letting in the rain to encourage a fine crop of mushrooms on the walls. Cob will last for ever, they say, provided it has dry feet and a dry head. The head of this house was now damp and it was surely only a matter of months before the walls began to slip away.

We sat in the kitchen, surrounded by sneezing cats and silver trophies won at gymkhanas by his wife, and discussed our PR campaign. We then repaired to the field where the caravans were supposed to be congregating and watched critically while Arthur erected a rickety wooden arch above the gateway and suspended a board on some baler twine from its apex. The board had 'Moorview Caravan Park', together with his address and telephone number, painted on it.

Bill instructed us to carry a few shovelfuls of mud from the ditch to add to the accumulation that already squelched in the gateway. He then carefully smoothed over the surface of the mud and summoned his dog which had been following these actions with a dubious expression on her face. The animal came, dragging her belly along the grass, and Bill forced her across the patch of mud. He examined the result, clicked his tongue in irritation, smoothed over the paw marks and tried again. This time he was satisfied.

The local paper came out the following Tuesday. There was a good splash. A picture across several columns showed Arthur standing in front of his sign above a large headline: 'LOCAL FARMER FINDS TRACKS IN FIELD – Threat to sheep in area'. Underneath was a lovely story. The tracks were thought to be those of a large black cat-like animal, according to the experts (Bill), and it did not seem to be thought strange that the animal's colour could be deduced from its footmarks. This theory was given further credence since the creature had been sighted by a retired vicar or verger who had been staying at the beautiful caravan site, with running water and hard stands, at the time. According to Arthur, this man of the cloth said that he had been woken by some animal breathing heavily in the night just outside his caravan. With considerable courage, he had opened the door and had received a confused impression of a large, dark, cat-like animal, flashing white teeth and a sinuous shape. No, it had not been Eartha Kitt.

Like all truly great public relations exercises, the story took on a life of its own. The next stage after the arrival of the local newspaper was the appearance of a reporter from the neighbourhood's radio station. He caught Arthur unawares as he had been busy processing two caravans that had been directed to his farm by a garage on the main road. Arthur shuffled his feet a bit but cantered through his hollow tale about footmarks and vicars who had failed to leave a forwarding address and was told that, all things being equal, the interview should be broadcast at lunch-time on Sunday in a magazine programme.

There was a radio in the pub and most of those in the know turned up to listen to it. We were feeling pretty proud of ourselves. The media coverage was already greater than we had expected and Arthur was already welcoming caravans whose inhabitants had come puma spotting.

Perhaps it could be said that the reporter had gone a little over the top. 'Fear stalks the peaceful countryside,' he intoned, 'as a mysterious and ferocious beast terrorizes farmers and ravages sheep.'

'Ravages sheep?' said the commander. 'We said nothing about ravaging sheep.'

Arthur was trotted out to say his piece, but the star of the item was one of his neighbours, Frank Mattock. He was not a party to the original plot, but he had never been a slouch when it came to turning circumstances to his own advantage. Frank had recently invested in large numbers of sheep as an addition to his highly profitable dairy herd, but he had a brother-in-law who was an insurance salesman, a terrible burden for any man to bear. Farmers are very vulnerable to the predatory excursions of such bandits as the risks to which a farmer is liable are legion, from cows being killed by lightning, to foot-and-mouth, to spontaneous combustion in hay and even to rape and pillage by one's bull or ram amid the neighbour's stock.

Frank had had a little too much to drink a few weeks earlier in his brother-in-law's company and had woken up in the morning to find that he was the owner of a policy which covered him in the event of unnatural death in his sheep, with the Transglobal Insurance Company based in the Cayman Islands. It cost a fortune as sheep are peculiarly prone to unnatural death. After some thought, Frank put in a claim for a bunch of sheep that he was sending to the abattoir, deciding, perfectly reasonably, that their death could hardly be described as natural.

He was just stirring a bit and, if the insurance company had shown any signs of a sense of humour, all would have been well. But bureaucrats are bureaucrats and they all find money a desperately serious business. They appreciated Frank's claim about as much as a feminist convention would appreciate a flasher. Letters of remarkable acrimony went back and forth and they tried to cancel Frank's policy, but they were damned if they would refund his premium.

Frank sensed an opportunity to fight back. The speaker of the radio tied itself in knots to achieve a faithful rendition of his rural accent. No, he had not actually seen this puma, but he had seen tracks and had lost at least a dozen lambs with their throats torn out, an unnatural and untimely end.

'How did you know that the killer was a puma?' asked the reporter.

'I've lived in the countryside, man and boy, for forty-two years and this sort of damage is only caused by pumas.'

'Can you afford this sort of loss?'

'Fortunately, unlike many farmers, I am insured. But it's got to stop. The sooner this ferocious beast is killed, the sooner we can all get back to proper farming again.'

'Will it be difficult to kill? One would think an animal like this would find it very difficult to hide itself.'

'Not really,' said Frank. 'It could disappear into the woods and copses and never be found. I stayed up for three nights on the trot last week and never even saw the beast.'

'And did you lose any animals?'

'Yes, we had four lambs die . . . sorry . . . killed and we never heard a thing.'

The reporter moved on to a potted history of pumas from the well-known Surrey strain to a Welsh manifestation a year or two before and closed with a 'watch this space' type of announcement to ensure that his next piece on the subject would be broadcast. The pub was well satisfied. The puma was coasting along nicely and it looked as though Arthur's caravan site would receive plenty of new customers.

The puma really began to take off the following week. Other farmers in neighbouring parishes suddenly found that the animal was taking their stock. It received publicity in the local morning paper and was then discovered by Fleet Street. We watched in awe as it grew in fame and ferocity. It killed a pony and ate it all so that not a trace was left. The pub began to talk about its latest exploits in whispers as one could never quite be sure who was in the bar. There were strangers about wearing camouflage jackets, stout boots and binoculars with clear-eyed, white-hunter-type expressions. They tended to grip your arm as you passed and engage you in earnest conversation about likely puma habitats.

One of them lectured to us one evening in the pub. A woman of middling years who claimed to be the nation's leading authority on British great cats, she told us of the time that not one but *two* lions appeared in the north of England before a lay preacher who was walking down a country lane in deep conversation with a commissioner of oaths. The beasts were grinning at them from the shelter of a bramble bush. They reported the matter to the police who, as they had to do on such occasions, scoured the countryside with sharpshooters, only to discover that the animals had vanished into thin air.

All in all, it appeared that the wild British great cat was a very shy animal. They were almost always pumas and the only fully authenticated sighting was in Scotland where the creature could hardly be overlooked since its body was found. It turned out to have been stuffed and was thought to be a hoax. We clicked our tongues in disapproval at this. It was a peculiarity of the British puma that it always seemed to be black although the normal colour was sandy brown.

'Perhaps its coloration is due to the vagaries of the British climate,' I hazarded.

'That is certainly one possibility,' she agreed. 'However, the theory which I favour is that the British puma is a separate species which became isolated after the last Ice Age and a few of them have managed to hang on and breed in the remoter parts of the country.'

'Like Surrey,' murmured the commander.

'The particular animal we have here is almost certainly a female with a litter of cubs.'

'How on earth do you know that?' inquired the commander curiously.

'I've seen her and I know where her den is.'

There was a stunned silence round the bar. 'Where exactly was this?' asked the commander.

The expert gave a mysterious smile. 'I'm sorry, but I am

unable to tell you. If I said where it was, it would be shot. I intend to photograph it.'

'I see. Have you photographed other pumas?'

'Not exactly. But look at these. This is the Welsh puma.' The expert produced her snaps. They were not of the puma itself, since the British species only appears in the flesh on foggy days before people whose cameras have just run out of film, but of puma tracks. Her prize shot produced a hot debate.

'That's a fox,' said Jimmy, who had been a professional rabbit catcher in his prime and knew about that sort of thing.

'Nonsense,' said the commander. 'It's a dog.'

The expert started to huff and puff with indignation.

'It's a vixen. As sure as I've got eyes in my head,' insisted Jimmy.

'It's far too broad in the pad,' said Bill decisively. The expert perked up a bit.

'Course it's a fox,' said Jimmy.

'Never,' asserted Bill. 'I've seen enough fox tracks round my pheasant pens to tell the difference between a fox and a dog and this is a dog if ever I saw one. It's a big dog, mind, something like a foxhound or . . .'

'A labrador?' asked the commander innocently. Bill looked rather shifty and the expert broke in indignantly.

'How dare you say it's a fox or a dog. It's a puma. It's as plain as a pikestaff.'

'Look, Missus,' said Bill patiently, 'the difference between the track of a dog and a cat is that a cat always retracts its claws when it's walking and a dog can't. So if you can see the indentation of a claw in front of each toe, then you know what you're looking at has to be the pug mark of a member of the dog family. And this photograph has not only got dents in front of the pads, but bloody great holes —'

'— which proves,' broke in the commander, 'that it's not only a dog of some kind but a pooch that is more at home sitting in front of someone's fire than out in a field. If it was a foxhound, its claws would be more worn than this.'

'It's a puma. I know it's a puma. The tracks are exactly the same as those by the caravan site,' said the expert.

It was obviously time for some sort of retreat. 'It could be a cheetah,' I said diplomatically. 'I believe the cheetah is the one member of the cat family that does not retract its claws.'

'Don't be silly,' said the expert. 'Everyone knows that the Welsh puma is black.'

That was a bit cheeky of her, I thought, since all I was trying to do was give her a face-saving excuse for one part of her aberration. However, I persevered.

'Well, they may be yellow and spotty in Africa where it's hot and dry, but it wouldn't take them long to be covered in mud if they were over here and that would make them look black.'

Bill was all for covering up as well. 'It could be a wolf, couldn't it, Jimmy?'

'Well, I suppose it just could be a wolf,' said Jimmy thoughtfully.

'If it's not a puma or a cheetah, it must be a wolf,' said the expert. 'But I'm pretty certain it's a puma.'

'But,' continued Jimmy inexorably, 'if you come across a footprint of a fox or a bloody dog in the English countryside, you have to be a bit soft in the head to decide it's a cheetah or a wolf.'

There was really no answer to that one, so Bill spilled his pint all over the bar to create a diversion while the commander hurriedly changed the conversation to the price of sugar beet nuts.

Arthur did his best to kill the story after a couple of weeks, but he was no longer in control. His cracking-point came when the BBC contacted him from London, wanting to send down a camera team to make a programme about the puma. To Bill's disgust, he beat a retreat. He said that he now thought the tracks could have been those of a dog and the vicar had been drunk and might have made a mistake.

The story thrashed around for a few more weeks but, without Arthur's assiduous attention to the various puma nutters who turned up, it gradually began to die away. It never disappeared completely, however. A year after the animal's 'discovery', Arthur found half a dozen Japanese with film cameras working on the story amid the caravans and he still receives a drizzle of enquiries from Americans working on their PhDs. Our puma was even brought in as provenance for the more famous Beast of Exmoor. According to many experts, it was the re-appearance of Arthur's puma, having spent the intervening year or two in travelling there from the caravan site.

Moorview Caravan Site grew rich on the puma. Frank even opened a camp site to sweep up Arthur's leavings but, when he came to the pub to report mysterious lights in the sky, nobody wanted to know.

Chapter Four

NOT MANY tourists made their mark upon our community. Mandy and Keith were one of the few pairs who came down to visit and stayed. They originated from the London area where Keith had been a butcher, owning a couple of amusement arcades on the side, stuffed full of space-invader machines and punk rockers.

Mandy and Keith were an odd pair. It was difficult to think of them as individuals rather than as a couple because they were always together and seemed to view the rest of the world as being populated by couples like them. Their talk was never of the doings of Ivor or of Beryl, but of Ivorandjane and Mickandberyl. In their pair-filled world, the male was always named first, but the village thought of them as Mandyand-keith. They seemed to be a thoroughly innocuous couple apart from their distressing habit of being too nice. They both went around with ingratiating grins on their faces and hers would only fade when she looked at him. He appeared to irritate her when his manner became too close to that of a cocker spaniel, but since hers was very close to that of a springer spaniel, it was felt that she had little to complain about.

They were both in their late forties with black hair. Mandy's must have come from a bottle, but Keith also had a little black moustache which was raven enough to give legitimacy to his hair colour. They bought a tumbledown house, part of a small row of thatched cottages down by the river, and began to do it up.

Mandy was musical, so she told us. Certainly we were all most impressed by the splendid melodies from Rachmaninov to ragtime which wafted through the window of her sitting room. Then Kelvin, the arrogant agricultural patriarch of the pub, passed by one day and spied her seated at the console of some marvellous electronic device. She had her tongue between her teeth in concentration as she laboriously picked out the tune of Beethoven's *Choral Symphony* with one finger, while the silicon chips played the violins and woodwind and harmonized with all the sorts of twiddly bits that suited them.

Mandyandkeith set out to transform their cottage into the ideal 'bijou residence'. Keith's first move was to rip off all the thatch. It was clearly necessary as the straw was rotten and was riddled with rat holes and birds' nests. This action created something of a stir because the local thatcher let it be known that he had not been booked to replace it. His waiting list was nine months long and his charges were quite extortionate, but this was not sufficient excuse to take business away from the community and place it in the hands of strangers. As a result, Mandyandkeith were closely questioned when they next came into the pub. Bill took on this important duty.

'Evening Mandyandkeith,' he said as they came to the bar. Keith ordered a rum and blackcurrant while Mandy asked for a vodka and peach juice. The current landlord found them a bit of a nuisance as he had to stock a variety of soft drinks of cloying sweetness which nobody but them ever ordered. They somewhat made up for this by pumping money into the juke-box in the next-door bar. Mandy liked Barry Manilow while Keith preferred Jim Reeves. They also borrowed all the romantic novels from the mobile library van, to the annoyance of Beryl who had previously had a monopoly on them.

'What are you doing to your cottage, then?' asked Bill bluntly.

'We're doing it up,' replied Mandyandkeith proudly.

'Who's doing the thatch?'

'Keith is,' answered his wife. The rest of the pub stopped playing darts, discussing the weather and trying to look down the front of the landlady's dress and stared at Mandyandkeith with delight and incredulity.

'Is Keith a thatcher, then?' asked Bill.

'Oh no. But it seems to be ever so easy,' replied Mandy. There was a sharp intake of breath round the bar. The villagers had heard the thatcher pontificating about the skills of his trade often enough to know something perilously close to heresy when they heard it. The thatcher specialized in the strong silent look, keeping himself to himself with the dignity of those professionals like brain surgeons, bomb-disposal experts and thatchers. He came from four generations who had crawled about on the roofs of the locality, and we were not used to hearing his trade being discussed with such flippancy.

'Are you going to use straw or reed?' asked Bill.

Keith looked at Bill uncomprehendingly. 'What for?'

'For your thatch, of course.'

Mandyandkeith laughed merrily. 'Goodness gracious!' said Mandy. 'We're not going to use anything like that. It's old-fashioned. Keith's going to use plastic thatch.'

Nobody had ever heard of plastic thatch and so most people found an excuse to walk past the cottage while it was being prepared for re-roofing. Keith ripped out all the old timbers and put in their place an ordinary set of rafters, although they had very little slope to them. This caused a bit of interest as thatch, even plastic thatch, has to have a steep slope, otherwise the water will just seep through the fibres.

Emily Jarrett, one of their neighbours, came into the pub while the roof was waiting for the plastic straw to be delivered. 'It's on,' she announced.

Bill swivelled on his stool and looked at her. She was an attractive woman, but Bill had more respect for the looks of heifers and ewes than for the female of his own species. 'What's on?'

'Mandyandkeith's roof.'

'Don't talk daft. I passed the cottage yesterday and the thatch hadn't even been delivered yet.'

'It came on the back of a lorry this morning and Keith had it tacked into place by mid-afternoon. It came in sheets.'

Everyone, including the landlord, emptied out of the pub and walked down the village to take a look. It was a remarkable sight, a curious yellowy-brown material which bore no resemblance to natural thatch at any stage of its weathering. It was not thick enough, either. A thatched roof billows. It is ample and luxurious, like a good feather duvet.

This looked skimpy, no more than 6 inches deep at the eaves, and one could see the seams between the slabs of moulded plastic.

The onlookers were dumbstruck. The slope on it made it look grotesque. Any raindrop falling on a natural thatch roof can expect an exhilarating ride down a reedy Cresta Run before hurtling off the edge to the ground. On this roof, a raindrop would have been faced with a few moments of grave uncertainty before it managed to work out in which direction it was supposed to travel. The village now contained an aesthetic disaster.

The thatcher went round the village saying 'I told you so' to anyone who would listen and there was some talk of getting the planning authorities involved to tell them to rip off their roof and start again, but an inbred distaste for bureaucrats prevented this from happening.

Mandyandkeith could not see what the fuss was about. Their roof was beautiful, even if it did have the disadvantage of crackling like machine-gun fire as it writhed whenever the sun hit it and forced it to expand. Dennis swore he saw it bring down a low-flying pigeon with a 6-inch nail that shot out of it just as the sun popped out from behind a cloud.

With their roof on, Mandyandkeith continued to beautify the exterior. They painted it baby-bum pink and put in window boxes crammed with poster-painted flowers which, having eerily lasted through the season, were found to be made from plastic. They paved over most of the tiny bit of ground in front of the cottage and filled it with white garden furniture and sun umbrellas surrounding a small fish pond which, Keith told the pub, was filled with shubunkin. Nobody was much the wiser but the word was researched by Ivor and it turned out to mean a kind of goldfish. They installed a wrought-iron gate with its interior in the shape of a heart with an arrow through it and, as a final touch, they changed the name of the cottage from 3 River Lane to 'Pixie's Bower'.

When it was all finished, they held a house-warming to celebrate. They had intended to hold a barbecue on their patio, but the weather had broken. The first gale of autumn was wuthering down from the moor and would have filled their garden with wind-blown umbrellas and shubunkin to the hazard of their guests. All the local heavies turned out. The party was too good a chance to miss of finding out whether the interior of the cottage could possibly match the glory of the exterior.

A bunch of us had come steaming down from the pub with several pints apiece inside us to dilute the sticky concoctions that would undoubtedly be on offer. Mandy had put the organ on automatic pilot and it was moodily amusing itself with a jam session in the background when she opened the door in response to the first few bars of *Home, Sweet Home* on the bell. Mandy, wearing a diaphonous garment the same colour as the outside of the house and bearing a cigarette in a long holder, asked us to take off our shoes to avoid marking the white shag-pile carpet. There was a small altercation in the door-way.

'I'm not taking off my boots,' said Kelvin.

'Do as you're told,' ordered Bill. 'You're not making mucky footmarks all over Mandyandkeith's nice carpet.'

'I'm not taking my boots off.'

'If you won't, you can't come in,' said Bill.

'In that case, I'm not coming in.'

Bill started to laugh. 'I know what it is. You've got holes in your socks and you're embarrassed.'

Kelvin looked sheepish. 'I haven't.'

'You bloody have.' Bill raised his voice: 'Here, Mandy. Kelvin's embarrassed to take off his boots because he's got holes in his socks.'

'Shut up, Bill,' muttered Kelvin.

Too late. Mandy glided up to him in her housecoat. 'Oh! Poor Kelvin! But there's no need to be shy. It doesn't matter if you've got holes in your socks. Just take them off.' Kelvin mumbled and shuffled his feet on the doorstep.

'Take them off!' was the cry that came from an assortment of throats inside the house while Kelvin shot a murderous glance into the hall. Mandy carefully put down her drink – a blue extravaganza – on the glass-topped telephone table inside the front door and placed her cigarette in a silver ashtray with a blue enamelled St Christopher set in the bottom. She turned her back to us and rummaged around inside her housecoat while we politely watched her reflection in the mirror that faced her and pulled down her tights. She turned and strung them gaily round Kelvin's neck.

'There,' she said. 'Now your hostess is barefoot as well and so you have no excuse.'

Grumbling, Kelvin sat down on the doorstep and slipped off his boots, carefully stuffing his thick blue woolly socks inside them before anyone could judge the extent of their holiness. He then entered the house and stood self-consciously inside the hall. We all looked down at his feet. They were a rather nasty pale grey with great gnarled yellow talons which contrasted ill with Mandy's neat little toes with their pearly nail varnish. Hers made one itch to play 'This little pig went to market' on them, while any self-respecting livestock farmer could have improved the look of Kelvin's with the liberal use of a hoof-knife.

'Well, then,' said Mandy brightly. 'Shall we go through to the lounge?' We went through to the lounge. It was already half-full with villagers and I was impressed to see that Barbara, the formidable relict of a colonial judge, had been persuaded to take her shoes off like everyone else and had one foot resting on an embroidered stool.

'The trouble with this village is that too many people talk about damn all,' she was saying, but she broke off and looked round ill-naturedly as the pub contingent came into the room. 'Good God! Now I know what they mean by a bum's rush.'

The lounge was well worth a visit. The ceiling was covered in polystyrene tiles, criss-crossed with beams which half a dozen sets of knuckles immediately investigated to discover that, in spite of worm holes, were plastic. Round the wall hung groups of flint-lock pistols. More surreptitious fondling revealed that these were constructed of the same material as the beams and a surprised buzz ran round the room.

There were four pictures on the wall. All were familiar: a posse of white horses were galloping out of a stormy sea; a blue oriental lady looked down from over the fireplace; Ophelia floated down a river on her back making a daisy chain, and there was a large coloured photograph of the Queen which would have looked more at home in the British consul's office in Benidorm.

Everything seemed to be brand new. There was no evidence of a previous life, no books, no photographs and just a rather pasty-faced teenager to prove that the marrige was of reasonable antiquity. The youth, introduced as Horatio, was helping Keith to ladle out the punch. Dennis graciously accepted a glass, took a sip, looked round for a vase in which to empty his glass and, thwarted, asked Horatio to be directed towards the loo. He came back a minute or so later, looking rather pleased with himself.

'Why are you looking so smug?' asked Bill, who was amusing himself by teasing the organ.

'The loo is just like the rest of this place. Shaggy carpet, fluffy jacket on the bog seat and a poem on the wall: "Please remember, don't forget. Never leave the bathroom wet." I've never seen anything like it.'

'Why should that make you happy?'

'I missed the lavatory and peed on the carpet.'

'That's disgusting,' said Bill.

'Disgusting, but enormously satisfying. I now feel really at home here. I can quite understand why a dog feels the need to cock its leg against the sofa when it enters a strange house.'

'What are you talking about?' It was Barbara who had come over to join us.

'Peeing on the carpet. I've just been to the loo,' replied Dennis, helpfully filling her in on the totality of the conversation.

'A particularly masculine topic. There is nothing more casually destructive to domestic hygiene than the uncircumsized drunken male. You are an appalling sex.'

Mandy came drifting up in a haze of black sobranie tobacco smoke. 'Did I hear someone talking about sex?' she asked archly.

'A greatly overrated pastime,' said Barbara. She looked down at her glass. 'This drink you're dishing out tastes like melted ice lollipops.'

Mandy took a Mata Hari drag on her cigarette while she tried to decide which part of Barbara's statement to respond to. I caught Dennis looking down at her toes which were peeking out from under the lacy hem of her garment. Her toes were definitely her best feature which was rather worrying since it made one wonder if one might be a foot fetishist.

'I don't think sex can be overrated if you are with the man of your dreams and there are lots of men to dream about round here,' said Mandy, fluttering her eyelashes to an extent that would be excessive for an actress in a silent film. Dennis looked at her in alarm. Peeing on her carpet was as intimate as he was prepared to get.

'Do you have any gin?' asked Barbara.

'Or any whisky?' added Dennis.

'Don't you like our Caribbean cocktail?' asked Mandy.

'No,' said Barbara.

'It's quite delicious, but it's wasted on me,' said Dennis. 'I'm perfectly happy with just whisky.'

'I'll go and see what I can do. I'm drinking Bols. It tastes of peppermint and it's a very pretty blue. Would you like to try some?'

'No, thank you,' said Barbara with a shudder. 'Just gin and a little bit of water.'

Barbara got her gin and Dennis his whisky. The room was nicely filled by this time and the level of Caribbean punch in the bowl was rapidly going down. Mandy brought out pretty little eats on the top of biscuits and sausages on sticks which Horatio handed round.

Kelvin found himself in difficulties. He had appropriated a spot which allowed him to tuck his feet beneath the sofa where they were invisible; this, however, meant that he could not go to the food, but had to wait for the food to come to him. He was talking to Mary Mowbray and her laugh, a delightful noise that sounded like a dirty old octogenarian crooning over a pornographic magazine of unspeakable filthiness, was bubbling through the conversation.

Once the food had gone, people began to go round the room making I-am-about-to-leave noises in order to go home to milk their cows and do the chores before the pub opened in the evening. Mandy stood at the bottom of the stairs to supervise the scrum as her guests scrabbled about on the floor trying to locate their footwear.

Kelvin was able to shoe himself first as his high ankle boots with their garland of woolly socks stood out from the ruck of more fashionable footgear. He opened the front door and began to retreat down the path uttering inarticulate cries of gratitude for the hospitality that had been afforded him.

Kelvin's day began to degenerate about then. It was blowing a brisk breeze outside which was ruffling his lank, grey locks. It was also ruffling the roof. Out of the sky, not unlike a particularly low-flying Vulcan bomber, swooped a 32-foot square of plastic thatch which scythed over his head and splashed down amid the shubunkin.

Kelvin's nervous system was never the most reliable of mechanisms, and this encounter with what would have been a

unique demise overloaded its circuits. He sat down on the
path. There was a crackling sound from on high and another
great bat skimmed over his head and bounced off the fence.
He uttered a squawk of dismay and scuttled back up the path
on his bottom like a large crab.

'What's going on?' asked Mandy, who was well inside the
hall.

'I'm afraid it looks as though the roof of your house may be
blowing off,' replied Dennis.

'Don't be silly,' said Mandy.

There was a flapping sound which seemed to come from the
upstairs landing and a couple more sheets of thatch thudded
down on to the patio outside.

'See?' said Dennis.

Mandy looked and she saw. Holding her cigarette tightly in
one hand and her glass in the other, she opened her mouth
and emitted one word.

'Keith!'

It was like standing over the vent of a volcano when it exploded. The sheer volume of sound and the quantity of venom contained in that one syllable made people clutch on to doorframes and the wall to prevent themselves being blasted out into the garden where they would have been picked off by the remaining sheets of thatch.

Keith must have known what was liable to be his due when Mandy's decibel count went off the scale in such a way. He moved across the sitting room towards the hall looking like a naughty member of the cabinet answering a prime ministerial summons. He crept through the door, his small black moustache quivering like the whiskers on a frightened hamster and grinned nervously.

'Yes, dear?'

The expression on Mandy's face would have made the Gorgon feel faint with envy. 'That fucking roof you put on is blowing all over the fucking garden!'

The rest of us blenched a little. The local dialect contained all sorts of words – zuggers is one example – which could be used to express any degree of emotion that was felt desirable. This meant that the more standard English epithets were rarely heard. Barbara stepped in where no angel would have dared to tread.

'Really! What appalling language!'

Dennis, a considerably better judge of character and situation than Barbara, tried to shush her, but he was too late. Mandy turned her head towards Barbara, her laser eyes scoring across the mirror that hung on the wall.

'Shut up, you drunken old hag.'

Barbara's mouth opened and shut like that of a shubunkin while Kelvin backed warily out into the garden again, willing to risk being decapitated by a gigantic thatched frisbee rather than face the wrath within.

'Let's go outside and take a look at the damage,' said the commander diplomatically, as Mandy drove Keith into the kitchen with a series of vicious prods in the chest from a rigidly extended forefinger. The door slammed shut behind them and the terrifying sound of a closet termagant letting go on all cylinders rapidly emptied the house of all its guests.

252

Many of them hurried off home, but the hard core of the curious waited in the garden to see what would happen next. At least two of the shubunkin appeared to have come to a sad end under the impact of the descending roof and were floating, bellies up, on the top of the water while the wind, having done its work, had died down leaving one piece of thatch still precariously stretched across the rafters with a corner of the panel still occasionally flapping sullenly in the breeze.

'Do you think that the party's over?' asked Jimmy, who had been downing Caribbean cocktails with lip-smacking delight.

'I expect so,' replied the commander. 'It doesn't seem right to continue to have a party under these circumstances and I expect that Mandyandkeith will be rather busy trying to weatherproof their house before nightfall.'

'I think we ought to help,' said Dennis.

'They've got a tarpaulin down at the fire station which they use to cover roofs after there's been a fire,' said Bill. 'I'm sure we could use it and it would give Mandyandkeith time to decide if they're going to get in a proper thatcher, or what.'

'I think you would be wise to check with Mandy first,' cautioned Dennis. 'She might have other ideas.'

'Me?' said Bill. 'I don't see why I should have to check.'

Almost unconsciously, we had been edging our way down the garden path to get away from the sounds of Keith having his character, morals and manhood torn to tatters in the kitchen.

'It was your idea about the tarpaulin. So it is you that ought to ask them,' said Dennis.

Bill looked apprehensive. 'But I don't think I ought to interrupt.'

There was the sound of thrown crockery coming from inside the kitchen.

'She always seemed such a pleasant woman,' mused the commander. 'Who would have thought she had a temper and tongue like that?'

The kitchen door was suddenly flung open and Mandy paused momentarily in the doorway, glaring down the hall and through the front door at us, before sniffing with contempt and sweeping up the staircase and out of our sight.

At some stage, the organ had changed over to Wagner and its chips were appropriately blasting out *The Ride of the Valkyries*.

After half a minute or so, a white-faced Keith slunk from the kitchen and came out of the house towards us. It was an awkward situation. Nobody quite knew how to react towards him; whether to make some sympathetic remark to show that we appreciated the ferocity of the roasting that he had just undergone, or whether to act as though nothing untoward had taken place. He cringed at us. Dennis patted him consolingly on the shoulder.

'Not to worry, old chap. We'll soon have a roof back on. Bill says that there is a tarpaulin down at the fire station and we can cover your rafters with it in a jiffy.'

There was a crash from above us and a dozen startled faces looked up. It was Mandy who had flung open her bedroom window and was now leaning out of it, her pink robe billowing round her making her look as if she was about to launch herself upon us like a candyfloss Dracula.

'Don't you dare put a filthy tarpaulin over my roof. It has got to be as good as new by tonight. Kelvin!' Kelvin was backing through the front gate. 'Where do you think you're going? You stay right there and help.' She swept the patio with her eyes. One of the shubunkin suddenly came back to life, sounding like a U-boat on the approach of a destroyer commanded by Jack Hawkins. She withdrew from the window and slammed it shut; a couple of plastic petunias fell out of the window box. There was a pause.

'Nobody talks to me like that,' whispered Kelvin.

'I think Mandy just did,' replied Dennis.

'Well, I'm going,' said Kelvin.

'How very brave of you,' murmured Dennis.

Kelvin hesitated. 'Anyone else coming?'

'I think I might as well come with you,' said Barbara. She looked at Dennis. 'Do you think it would be all right?'

'I'm sure it would be O.K. I can't see our hostess expecting you to clamber all over her roof.'

'Er . . .' said Keith. It was the first time he had opened his mouth since he had come out of the house. There was a bit of

254

colour back in his cheeks. 'I think it would be safer if you stayed.'

Barbara looked uneasily at Dennis who risked a quick glance up at the bedroom window. It was reassuringly closed and the curtains had even been drawn across it. 'I think you can go home, Barbara,' he repeated firmly. 'But I'm not sure that Kelvin had better risk it.'

Barbara scuttled off down the path and along River Lane faster than she had ever been known to move before, without hazarding a backward look. The rest of us stared longingly after her.

'Right,' said Dennis, breaking the spell. 'Let's get going or we'll be here all day.'

We sorted ourselves into a work party to replace the thatch as we had been commanded. There were a couple of difficulties; the workers were wearing their party clothes which were not the most appropriate garments for scrambling about on ladders or on roofs. However, it was Mandyandkeith's ladder and Mandyandkeith's roof where dirt was banned. Even the rafters had been planed and varnished. The other problem was that one of the slabs of roof had disappeared. Eleven had blown off in all and we could find only ten of them. Two were in the pond and the others were either scattered around the garden or over the fence with the neighbours.

Rather surprisingly, Dennis turned out to be the natural leader during this time of crisis and he dispatched the halter, the lamer, the blinder and the older members of the team on a quest to find the missing panel. He was a bit like the captain of a sinking ship sending the weaker passengers to safety before the others.

Keith put up his ladder, which had to cross the window of the bedroom where Mandy was closeted, and Dennis instructed the commander to scale it, reasoning that he must have clambered up plenty of mainmasts and futtock shrouds during his formative years and so would be used to heights. We stuffed hammers, nails and bits of string into his pockets and pushed him, protesting, up the ladder.

He'd got about half-way up, gallantly overcoming the

deleterious effects of the Caribbean cocktails, when the curtain on the bedroom window was whisked aside and Mandy glared out at him from behind the glass. The commander let out a hoarse croak of terror and let go the ladder with both hands. Those on the ground held their breath as he stood on the rungs windmilling his arms and fighting to retain his balance. After a few seconds, he managed to slump forwards and wrap his flailing upper limbs round the uprights.

Mandy must have had experience of the sort of effect that she could have on the weaker sex when she was in the mood because, as the commander watched through the widow like a rabbit paralysed before a stoat, she left the bedroom, shaking the house and making his ladder sway as she slammed the door. We heard her descend the stairs to the kitchen where the odd crashing sound established that she was safely occupied in washing up the party glasses.

It was not difficult to put the thatch back on. The sheets slotted together like Lego and the only complication lay in the fact that Keith had nailed them on and the wind had ripped the plastic off, leaving the nails still embedded in the rafters. Once the commander had hammered them flat, Dennis produced an electric soldering iron and, with the help of a long extension lead, the commander melted dozens of holes in the thatch through which we threaded yards of baler twine, creating a cat's cradle of support that bound the roof to its rafters. The search-and-rescue team found the last panel in the river 200 yards downstream, lodged against a rock, and the commander tied it into place just before the last of the daylight faded.

The roof held safely through the gales of the following winter. It was not quite as pretty as it had been, for the twine made it look as if it had undergone a serious operation and was waiting for the stitches to be removed. It was also rather noisy. Given a stiff breeze, it sounded like a man o' war beating across the Bay of Biscay against a nor'westerly gale and the creak and heave of the straining slabs intermingled with the crash as they fell back against the rafters could be heard over most of the village.

Mandyandkeith settled into the community. Keith found a job in the nearest town as a Kosher butcher with a firm that exported correctly slaughtered and chopped-up bits of animal to London. Mandy sloughed off the air that gave the impression she was always trying to screw up her courage to invite you to a Tupperware party and went around in her true colours as a woman of great power and determination. She even stood for the parish council and achieved the rare distinction of winning only eight votes. Kelvin was distraught. Given that she voted for herself, it still left seven other people in the village who had put their cross next to her name. As Kelvin said, there were seven people who were either mad or bad and he did not know who they were.

Chapter Five

EVERY COMMUNITY has its Shangri-la. For some, it will be the bright lights of London or Borchester. Conversely, the Londoners and Borchesterians will look to Ambridge and the cottage-infested English countryside as the places where the Arcadian myths become reality. As long as the townsmen and the countrymen have the sense to stay at home and dream, all is well. The country cottage is one of the goals for which it is better to strive than to obtain, as the reality can never match the dream. The drains, the water supply and the services are unreliable, while the banks of wild flowers hide piles of garbage because the refuse collector does not call and the centuries of rubbish have to be put somewhere.

Country people no longer spend their idle hours skipping round the may-pole or morris dancing, but watch *Coronation Street* or amuse themselves by observing newcomers with beady, implacable eyes, waiting for the tell-tale signs that show their alienness and their incapacity to handle the simple, everyday problems of the countryside, like overflowing cess-pits and the moles that rampage through their carefully tended lawns.

For our village, the yellow-brick road ended in Canada. Nobody quite knew why this should be but, for generations, those second sons who did not stand to inherit the ancestral acres, and those with some wild oats to sow, went out to the Canadian mid-west for a year or two or for a lifetime.

One of those with a relative somewhere near the Rockies was Jimmy. He was the village's oldest inhabitant who had been a rabbit catcher, retiring with the arrival of myxomatosis. His trade was as irrevocably part of the past as that of a cartwright or a fletcher. Gone are the days when a shotgun fired in the evening at the edge of virtually any field in the parish would have resulted in the death of half a dozen rabbits. The market he supplied has vanished as well, since the housewife no longer buys rabbit to feed her family, the beast having been elbowed out of her cooking pot by the ubiquitous chicken. Gone, too, has the distribution system. The weekly rabbit train, with its wagons groaning under the weight of thousands of furry little carcasses, no longer chuffs along the rural branch lines towards Smithfield. The very lines themselves have disappeared and their routes, marked by neat signposts, are tramped by earnest ramblers from the cities, exclaiming with delight over each weed that infests the decaying foundations of their tracks.

Jimmy was marooned in the last quarter of the twentieth century, a rather small and bow-legged human dinosaur, while the environment which had supported him had vanished forever and even its memory was beginning to fade from people's minds.

Jimmy's life now centred on the pub where he sat for hour after hour over a pint of beer or cider with a baffled look in his eye. The changes that he had seen did not excite or disturb him. He just never understood them or was able to adapt to them. They had just happened. Jimmy never talked much, except when the subject of dogs or cricket came up. Then he would become animated and talk at great length in an accent which Kelvin, no master of the Queen's English himself, described as being as thick as his head.

Jimmy was always listened to, not because his conversation was particularly interesting, but because the hand-rolled cigarette that was always in his mouth stuck to his lower lip as he talked, spraying ash in all directions. Nobody could work out how the cigarette stayed in position and it was a matter of great fascination.

Like many of the old men of the community, he was a widower, living in a cottage in the middle of the village by himself with the granddaughter of his last great rabbiting lurcher for company. In the ancient patriarchal society of the countryside, women have either to dominate their men and make them quake at their every utterance, or risk becoming little better than slaves and be driven to an early grave. Jimmy's wife had died a decade earlier and her epitaph was that she had been 'a good worker'.

A couple of times a year, Jimmy toiled his way past the pub to the churchyard, bearing a bunch of flowers from his garden. These he would place, scattering cigarette ash the while, on the hump under which lay his departed spouse. He would stand there for a few contemplative minutes over her grave and the space beside it reserved for himself before hawking up a gobbet of phlegm which he would send shooting skilfully past his cigarette to the ground.

The tangible product of Jimmy's marriage was a son in Calgary, improbably employed as the financial director of an oil company, who sent his father a Christmas card every year which was shown round the pub. The front always bore a picture of the family. There would be Jimmy's son, looking fat, soft, smug and forty-five in the company of a pretty blonde wife and three fair-haired discontented-looking teenage children. They were always standing in front of a house that looked as if it had been part of the set for *Gone with the Wind*.

Jimmy never expressed any pride in this incongruous outcome of what must have been a very primitive rural coupling, and the rest of the villagers were equally unsure of the correct response. This family seemed to have so little in common with Jimmy that we would look at the picture, clear our throats uneasily and hand it back to the unemotional grandparent.

One Christmas, the card contained more than the usual 'To the best grandpop in all the world'. There was a PS at the end in a female hand: 'Why don't you come out and spend the summer with us?' The card did its usual round of the pub and we all gazed at the picture, opening it up to study the legend inside before passing it on to our neighbours. It was returned to Jimmy before Winnie asked the question.

'Well, Jimmy?'

'Well, what?' waggled back Jimmy's cigarette.

'Are you going to spend the summer with your family?'

Jimmy screwed up his eyes as a wreath of smoke climbed up over his nose. 'No,' he replied.

'Oh! What a shame. It would be a wonderful chance to see your grandchildren. After all, you may not have many chances left.'

Jimmy looked at her blankly. It had obviously not occurred to him that he might go, any more than he might expect to be asked to lunch by the Queen or go to the moon. Such matters were not part of his life. Others present in the pub also considered Winnie's suggestion. Against it was the fact that Winnie had come up with it. She was fey, arty, wrote doggerel poetry about skipping lambkins and puppies and was a medium who believed that she had a direct line to King Arthur, but, on the other hand, there was no good reason that came to mind why he should not go to Canada. The commander swivelled on his bar-stool and looked over at Jimmy.

'I think it's a damn good idea.'

'I agree,' said Kelvin.

'That's it then, Jimmy,' said the commander. 'The oracle has spoken. If Kelvin says you should go, then you have no choice.'

Jimmy was having none of it. 'Sod off. What would I be doing going to Canada? In summer, too. Who would look after my garden? And who would look after Flossie?'

'I would love to have Flossie to stay,' said Winnie. 'I'd take her for a good long walk every day and the commander would look after your garden, wouldn't you, commander?'

'Get stuffed,' said Jimmy. 'He'd make a mess of everything.'

The commander augmented his pension by market gardening and there was deadly rivalry between him and Jimmy for the Onion Shield at the Horticultural Show every year. The commander may have come to the village wise in the ways of the sea, but his knowledge of the soil was so scanty that he had dug up the best asparagus bed in the county because he wished to clear those odd-looking ferns so that he could grow asparagus. He had eradicated his ignorance through vigorous application, but this was not enough to win the respect of Jimmy who gardened with the instinct inherited from countless generations of peasant ancestors.

'I'll tell you one thing, Jimmy. If you're away over the summer, you'll keep a bit of your pride because you've no hope of winning anything this year. I was talking to one of those northerners who feeds his vegetables on bat's blood and newt's eyeballs. He gave me some tips and my onions'll be like footballs this year.'

Jimmy's cigarette described a derisive parabola in the air. 'I could grow a bigger onion than you if I planted one of those things in the pickle jar behind the bar. Anyway, it makes no difference because I'm not going.'

The door of the pub was flung open and Lindy came bustling in from her rounds. She built up quite a thirst during her district nursing and usually came in to quench it while her husband put their children to bed. 'Not going where?' she asked.

'To Canada,' replied Winnie. 'Jimmy's son has asked him over for the summer.'

'What an excellent idea!'

'I'm not going,' said Jimmy.

'Of course you're going. If you think I'm going to spend another summer cutting your bloody toenails, you can think again. Let some poor Canadian hack away at them for a change.'

'I'm not going,' said Jimmy firmly.

262

He did not have a chance. Jimmy was no great hand at penmanship and so Winnie wrote off the letter of acceptance to his family and received an effusive reply which made the machinery grind into action. It appeared that Jimmy needed a visa because there was some talk of him having to emigrate due to the intended length of his stay and visas were presented at the regional emigration centre. Jimmy was given a lift up to town by the squire's wife who combined it with a day's shopping. We were told all about the trip that evening. Jimmy was beginning to adjust to the idea of his journey and was quite full of himself.

'I had to answer all sorts of questions and the fellow filled in a great form, all about who I was and even about who my mother and father were. I said you could never be too sure about who your father was and we had a good laugh. He was a Canadian, you know. You could tell by his American accent.'

'Are you all right to go then, Jimmy?' someone asked.

'I reckon so. It all depends on the result of my medical examination.'

There was a rather gloomy silence. Jimmy was thought to be in his late seventies; he smoked thirty lethal roll-ups a day and had done for over sixty years and he sounded as though he suffered from tuberculosis, asthma and farmer's lung all at the same time. He could kill a bluebottle at thirty paces with one of the cannonball gobs of phlegm that he scattered as he went and this, combined with a leg that had been crushed by a carthorse in his childhood, made him look and sound about as healthy as an Egyptian mummy.

'They gave you a medical, then?' asked the commander.

'Yes, it was a rum business.'

'A bit of a cheek, if you ask me,' said Lindy. 'They could have asked your own doctor to do it. What happened?'

'Well, the doctor asked me to cough and, of course, once I'd started, I couldn't stop and that seemed to upset the fellow a bit. Then he stood me up and listened to my chest and then he told me to look at the wall and drop my pants.'

There was a gasp of horror at the idea. Having to examine Jimmy's skinny torso was bad enough, but it paled into insignificance before the prospect of having to root around

263

among the layers of tweed and grimy long-johns that clothed his nether regions with only the manifest existence of his son to demonstrate that the brave Canadian was boldly going where any human being had gone before. The commander asked the distasteful question.

'And did you drop them?'

Jimmy was unused to being the centre of attention and took a long sip of his cider to fortify himself before answering.

'Well, there was a bit of a problem. You see I didn't quite know what he meant. He was a Yank and so I didn't know whether he wanted me to take down my trousers or my pants. On TV when an American says pants, he doesn't mean pants. He means trousers.'

'So what did you do?'

'I took them all down.' There was a collective shudder. 'Mind you, I didn't like it much. He told me to look at the wall when I was doing it and I didn't like the sound of that. I was a bit frightened that he might make a dive at me. You hear so much about these happies, nowadays.'

'Gays, Jimmy. But I shouldn't have thought that your virtue was in much danger,' said Lindy. 'Did he seem to like what he saw?'

'He didn't exactly say that he liked it. But he did say that he was satisfied.'

'Have you got your visa, then?'

'They said they'd let me know in a week or two.'

The atmosphere in the pub the week or two later could only be described as agitated. Jimmy was gesticulating in the corner while the commander and Kelvin were trying to calm him down with Winnie flapping her arms ineffectually in the background.

'I'm not bloody doing it,' Jimmy bellowed. 'They can take their sodding visa and stick it up their arses.'

'What's up?' I asked Winie. I would have asked Ivor, but he was having a fit of the giggles into his beer.

'Jimmy's been sent a letter by the Canadian doctor. He wants Jimmy to send him a stool sample for analysis.'

'A stool sample!'

'Yes. He's afraid that Jimmy might be harbouring parasites which he would bring into Canada.' She looked across at the indignant Jimmy who had dribbled some cider down his three-day growth of beard. 'I can't say I altogether blame him for wanting to make sure.'

'It's a bloody insult,' said Jimmy.

'Come on,' said the commander. 'It's a very little thing to ask in exchange for a lovely holiday in the Rocky Mountains. Especially when you don't have to pay a bean.'

'It's all very well for you to talk like that, but have you thought about it? Just how do you go about getting a stool sample?'

'Oh, I would think it would be quite easy.'

'Easy? I suppose it would be easy right enough, but so is throwing my cider in your great stupid face. Just because it's easy doesn't mean I want to do it. And sending it to that bloody doctor. What am I supposed to do? Put it in a sodding envelope?'

'A plastic bag might be more appropriate,' said Ivor, controlling his mirth with some difficulty. 'Let's have a look at the letter.' The offending document was passed over for his inspection. 'Hm. It does seem very clear. You have to send a stool for analysis. Right. Have you thought about how you go about it?'

'No,' said Jimmy huffily.

'Well, think about it, man. Don't be so useless. The obvious thing to do is to fish out the sample with a spoon.' We looked at him with distaste. It was Ivor's turn to look huffy. 'What are you all looking at me for? If Jimmy's got to produce a sample, there's no other way of going about it. I would suggest he uses one of those spoons with holes that you use to fish out vegetables and boiled eggs.' There was a heavy silence.

'I ain't got one of those spoons,' said Jimmy eventually. 'Ivor, you must have one. Could you lend it to me?'

'Er . . . well, I'd love to but it belongs to my wife and she's away at the moment and it would be more than my life was worth to lend out any of her stuff.' The commander chortled his disbelief. 'But,' continued Ivor, 'I'm sure that the commander would be delighted to oblige.'

The commander stopped chuckling and looked thoughtful. Jimmy continued to mull over the problem. 'Right, assuming we get as far as using the spoon —'

'I'd cut out the "we", if you don't mind,' said Ivor with a shudder.

'All right. That's fair enough. Assuming that I get hold of a sample. How much do you think that Canadian doctor will want? How big a sample?'

Without Lindy being present to advise, we were all breaking new ground and nobody quite knew. Kelvin was the person who felt he might have something useful to contribute.

'I had the vet round the other day and he took dung samples from the cows to check for worms. He didn't use a spoon but a polythene glove and he just turned it inside out when he'd got a handful and tied a knot in the top to stop any of the shit from leaking out. It seemed quite a good way of doing it.'

'Have you got any of those gloves?' asked Jimmy.

'No.'

'Well, that's a fat lot of good then. We're back with the commander's spoon.'

'You won't need a very big sample if the amount that the vet took is anything to go by,' said Kelvin.

'All right. So I get a little bit. What do I put it in?'

There was a pause while everyone tried to figure that one out. Ivor spoke first. 'Isn't there some sort of law against sending perishable or noxious substances through Her Majesty's mail?'

'I don't see how there can be. Hospitals must be doing it the whole time and Frank Mattock keeps receiving parcels of boar semen which he stuffs into his sows and I wouldn't think you'd be able to get much more perishable or noxious than that,' said the commander. 'I think Jimmy had better use a plastic bag.'

Ivor looked dubious. 'It would be a bit fragile. And if there was a hole in it, as there often is in a plastic bag, it wouldn't be very funny. Although I suppose we could put the bag in a tin to protect it.'

'I know!' said Winnie. 'I've got a little transparent plastic tub of cheese. It's one of those smelly French cheeses but you can't smell a thing. It would be just the job.'

'Have you got an empty pot?' asked Ivor.

'No, but I'd be quite happy to sell Jimmy the one I've got.'

'But I don't like smelly cheese,' said Jimmy.

'You can always give it to someone else,' said Winnie.

'I'll take it off your hands, if you like,' said the publican. 'I always think it's quite nice if there are crisps, olives and cheesy bits around at lunch time on Sunday. It makes the pub a bit classy. I'll use the cheese and you can come round and pick up the empty pot.'

It could never really have been a classy pub but, come Sunday, there were quite a few people around for the moment when Jimmy sidled in, defiantly meeting the stares of the other customers and picked up his tub, the contents of which were covering the little biscuits which mine host had spread over the bar in his attempt to add sophistication to the spit-and-slurry atmosphere of his establishment.

That evening Jimmy was back in his usual chair by the side of the bar.

'All right, Jimmy?' was the greeting that was thrown at him, followed by a more or less subtle request for information on how the proceedings had gone. But Jimmy held his peace, with the ghost of a Mona Lisa smile hovering enigmatically at the corner of his lips.

It was only a couple of days before Jimmy received a response and the letter ended up pinned to the pub wall where it gently turned yellow over the years:

Dear Sir,
Thank you very much for the most interesting parcel that enlivened our postbag this morning. However, our doctor actually meant you to take a sample to your nearest hospital for analysis and send the results to this office. I would be grateful if you would have another shit at it.
     Yours faithfully, etc.

Chapter Six

COUNTRY POLITICS are not quite the same as urban politics. Some people do take them desperately seriously, particularly those from the urban middle classes who retire to the countryside and bring their prejudices and fanaticisms with them. They are always to be found as the treasurers and secretaries of the local Conservative associations since nobody else cares sufficiently to see that these mundane political chores are carried out.

The true-born countryman finds politics of lesser importance. They can be a lot of fun, particularly at election time when candidates have their tyres let down and are booed by rival supporters, but the subject of politics is generally a bit of a bore.

This is not an unreasonable attitude to take under the circumstances. The country person's prime interests in life are sex, which politics influences not at all; sport, where again politics has little to offer; and money. On money, politicians do have a peripheral effect but, in the countryside, the main influence on income is not their decisions, world recession or even the doings of Brussels but the weather – droughts, thunderstorms on the ripening corn, or the rain that keeps the tourists away. Since politics do not matter very much, the subject can afford to be treated rather more lightly than it is in the cities and people try to get some fun out of it.

The Bart understood this perfectly. The village was actually situated on the junction between three constituencies, in all of which the Liberals sometimes came first and in all of which the Socialists invariably lost their deposit. One constituency was currently occupied by a rather eccentric Liberal farmer, another by a ghastly new-style Identikit Tory who had been in public relations, and we had the Bart.

The Bart was one of the very last of the great Tory knights of the shires, although he was actually a baronet. He was magnificent from his bristling white moustache down to his Oxford brogues, handmade by Lobb of St James's. He was not part of the new right-wing radical party or even the old liberal wing of the Tories, but believed in an even older tradition which held that the unemployed were all shirkers; those with dark complexions made very good houseboys but were incapable of governing themselves; and that wogs began on the other side of Hadrian's Wall, although there was quite good shooting and salmon fishing to be had to the north of it. He was a much-loved local figure and it was thought that it was only his personal vote that kept the constituency blue.

The Bart used to organize fine, blood-curdling elections. Mobility was the key factor, with the candidates having to rush along the country lanes from village to village to make speeches in schools and halls to stolid voters who were damned if they would give the speaker any encouragement or indication of how they might vote. The Bart would travel with a loudspeaker strapped to the top of his car, greeting most of those he saw working in the fields by name, together with an enquiry as to the state of health of their relations. If the worker

271

was a known Liberal, he would be subjected to jocular abuse in the Bart's dreadful attempt at a local accent.

It was a tradition that Dick Hunniford, the local Liberal chairman and sheep farmer, should wait in ambush for the Bart when he came to our village and slide in behind his car in a Land Rover with its own speaker on top. Then the two vehicles would cruise round the parish shouting insults at each other with the Bart kneeling on his seat, glaring at Dick through the back window, and thumping on the upholstery in his excitement.

When the Bart decided to retire, even though his party seemed to be re-embracing the principles in which he believed, there were a series of meetings and elections at Tory Party Constituency HQ to select a new candidate. Nobody from our area bothered to attend, and the new man was wheeled round the voters in order to introduce him. It was rumoured that the Bart did not approve of his successor; at any rate, he seemed to have pressing alternative engagements whenever his replacement was scheduled to speak and they never shared a platform. Our village was not one of the more politically significant communities within the constituency and it was not until a good three months after selection that we were honoured by a visit.

The new candidate's publicity had preceded him. He was in his thirties and was an accountant, specializing in corporate taxation. We tried not to hold this against him and turned up *en masse* on the advertised Friday evening. The meeting was at 8.30 pm – a very dangerous time to hold a political meeting, but we were the second engagement of the evening. The pub had been open for several hours and, on a Friday, those were hours that were not to be wasted. So the atmosphere inside the school hall was not ideal.

The room was crowded, rivalling the attendance at the annual pantomime. The venue had advantages as the main meeting place of the village. It was dirt cheap and it was small, which meant that parishioners could easily build up the Roman amphitheatre atmosphere which made for a good political meeting. It also had its drawbacks. The walls were papered with poster-painted children's drawings which could be distracting, while the chairs with which it was furnished were designed to accommodate well-built six-year-olds. The sight of ranks of adults seated about a foot off the ground, all solemnly staring at the speaker while resting their chins on their knees, had put more than one passionate advocate off his stroke.

The front two rows were occupied by the squire and the rest of the local gentry – all of them a little unruly and nudging at each other. Most of them were slightly drunk and felt themselves back at the level they had last encountered during their first term at prep school.

When Dick Hunniford and the rest of the Liberal committee entered and took up their positions in a standing line along the back wall, there was a murmur of dismay. They had achieved a distinct tactical advantage as they were able to stare commandingly and intimidatingly over the heads of the rest of the voting fodder towards the speaker's podium. The gentry hissed and catcalled their disapproval and one could see their fingers twitching to be filled with bread rolls with which to pelt their rivals. Most of the solidly sober citizens in the rows behind them tut-tutted at their lack of decorum.

The candidate was late and it was 8.45 before Ivor led him in from the school kitchens to a scattering of applause. The candidate looked dangerously smooth – blue pin-striped three-piece suit, black sleek hair and a romantic hero's smile playing at the edge of his lips. Ivor introduced him. Ivor could have mumbled the appropriate grace at a cannibal feast, should he have wanted to. It was one of his greatest talents, and he never wasted an opportunity to fill half an hour with his oratory. All eyes examined the candidate as Ivor chuntered out his skilful platitudes.

He regretfully brought his introduction to an end and sat down to a huge round of applause. The candidate stood up and naturally acknowledged it as his own, while the gentry in the front rows waved their arms about in the air and yelled, 'Encore!' We all knew that Ivor liked to be loved and appreciated, so the clapping continued while the candidate smiled modestly and fiddled with his watch chain. Ivor wore a smirk of delight and self-satisfaction.

The candidate held up a slim, manicured hand in a request for silence. It was not a particularly wise move, although he could hardly have known it. Half his audience were Liberals who were damned if they would do anything that a Tory asked of them and, although the other half were Conservatives, they were enjoying the sight of Ivor grinning like a watermelon as he soaked in the applause and saw no reason why it should stop.

The din of appreciation grew with wild whoops and shouts of 'Speech!' coming from odd corners of the room. Ivor began to realize that the piss was being taken out of him and the mood of barely suppressed hilarity that had taken over the audience infected him as well. It became a joke from which only the candidate, rather pink with pleasure at all the cheering, was excluded.

Eventually Ivor, seated behind the candidate, raised his arm and managed to restore order – barring a few stifled snorts of laughter – and we settled our attention to the serious

274

business of trying to evaluate the Bart's successor. He smiled at us, his head cocked slightly to one side so that the light shone on his glossy black hair creating a halo effect. It was not a smile that said, 'I am trying to be friendly', but a smile that said, 'Look at me. Am I not wonderful? Don't you wish you could smile as attractively as I can?' We shifted uneasily in our seats, but the candidate continued his smile unrelentingly until he was absolutely sure that we had had a chance to savour its full glory.

'Good evening, ladies and gentlemen,' he eventually began. 'I would like first to thank my very good friend, Ivor here, for asking me to come here tonight and for saying such kind words about me and also to say how long I have been looking forward to visiting you.' Ivor looked a little startled at being described as the candidate's very good friend. Not surprisingly, since I had seen him that afternoon hunting worriedly through his desk amid the cow records trying to find the scrap of paper which had been given to him by the constituency agent on which was inscribed the candidate's name. The rest of us just wondered how long he had been looking forward to visiting us. Six hours? Six weeks? Six months?

'This evening I would like to talk about politics and the countryside and how our great party will transform the rural scene.' One of the absurdities about politicians is that they have a grossly inflated conception of the importance of their ideas and actions on the lives of ordinary people. The candidate was no exception.

'We, as a party, are particularly identified with rural issues. We think they are of prime importance, if not of paramount importance. After all, our cities are situated amid the countryside and so it follows that the country is at the basis of our nation. We talk of England as "our country". We do not talk of it as our city. It is our country and not our cities that we talk of fighting to preserve. Ours is the party that wishes to make our country great again. The voice of the country must be heard again, clearly and resolutely, at the conference tables of the superpowers.'

The voice of the country at a summit meeting was a charming idea. A good, clear 'moo' would probably make as valuable a contribution as anything else. However, the candidate had lost most of his audience when it became apparent that he was not one of those politicians who made jokes, and many of them started to doze.

It did not really matter. The gentry, quietly picking their noses in the front row, would have voted for Caligula's horse, had it been a Tory. In fact, they would probably have preferred a horse to anything else. They knew where they stood with a horse: they are honest, reliable, hard-working and have very little of the vanity that drives so many of those who would wish to become our leaders.

The Liberals were also dozing quietly. Even if the candidate had transformed the contents of his water jug into Chateau Lafite before their very eyes, they would have remained implacably opposed to him. They were waiting patiently for question time when they hoped to embarrass him with some carefully planned queries handed to them by the Liberal constituency agent.

Meanwhile the knitting was out in the body of the hall and Kelvin was discussing his harvest prospects with his neighbour. If the candidate had had the sensitivity to be aware of the world beyond the boundaries of his sleek hide, he might have wondered how he had managed to lose his audience so quickly after the rapturous reception he had been accorded.

As Ivor slipped his penknife from his pocket and began to scrape at the accumulation of cow dung beneath his fingernails, the candidate fixed his eyes on the distant landscape of his political Utopia and marched towards the sound of the trumpets.

'I know the importance of the environmental issue and how hard the farmer has to work in ploughing the soil to pay for tractors and . . . er . . . things. I believe that our party does not give sufficient emphasis to the needs of farmers.' He looked at the audience and gathered that not all before him were farmers. 'We intend to give *all* those who live in our rural communities more jobs, better roads and greater access to the landscape. We will give far greater protection to the environment and —' he hurriedly added as a few pairs of cold farming

276

eyes opened and looked at him, '— we will ensure that any such protection does not interfere with the freedom to produce as much food as possible at a good price, which is the glory of our agricultural industry.'

He rambled on as the audience began to shuffle its feet and some of its members, who had partaken of a pint or two earlier, uncoiled themselves from their seats and tripped over feet on their way back to the pub to empty their bladders and pour in some more beer. Seth Matravers heaved himself off his backside and lumbered down his row. His need for a loo was patently absurd as he had the capacity of an oil tanker and he obviously just fancied some more beer. He stumbled over a knitter who stuck a needle into his behind, causing him to fall over the line of gnomes in front of him. The speaker paused while the kerfuffle was sorted out and Ivor seized his silence to tap the side of his water glass with his penknife.

'I am sure the speaker is about to finish and so if people would contain themselves for a minute or two, we shall have a break before questions,' he said.

'Can't you shut the bugger up now, Ivor?' yelled a Liberal wag from the back. The audience, even the Conservatives, murmured their approval and Ivor whispered a few words into the candidate's ear who nodded vigorously.

'In conclusion . . .' he began, but his words were lost in a rising buzz of conversation, the shifting of feet and the machine-gun-fire cracking of joints as people stretched themselves in their cramped seats. The candidate had enough sense to sit down.

'Any questions?' asked Ivor.

Dick Hunniford jumped straight in: 'How are you going to increase returns to sheep farmers?' It was a question that was thrown at every politician who came within hailing distance of the constituency. Not many could give a coherent answer. The Bart's reply had usually been on the lines of, 'I haven't a clue and it's obviously too high as it is, since you look so disgustingly prosperous, Hunniford.' Most politicians tried to bluster to cover their ignorance. The candidate did rather well.

'I am pleased you raised this important topic. The returns

for sheep should undoubtedly be maximized and I believe that our policy should incorporate a double-rated regime in which the cost factor should be in inverse proportion to the EEC unit of account's standing *vis-à-vis* sterling.'

It shut Dick up. In fact, the answer was eventually handed upstairs to the county headquarters of the National Farmers' Union and it took them a fortnight to deliver their opinion that it was probably gobbledygook, but even they were not entirely sure. Dick looked as if he might want to ask a supplementary question after the pause during which we tried to digest the last answer, but Ivor was too experienced to allow his man to be backed into a corner and he slid smoothly on to a more innocuous questioner.

'Thank you. Mrs Baggins, you were next. Would you give your question, please?'

Mrs Baggins was one of the stalwarts of the Women's Institute. There are WIs and WIs. Some are part of the whiteheat of the feminist revolution and organize provocative discussions on the role of rural women in the twenty-first century. Others, more traditional, deal with the interests of their members in the present day. Others, still, prefer to work in the past as most of their members are approaching senility. Ours was into favourite nursery rhymes and competitions about who can produce the prettiest tea-towel and Mrs Baggins was its leading light.

She liked to give the impression of total serenity of nature – a sort of Mother Theresa of the village – but she rather belied the image by dispensing lethal gossip to anyone who would listen, delivered in a breathy whisper through the saintly smile that always adorned her lips. The candidate matched her, smile for smile, as she rose to her feet.

'Our branch of the Women's Institute favours legislation to outlaw glue sniffing. I would like to know whether we can count on your support in parliament.'

'He's not in parliament yet,' shouted a Liberal, and there were a few titters as we waited for his inevitably boring reply.

The smile suddenly disappeared from the candidate's face. 'Er . . .' he said and looked worriedly down at Ivor.

'Did you understand the question?' asked Ivor helpfully.

'Yes,' said the candidate.

'Well, then,' said Ivor encouragingly.

The candidate took a deep beath. 'I feel that this is a very difficult question to answer.' It seemed simple enough and one or two of his listeners forced their eyes open and tried to take an interest. 'It seems to me to be a question of personal morality rather than a subject for legislation. And consequently I would leave it to each individual to make up his or her mind on the matter.' There was a mutter of conversation round the room. Everyone was awake now. Mrs Baggins rose like an avenging angel.

'Do you mean that you won't support such legislation?'

The candidate looked round nervously. His smile was very fixed. 'I am afraid you are correct. Such a law would be a step back to Victorian times and, although I heartily disapprove of such practices and avoid it myself, I feel that parliament should not become involved. I think it would be electorally disastrous to pass such a law and the law itself would be unenforcable.'

This was baffling stuff indeed. Most unexpectedly, the candidate appeared to have at least one opinion of his own. Even more unexpected was the nature of that one opinion. Mrs Baggins rose to her feet again, her smile of serenity now absent.

'I've voted Tory all my life, but I think your attitude is disgraceful. I don't think you deserve the support of decent people. You seem perfectly content to watch our children corrupted and destroyed.'

There was an outraged rumble of support from the Liberal contingent and even the Tories looked a little shocked. It had been a perfectly mundane question, requiring a perfectly mundane answer, but the candidate had skidded wildly beyond the barriers of mainstream politics and was thrashing his way through a minefield of his own creation. He looked at Ivor for support with a film of sweat on his brow, but Ivor was embarrassedly examining his nails once more. The candidate was on his own.

'I am very sorry that you feel that way but, I repeat, however unpopular it might make me in some reactionary quarters, I feel that the problem is one of personal morality and is not a fit subject for legislation.'

There was a storm of hissing, in the middle of which Dick rose majestically to his feet.

'I am sure I speak for everyone in our community when I say that reactionary is not the word that I would consider applying to this dangerous practice. Any man who is not prepared to do all he can to stamp out glue sniffing does not deserve to get to the House of Commons.'

There was a bay of agreement from the audience, even from the front rows. The candidate looked wildly round him and suddenly began to snort with laughter, doubling up over the desk in front of him. Ivor looked at him in consternation and jumped to his feet, ready to bring the meeting to a close in case the man was about to break down. The candidate waved him down, still laughing. The audience quietened down, wondering what on earth he was about to do or say next.

He took a large silk handkerchief out of his pocket and mopped his eyes. 'I am most frightfully sorry. Of course I support legislation against glue sniffing.' He started to giggle again. 'I thought the questioner said she wanted legislation outlawing loose living.'

That was the making of the candidate. It had looked as if there would be serious defections from the ranks of Tory supporters with the retirement of the Bart, but now we had the Sniffer. In the next twenty-four hours, the tale went round the constituency and his succession to the Bart was secured.

He even managed to increase the Tory majority.

Chapter Seven

LOVE MAY make the rest of the world go round; in our village, however, it wasn't love that did the trick, but gossip – often gossip about love. If the facts were not available, they were invented, and so it was usually in the interests of those who feared they might be gossiped about to make sure that the information in general currency was accurate. If accuracy could be compromising, their story had to be sufficiently convincing or interesting to ensure that their desired version would be accepted rather than the reality.

The pub, of course, was the general clearing house for news and scandal, where anything doing the rounds could be tested and embellished. How queer was the local hotelier? Was his *penchant* for the sort of sweaters that are worn on breakfast television sufficient evidence to confirm his aberration? Was Tony nicking diesel fuel from Ivor? And were the remarkable efforts of the shepherd to guard his privacy proof that he had something to hide? Could he be more attached to his charges than he might care to admit? Such things were not particularly rare in the countryside and he always wore gumboots.

Kelvin was sophisticated enough to know that very little can ever remain a secret in the country and, when he decided to enliven his private life, he instinctively involved everyone else in the affair. Kelvin had been quiet on his domestic front for years, ever since his long-suffering wife had died during a nasty dose of influenza. It had been felt that she had probably seized the opportunity of a peaceful demise and put a half-nelson on the Grim Reaper until he agreed to take her away with him.

Kelvin's life had been a model of decorum since then. His mousy, middle-aged daughter, Prudence, kept house for him and it was presumed that he got his jollies by tyrannizing her, just as he had tyrannized his wife. But Kelvin came into the pub one day bearing a copy of a farming magazine, looking as smug as a Friesian calf who was suckling a Jersey cow.

'Why are you looking so pleased with yourself?' asked the commander. His only concession to his naval past was that he occasionally wore a dark blue blazer with anchors on the brass buttons.

'Have you read *Farmers Weekly*, then?'

'Why? They're not featuring the amazing Kelvin Morchard cattle-rearing system, are they? Stick them in a field for eight years and then sell any that haven't died of old age.'

'I make a better living than you,' replied Kelvin, rather nettled at being summed up so easily and accurately.

'I doubt that. You don't have a munificent index-linked pension as do we who have retired from the sounds of strife.'

'That sound being ice cubes clinking in your pink gins.'

'We can all choose our own careers and you will not have heard me complain. Anyway, why are you looking so uncharacteristically cheerful?'

'I've got an advert in this week.'

'What's it about? Trying to sell your soul? It won't be worth much.'

Kelvin's sense of humour was the least developed of his faculties and so he ignored this crack. 'Read my advert,' he said, brandishing his magazine at the commander. The latter took it, placed it on the bar, put on a pair of gold-rimmed spectacles and read at the indicated place in a loud, clear voice so that the rest of the pub could hear.

'Personable, middle-aged widower with own farm seeks housekeeper/companion. No dogs. Send photograph. Apply Box.' The commander took off his glasses and howled with laughter. Kelvin bristled as the rest of the pub joined in.

'What's the joke?'

The commander wiped his eyes. 'Kelvin, you shocker. It's against the law.'

'What's against the law? You're allowed to advertise for a companion. It's not as if I'm asking for someone to give

French lessons or to administer discipline or do one of those kinky things.'

'No, it's not that. The Trades Description Act. You haven't been middle-aged for twenty years and nobody has considered you personable since the day your mother died.'

'Don't be so bloody rude. I'm still in the prime of my life. I can still put in a day's work that would see off any of the young whipper-snappers about nowadays.'

'Kelvin, my dear. This advert of yours is going to bring down hordes of women, all of whom will be after your money. It'll even bring down men as well, because there's nothing about which sex you require.'

Kelvin snatched the magazine. 'Isn't there?' He read the

advertisement again. 'But it's obvious isn't it? Housekeepers are always ladies, aren't they?'

'I wouldn't count on it. If you can have female prime ministers, you can just as easily have male housekeepers.'

'That sort of fellow won't read *Farmers Weekly*. I'm just after a nice lady who might be able to help a bit with the bullocks and that sort of thing.'

'You might find someone who's good at "that sort of thing",' agreed the commander. 'But I doubt if she'd be much good with the bullocks. And what's Prudence got to say about this? She's been looking after you for ages and she'll be a bit put out if some woman moves in as lady of the manor.'

Kelvin had obviously not given much consideration to Prudence's feelings. She was only a heifer, after all, and it was beginning to look very unlikely that she would be bred from. A few young bulls had sniffed around her when she had reached prime breeding condition fifteen years earlier, but her unfortunate conformation, temperament and her highly suspect pedigree, having a sire like Kelvin, had frightened them all off. This was in spite of the fact that she would be the sole inheritor of the farm when Kelvin went to the Great Pastureland in the Sky.

'Prudence? Oh, she won't complain. She always does what she's told.'

'What do you want someone else for, then?'

'Well,' replied Kelvin coyly, 'you never know what might turn up. I might even want to get married again.'

'Who would want to marry an old goat like you?' said Bill scornfully.

'You'd be surprised,' said the commander. 'Clean him up a bit and he'd be quite a good catch. Single man with a few bob.'

'I ain't got a few bob,' said Kelvin hurriedly. Like all established farmers, he liked to look over his rolling acres and claim that the bailiff was virtually at his door. 'So why don't you buy me a drink?'

Kelvin thrived in a rural habitat among those of his own kind, but he was smart enough to be aware that the wool could be very easily pulled over his eyes by his urban brothers, let alone their sisters. Although there was the obvious danger of exposing himself to ridicule, he knew that he could get himself into terrible trouble if he tried to deal with the replies to his advertisement by himself. Quite apart from anything else, he, like so many of his generation of farmers, was barely literate. So both he and the rest of us thought it would be a good idea to go over the replies to his advertisement together. That way he could at least share the responsibility for any disaster.

We did not see anything of Kelvin for a while, during which time we assumed that all the ardent damsels of the country who fancied the idea of a personable middle-aged widower with a farm were licking the tip of their pencils and rushing out to buy stamps and writing paper. Kelvin came back into the pub a couple of weeks later, bearing a sackful of potatoes.

Being one of the godfathers of the parish through his possession of the only flat field in the area – the sole possible venue for fêtes and gymkhanas, for which his permission was consequently required – he could enjoy certain little perks. His main one was the right to supply the pub with agricultural produce of all kinds.

The pub provided sandwiches and snacks for the benefit of culinarily primitive tourists, which meant that potatoes, milk and eggs were all needed, and the landlord paid cash, or with credit in the bar which was just as good. Every time a new landlord took over after the previous one had declined into helpless alcoholism, all these supplies would be put out for tender, but the other farmers respected the conventions and Kelvin's tender was always unopposed. So Kelvin entering bearing a sack of spuds, dead chickens or milk was a normal event. The fact that his bar chit was usually well in credit, did not make him any more generous when it should have been his round.

'Is that my spuds?' asked the landlord.

Kelvin looked shifty. He often did. In fact he usually wore a shifty expression on his face, or else one of bluff bonhomie which he used to cover the fact that he was feeling guilty.

'Spuds? I haven't got time to do spuds at the moment. Me and Prudence are flat out doing the haymaking. It's the first decent bit of haymaking weather we've had this summer. We've baled 10 acres today and, if the weather holds, we'll do the same tomorrow. Prudence is turning the swaths now.'

Kelvin was one of the very few local farmers who still relied on hay as the mainstay of his winter stock-feeding system. It had dawned on most of the others that the weather was the great unpredictable in their working lives and, in order to make decent hay without resorting to expensive artificial drying, they needed to be able to count on four or five days of settled weather.

It has been proved over countless years of careful observation that Nature waits until haymakers cut their grass, ruffle it, and backcomb it into neat rows, before she releases a barrage of good rollicking thunderstorms. The thunder was grumbling in the distance even as Kelvin ducked in the pub door.

'Did you have any replies to your advert?' asked the commander.

'Which advert?' asked Kelvin.

'The one for housekeeper and things.'

'Oh! That advert. Well, now you mention it, there were one or two. I was hoping you might be able to help me a bit.' Slightly shame-faced, Kelvin lifted the potato sack on to the bar and plunged his hand inside. He brought out a fistful of letters and handed them to the commander.

'Good grief!' exclaimed his companion. Kelvin put his hand inside the sack and brought out more letters, and then more and handed them round.

'This is positively terrifying,' said the commander.

'That it is,' replied Kelvin. 'I've even had women writing to me from abroad.'

'What are you going to do about them all?' asked Lindy, who also constituted part of Kelvin's fascinated audience.

'I thought I might have an open day on the farm and ask them all down.'

'You'd be crazy!' said the commander, to grunts of agreement from everyone else. 'Can you imagine a hundred women, all wanting a personable middle-aged widower, being confronted by an arrogant old lecher like you? Not to mention

286

Prudence. You'd need police protection and they'd still probably murder you. And they could claim justifiable homicide and no jury would ever convict them.'

'But how else can I ever select from this lot?' said Kelvin despairingly.

'Are you sure you want to get involved with the sort of women who would reply to an advert like this?' asked Lindy.

'Oh yes. There are enough of them here to make sure I can get a woman who will do what I tell her. That's the trouble with the country today. Too many women have got minds of their own. A woman needs a man like me to do her thinking for her.'

'In that case, there would be no thinking at all taking place,' said Lindy sarcastically.

'That's the sort of thing I mean. No woman that I would want would ever talk to me disrespectfully like that.'

As Kelvin did not appear to know how to begin the process of selection, the commander took charge in a manner befitting someone with his experience of administration and man-management. 'First of all, we need to know the parameters of your requirements,' he said, preparing to make a list.

Kelvin looked uncertainly at Lindy who explained for him. 'He means we need to know what you want. Like blonde hair or long legs, for example.'

'Oh yes. Well, I'm not so worried about the legs or the colour of her hair, but I wouldn't mind a big pair of . . . er . . . bosoms.'

The commander looked distastefully at Kelvin. 'That's not quite what I meant, but we'll mark it down. Age?'

'Sixty-three.'

'Not you, you fool. What age do you want your lady to be?'

'Oh, sorry. I hadn't really thought about it.'

'Well, think about it now, man. What's the oldest that you want her to be?'

'Hmm. I certainly wouldn't want her to be too old although, if she was over sixty, she would be collecting a pension. How about fifty-five? That's a good age.'

'Right,' said the commander, marking it down. 'What's your bottom limit?'

'I don't really think that matters, do you?'

'Would you want a seventeen-year-old?'

'That would be a bit young, I think. She ought to have had some experience of life.'

Lindy snorted. 'I should think the average seventeen-year-old these days has had a damn sight more experience of life than you, Kelvin.'

'I don't reckon so. Anyway, I think it's only right that she shouldn't be any younger than Prudence. Prudence might find it difficult to get on with a stepmother who was younger than her, if it comes to that.'

'That's sensible,' said the commander approvingly. 'How old is Prudence?'

'She'll be thirty-eight this Michaelmas.'

'Right. We'll put a bottom limit of forty. Now, height and weight?'

'I don't mind about that.'

'Looks?'

'No, I don't mind. So long as she's not really ugly. I mean, I've got my pride. I wouldn't like people to think I was desperate. And she's got to be, you know, big.' He sketched a curve in the air with his hands.

'You've already said that, Kelvin,' said Lindy.

'But the commander didn't mark it down. I was watching.'

'All right, Kelvin.' The commander scribbled 'Knockers, two, enormous.' 'How's that?'

'That's fine.'

'How about children?'

'Oh, I'm not so sure about that. I'm a bit old to be a father now, and Prudence might get a bit upset if I went and sired any more.'

'No,' said the commander patiently. 'I was not talking about your future plans. Would you mind if she brought any children with her? I would imagine that quite a lot of these women might be divorced or separated and might well have children in their charge.'

'Oh, sorry. I see what you mean.' Kelvin thought for a bit. 'I think it would be best if I said no female children and no boys under twelve.'

'What have boys got that girls haven't?' asked Lindy curiously. 'Apart from the obvious?'

'I could do with a bit of help round the farm and a strapping teenager could be quite useful.'

'Ah! I see. Cheap labour.'

'That's right,' replied Kelvin without a qualm.

'It's going to be a very spiritual relationship,' said the commander. 'However, we're beginning to get some sort of picture. I think we should move on to interests. There may not be any indication in the letters, but are there any hobbies or interests or anything like that which you feel are important?'

Kelvin thought again. You could always tell when Kelvin was thinking deeply because you could see his lips move. When he was reading, he not only moved his lips but whispered aloud. He came to his conclusions: 'Cooking, sewing, cleaning, working on farms, sheep, cattle, hens, calves —'

'Slow down a bit, I'm trying to write all this down.'

Lindy looked at the list with distaste: 'I pity anyone who ends up with you, Kelvin.'

The commander also examined the finished list. 'Right. I suppose we'd better start looking through these letters to see if we can find anyone who remotely matches this paragon.'

There was a general filling of pints as the letters were distributed round to those who could read anything more than the figures on their market cheques. Most of the letters contained photographs and these were passed over to Kelvin for his examination. We took an unspoken mutual decision to ignore any letters whose writers showed that they possessed any degree of refinement or sensitivity. No delicate flower or hothouse plant could be subjected to the crude blasts of Kelvin.

We ended up with three candidates. One was a fifty-year-old who showed all the desirable interests, having been a farmer's housekeeper for years. Against her was her demand for a bedsit of her own with a colour TV with a minimum screen size of 22 inches. It was thought that this showed a hard-headedness which militated against Kelvin consummating his carnal desires with her.

The second letter came from a farmer's widow, age unmentioned, but she had a son of thirty. Her application seemed to be rather ulterior in its motives as she wrote of how her son had been cruelly deprived of the opportunity of taking on her late husband's tenancy. It appeared that there might be a distinct possibility that Kelvin might find himself poisoned once she had managed to change his will in her favour.

The third candidate was the one that was most interesting.

She enclosed a photograph that showed her in a bikini on a Costa Brava holiday. The applicant stated that she was forty-two and the picture must have been taken, according to Lindy, at least a decade earlier since she was sure that the remarkable suspension of her two huge mammary glands would have begun to fail under the forces of gravity by her fourth decade. She was childless, twice divorced, lived in London, was fond of the countryside and 'a good time'.

Kelvin found himself in a bit of a dilemma. He liked the idea of a thirty-year-old, an experienced farm worker, who could be strung along with a series of vague promises about the future and who might even provide a partner for Prudence. But the photograph of the two enormous knockers, even if they had begun to succumb to fair wear and tear, had him dribbling into his beer with excitement. Lust won. He decided to write to her.

'What sort of salary do you intend to offer?' asked Bill.

Kelvin looked at him in alarm.

'Salary? Do you think I will need to pay her? I would have thought that offering her board and lodging would have been enough. You don't pay a wife a salary.'

'You don't pay a wife because all your worldly goods are already endowed to her. Unless you intend to do that on the strength of a magnificent pair of breasts, I'm afraid you will have to pay her. After all, you did advertise in the "Jobs Vacant" column,' said the commander.

'I suppose I'll have to come to some arrangement then,' he said begrudgingly. 'But let's not dwell on the subject of money. What's the next step?'

'How do you mean?'

'Well, do I ask her down for an interview, or should I just hire her?'

'I think the best thing to do would be to write as honest a letter as you can manage so that you don't waste each other's time. She might have her own parameters. For example, middle aged, to her, might mean around thirty-five instead of sixty-three. It would be a shame if you paid her fare down and she got straight back on the train as soon as she clapped eyes on you.'

Kelvin pondered deeply over this. 'Do you think you could help me to write a letter, Commander?'

'With pleasure. I'll draw something up and you can copy it out.' The commander selected an envelope from the pile of letters – a pink one that smelled of Lily of the Valley. 'Dear Madam,' he said as he wrote.

'Don't you think that's just a little formal under the circumstances?' asked Bill.

The commander considered. 'I wouldn't have thought so. Kelvin hasn't met her so she doesn't know his name or anything. I would certainly use "Dear Madam" and sign off with "yours faithfully".'

'It's a bit old-fashioned and even intimidating,' said Lindy. She might disapprove, but she was not going to be left out.

'Good manners are never old-fashioned,' said the commander. 'And Kelvin is supposed to be her prospective employer.'

'From what I can make out, neither she nor Kelvin are aiming for a conventional working relationship. She's more likely to chuck him under the chin and call him "ducks", rather than stand to attention and call him "sir". Don't you agree, Kelvin?'

'I think "madam" is a bit formal. Couldn't I just say "Dear Missus"?'

The commander frowned. 'I suppose you can call someone "missus" in speech, if you must. But you certainly can't when you're writing a letter. I suppose we'd better use names.'

Kelvin picked up her letter and studied it. 'She's called Matilda Billingsley.'

'Right,' said the commander. 'We'll start off: "Dear Mrs Billingsley, Thank you for your letter in reply to my advertisement for a housekeeper/companion. It is only right that I should tell you a bit more about myself. I am sixty-three —" '

'I don't think I ought to say that,' interrupted Kelvin.

'I don't see why not. It's true, isn't it?'

'Yes, but it's a bit blunt. There's sixty-three and sixty-three. Jimmy there has looked at least ninety ever since he has been in his fifties and I wouldn't want her to think I was like that.'

'You don't want to mention your age?'

'I think we ought to mention it, but just lie a bit.'

'How big a bit?'

'Say I am a young fifty-seven.'

'Right: "I am a young fifty-seven and I have been a farmer all my life." How's that?'

'That's fine. I think it would be a good idea if you said I was good-looking or something like that.'

'I don't honestly think you can get away with that,' said Lindy, looking at Kelvin critically. 'Unusual looking, perhaps, but your nose is too big and your false teeth don't fit well enough for you to be described as good-looking.'

'You ain't no oil painting yourself.'

'I agree. But it is not me that is claiming to be one. I think you could fairly call yourself interesting-looking.'

'Thank you,' said Kelvin.

'Because that could have even taken care of Quasimodo.'

'Who's he?'

'A Frenchman who looked not unlike you.'

'I see. OK. I'll agree to that. Say: "I am an interesting-looking young fifty-seven."'

'If that's what you want,' said the commander. 'It's a bit personal, though, isn't it? After all, you're just offering a job.'

'It's a personal sort of a job. What else does she say in her letter?'

Lindy picked it up and skimmed through it. 'She says she is a driver and has a mini. Perhaps we should say that you have a car.'

'I don't think Kelvin's clapped-out van is worth mentioning,' said Bill. Kelvin's clapped-out van was looking even worse than usual. He used it to transport lambs and bales of hay round the farm. Moreover, the previous week, a curious cow had put its head through the window and, when it had tried to pull its head back out, the whole door had come off its hinges and the animal had worn it like a giant collar for several hours before it could be removed.

'I've got a Morris Minor,' said Kelvin.

'But that belongs to Prudence,' said Bill.

'It's in my name. Put down a car, a Land Rover and two tractors. That ought to impress her.'

The letter was duly written and sent off. The village waited for Matilda Billingsley's response with as much patience as it could muster.

Chapter Eight

BILL STARTED up a book, offering odds of 2 to 1, that Matilda Billingsley would not turn up and, if she did, the odds climbed to 20 to 1 against her taking the job. He found few takers.

It took a week for a reply to come back from London where the lady lived. 'Dear Kelvin,' it started off, without any of the formality that we had agonized over, 'I am most interested in this position,' which occasioned much ribald delight. Since she was a 'shy girl at heart', she would much rather meet Kelvin in London for the first time than come down to stay. She found Kelvin a very pretty name and preferred 'mature men rather than young men because they are older'. The gist was that she would meet Kelvin at Paddington and they could spend a week-end together to see how they would get on.

Kelvin was terrified at the prospect. He had once been to Smithfield, but his only other forays out of the parish were his fortnightly trips to the local market where he met his cronies in the pub and they became gently sozzled together. Kelvin was as territorial as a cockerel and his patch was the parish and the thin ribbon of land to the market. He knew almost everybody on his territory and they knew him and he understood all the surprises and emergencies that were likely to arise and how to deal with them.

Away from his own patch, particularly in London, Kelvin knew that he would be nothing but an elderly man with scruffy clothes and a country-bumpkin accent. He would be in no position to impress Matilda Billingsley with his land, his cattle, his friends; that he was the only man in the village who could run a slate at the pub or that he had been on the parish council for thirty years. Not even for the sight of Matilda's chest was he prepared to strip himself of his identity to that extent.

Perhaps Matilda felt the same. At any rate, it took another five weeks of negotiation before she agreed to come down to the countryside to investigate the position that was vacant. Kelvin had even been forced to mention money and had thrashed out a salary of £42.50 a week, plus room and board.

The great day arrived. Kelvin had to go into town to meet the train at about 8.00 pm and he visited the pub to give himself a bit of Dutch courage before he left. He looked ghastly, wearing his wedding/funeral suit with a white carnation in his button-hole to aid recognition. His collar was sawing into his neck and already grey spikes of hair were slowly re-erecting themselves on top of his thoroughly watered scalp. If his false teeth had been up to the challenge, he would have been biting his fingernails. A couple of whiskies were poured down his throat and he departed to meet his destiny.

This was on a Friday evening. The next night was the communards' barbecue. This had become one of the social high spots of the year, along with the Christmas dance in the skittle hall behind the pub and the midsummer Strawberry Ball organized by the hunt.

The barbecue was usually a highly successful affair. The commune lived secretively for most of the year, trying to be self-sufficient, creating dreadful pieces of pottery and paintings, studying strange religions and descending like locusts on the local jumble sales to rummage through the clothes. Three centuries ago, the villagers would probably have raided the commune and burned most of its inhabitants at the stake, but now they were just looked at with amused tolerance and this they repaid at the barbecue. The commune laid on a rodent's feast of nut stews and home-fermented wines while the locals brought along bits of pig and chicken for barbecuing and hip-flasks full of spirits so that the country wines could have a rocket-assisted start in the task of inebriating everyone.

There had actually been a moment earlier in the year when it looked as though the communards might be cast out into social darkness. One of them had given birth to a child, thus settling a local controversy as to her sex, and had thrown a party to celebrate the event. Unlike the barbecue, it was primarily a communard party with alternative livers from all round the county coming together to get pissed, stoned, pass round the infant's horoscope and gibber to the moon. A few locals had attended just to be sociable, and an awful tale had emerged through them.

One of the dishes on offer had been a pâté. Since it was the only meat as opposed to veg dish, the locals had tucked in. The hostess had drifted up to them in her kaftan, offering a puff of her acrid, hand-rolled cigarette.

'Do you like the pâté?'

'Oh yes. It's delicious.'

'I'm so glad. In nature, I noticed that all animals like to eat their own placentas and so I made the pâté out of mine.'

During the ensuing uproar, even the other communards had thought that this was just a little over the top and the lady had been asked to leave. She had moved on to a more sympathetic establishment in Cornwall, but there was still a degree of gastronomic unease about the barbecue, while the grass-and-dandelion salad was even less in demand than usual.

It was known that Kelvin would be bringing his Matilda to the barbecue and so most people turned up promptly at 9.00 pm, rather than drifting in as the pubs closed. The party was held in the courtyard of the old stable block. Given a hundred thousand pounds or so, the communards could have had an establishment fit for a merchant banker wishing to become a country gentleman. Their house was a late Georgian vicarage, but it had been browsed over by pests for decades, housed thriving colonies of fungi and had been empty for five years before the communards had taken it over.

The communards themselves had come down to the neighbourhood with a reputation of being drug-sodden degenerates. For all we knew they probably were, but they seemed quite harmless as they pottered about on their 6 acres of land, trying to grow their food organically and fighting a losing war against the hordes of encroaching nettles and thistles which had not had such an easy life since the invention of herbicides.

The only member of the community who worried much about the habits of the communards was Percy the policeman, and he had been keeping a low profile since his last brush with them. He had espied two of their number walking through the village towards the river and had observed one of the communards pass an object to the other in a furtive and suspicious manner. As he approached them, the communard holding the suspicious substance had stuffed it into his mouth in a clear attempt to get rid of the evidence. Percy had pounced with an outstretched hand and commanded the masticator to spit the evidence into his waiting palm. The obliging fellow duly disgorged a mouthful of well-chewed peanuts, to the delight of the dozen or so watching tourists. Over the ensuing couple of weeks, Percy had been greeted by locals offering to spit in his hand wherever he went and he had become rather browned off by it.

As it happened, the communards had fortuitously entered an area that was probably more tolerant of drugs than most. There was nothing particularly exceptional about the amount of alcohol that was consumed, massive though it was, but the older families in the neighbourhood had always enjoyed their own means of intoxication. On the moors above the village grew quantities of hallucinogenic fungi which were latched on to by the hippies of the sixties as one of the paths to enlightenment. For centuries the locals had harvested them for consumption at autumn social get-togethers and nobody had ever given it a thought. It was really rather embarrassing for so many solid citizens to discover that they were among the pioneers of the drug culture. So we tolerated the strange customs of the communards where other communities may not have done.

The barbecue got under way, running its loud, midgy, smoky course. The fire lay at the centre of the courtyard surrounded by bales of straw on which to sit where one swithered between the twin evils of being eaten alive by insects or swathed in the greasy smoke coming from the broiling pigs and chickens on the grill.

The squire's wife was deep in conversation with Ben Moggridge on the breeding habits of the goat. Ben called

298

himself a tree surgeon, which meant that he spent the summer sawing up logs to stoke all the wood-burning stoves in the locality, owned by those who had not yet worked out that they were both highly expensive to run and very inefficient.

There was still no sign of Kelvin and Matilda, and an air of restless anticipation prevailed. The dancing that was going on in one of the stables had a frantic feel to it and some of the old ladies of the parish were kicking up their heels for the first time in decades to the heavy metal music being pumped out by the commune's ghetto blaster. Assorted dogs scrabbled and snarled like their ancestors at medieval banquets for scraps of meat thrown into the darkness beyond the circle of straw bales. Not just bones were coming their way, but prime New Zealand lamb chops and sausages, sent spinning into the night after one horrified bite through the carbonized exterior had revealed the chill, deep-frozen heart within.

Then things began to happen. Whether Kelvin arrived late so that he could make a grand entrance or so that he could sneak in and lose himself in the milling throng was unclear – although his choosing the modest alternative would have been totally out of character, however exceptional the circumstances.

Kelvin was not wearing his suit and was looking more comfortable in his 'number two' dress of wide-bottom grey trousers and dung-coloured sports jacket. However, the sudden hush that fell over the assembled multitude as the murmur of talk died away and the auditory vacuum was filled by the sound of sizzling fat and the thump of music from the stable was not because we were interested in the fine detail of Kelvin's dress but because we were interested in the lady.

The first noticeable thing about her was that she tottered on heels that appeared dangerously high. High heels are not common in the countryside as they sink in where the tarmac stops and a slip on a cowpat can have dangerous consequences. Her stated age of forty-two seemed to be a fair approximation, but the extent to which the passing of the years had slackened the ligatory guy-ropes that kept her undeniably astounding breasts in their state of suspension was difficult to ascertain since they seemed to be incarcerated in a curious conical brassiere.

With a hand resting genteelly on Kelvin's arm, she tottered into the light of the fire and there was a mighty hiss of indrawn breath. She was wearing a cotton frock covered in pictures of ponies, a concession no doubt to the countryside, but it was a very thin garment and there was a definite nipple-shaped protuberance to the fore – well to the fore. Either she was not wearing a bra at all, in which case she was a physical phenomenon on a par with Cliff Richard, or she had holes in the front of it which gave rise to all sorts of erotic speculation. She was a powerful-looking woman – not tall, but broad, with her superstructure neatly balanced by an equally formidable backside. Her face, with its surrounding tight blonde curls, was saved from vapid prettiness by a slightly underslung jaw which gave her a faint resemblance to a salmon.

There was something odd about her manner. Apparently not at all shy about being thrown among strangers in rather unusual circumstances, she seemed totally unaware of being scrutinized by a score of pairs of eyes. She stared intently at the barbecuing meat and, after a decent interval of contemplation, switched her attention to the bar with its barrel of cider and boxes of British wine spread amongst the odd-shaped assortment of bottles of home-brewed beer and wine.

With Kelvin standing by her side like an abashed schoolboy, she then switched again, letting her eyes travel round the courtyard, taking in the straw bales, the people sitting on them and the stable doors through which the music was coming. She then finished up by staring back at the fire and following the plume of smoke upwards to the moonlit sky. It was almost as if she could take in only one visual stimulus at a time and had to savour and evaluate it before allowing herself to move on to the next.

She turned to Kelvin, who was looking anxiously at her. 'Get me a sherry,' she said.

We considered her request. Crisp, clear, to the point and no messing about. She knew what she wanted and asked for it. Kelvin went over to try to find a sherry as she stood placidly by the fire, her legs slightly apart, examining the sizzling sausages rather hungrily. She seemed perfectly content just to stand and cogitate on the grilling pigmeat, but her self-possession and calm created a little circle of disturbance. It was as if a bacterium had invaded the bloodstream and the white corpuscles were twitching and heaving about, wondering quite what they ought to do about it.

Dennis, bless his heart, took it upon himself to try to integrate her into the party. He approached her with an ingratiating smile wreathed across his lips. Conversation, which had begun to start up again after the initial impact of the couple's arrival, died away again as we all stretched our ears to hear the exchange. As Dennis walked towards her, she turned her head and looked at him warily, as if she expected him to turn somersaults or do something equally unexpected.

'Good evening. My name is Dennis. I'm a friend of Kelvin's. Er . . . Welcome to the village.' She continued to look stolidly at him. 'Er . . . Do you come from round here?'

We appreciated the question. It would not do to embarrass her by making her think we had been talking about her or knew too much about her.

'No,' she replied. Dennis smiled at her encouragingly, but it appeared that she had nothing more to say on the subject. He took a hurried gulp of his whisky as Kelvin lurched over to join them, bearing a couple of glasses of wine.

'Evening, Dennis.'

'Evening, Kelvin.'

'Good party, innit?'

'Yes,' replied Dennis. 'I was just talking to your companion.'

'Oh? What about?' Kelvin seemed desperately eager to find out.

'We hadn't actually got very far. I was just introducing myself, but your friend hasn't yet told me her name.'

Something seemed to stir deep behind the lady's eyes and she looked as if she was about to speak, but Kelvin clumsily destroyed the magic of the moment before she had time to sift through all the considerations and actually commit herself to utterance.

''Course you know her name. She's Matilda from London. The one that sent the letter. Who else do you think I'd bring along here?'

Dennis raised his eyes to the stars in exasperation. Lindy saw the difficulty that Kelvin's obtuseness was creating in the search for information, and so she went across to lend a hand. Dennis flashed her a look of gratitude. There was nothing else that Lindy could be except the district nurse: she looked so capable with her short hair, square, strong hands and air of being able to handle all the nasties that life might throw at her and come bouncing back for more. She donned her bedside manner which put at ease her most awkward patients.

'Hullo. What a lovely dress.' She paused for a split second, realized that she was not going to get an answer and carried smoothly on. 'Where did you manage to find it?'

A slight look of alarm crossed Matilda's face as she swivelled her head towards Lindy. The hush as she opened her mouth was almost palpable. 'Don't remember.'

'Oh, come on,' said Lindy encouragingly. 'You must remember where you bought a lovely dress like that.'

'A present, it was.'

'How nice! And who gave it to you?'

'I can't remember.'

The conversation, as Lindy put it later, was like taking out stitches. She and Kelvin were studying Matilda's face, willing her to utter, while Dennis had given up and was trying to solve the conundrum of her breasts under the guise of studying the bottom of his whisky glass. It was not made easy by the flickering light of the fire which forced him to lean down and squint a bit. Lindy girded her loins and moved back into the conversational fray.

'How long are you here for?'

'Dunno,' replied Matilda. 'It depends.'

Lindy looked across at Kelvin for some help. A look of panic crossed his face and he hurriedly backed away, moving over to where Bill and the commander were standing surveying Matilda.

'Did you come down from London?' continued Lindy doggedly.

'That's right. On a train. From Paddington.' She paused again and then suddenly spoke, making both Lindy and Dennis jump. 'It took ever such a short time and that gentleman was waiting for me at the station.' She indicated Kelvin. She delved into her handbag and produced a small piece of paper which she studied carefully. Dennis tried to read it too, but it was upside down. She grinned. She was one of those rare people who look less attractive when they smile. 'Kelvin, that's what he's called. He's ever so nice although he's quite old.' She sank her voice to a whisper as all and sundry strained their ears to hear and there was complete silence, except for the yelp of a dog as someone sank their foot into its ribs to stop it making the night hideous with its scratching. 'He might offer me a job. He's a very important man round here, you know. He used to be a very senior policeman and they asked him if he would be the local mayor, or something, but he said he was too busy. Everyone in the district is very jealous of him because he's so popular.'

'Is that right?' said Lindy. 'What else did he tell you?'

'Oh, I shouldn't go round repeating confidences. That's one thing I told Kelvin. I never gossip. I don't believe in that sort of thing.'

'You're absolutely right,' said Dennis. 'Gossip is a terrible thing and it's easy to see that you're the sort of person who never gossips about other people. Isn't it, Lindy?'

Lindy nodded assent.

'Oh! Is your name Lindy?' asked Matilda.

'That's right.'

'What a coincidence! Kelvin was talking about someone called Lindy earlier on.'

'Really?' said Lindy. 'That must be the district nurse. She's called Lindy, just the same as me. What did he say about her?'

'I shouldn't say, really.'

'No, of course you shouldn't,' said Dennis, perceiving minefields ahead.

'— But he said she was very bossy.'

'Oh, did he?' said Lindy grimly. One couldn't help hoping that Kelvin would never need an enema. Others at the party had begun to close in on Matilda, desirous of overhearing further indiscretions. Ivor did the gentlemanly thing and made sure that Kelvin's attention was fully occupied by bringing up some query about communications after the atomic holocaust. This was Kelvin's current obsession since he had taken over the planning of the parish's survival after the bomb had dropped. When he was safely out of earshot, Lindy did not so much have to pump Matilda as pull out her plug.

'He's awfully clever, that Kelvin, and a very shrewd businessman, you know.'

'In what way?' cooed Lindy.

'He was saying that there was some old lady who owned a small bit of land at the edge of the churchyard and he went and bought it very cheaply the other day, because he knows that they'll have to buy it when they want some more room and he'll be able to name his own price. Isn't that clever?'

There was a stunned silence. It had come up in a meeting of the parochial church council a few weeks earlier that the graveyard was getting a bit crowded and that something would have to be done about it. Kelvin, being a heathen, was not a member, but he must have heard someone mention it in the pub.

It was evident that Matilda was far too precious an insertion into the shady areas of Kelvin's soul to be allowed to vanish back to her urban rookery and Lindy and Dennis left her in the capable hands of the commander while they went to join Ivor in his distraction display.

'What a splendid woman, Kelvin. You are a lucky chap,' was Dennis's greeting.

Ivor looked startled, while Kelvin examined Dennis suspiciously to try to establish whether or not the mickey was being taken out of him.

'Yes. She seems awfully nice,' echoed Lindy.

Kelvin peered at her in turn. 'Do you really think so? I was wondering if she might not be all that bright. I'm not sure that I could stand her round the farm all day.'

'Not all that bright?' said Dennis in amazement. 'I thought she was very bright. Didn't you, Lindy?'

Lindy corroborated with a vigorous nod of her head. 'Certainly. She may not be in line for a double first at Oxford, but she's certainly sharp enough. And witty.'

'Witty!' said Kelvin. 'I haven't heard her crack many jokes. Come to think on it, I've hardly heard her say anything at all.'

'Really? Well, I find her very witty.' Lindy emitted a peal of laughter to show how witty Matilda was. It was so unlike her usual earthy chuckle that Kelvin and Dennis gave her a startled look. She tried another peal and managed to produce a more normal sound.

'Hmm,' said Kelvin. 'I'm not sure that I want to live in the same house as someone who cracks jokes the whole time.'

'She's not *that* funny,' said Lindy, rather more scathingly than was appropriate.

'Certainly not,' agreed Dennis. 'Just about right. Witty without being tedious. I would have thought that she was exactly the sort of person that you should be looking for.'

Kelvin rubbed his chin thoughtfully. 'Well, I have to admit she's pretty near to it, but don't you think she's a little plain? She's not as pretty as the photograph she sent.'

'I think she's very pretty,' replied Dennis gallantly. 'And her most impressive features certainly live up to expectations.'

'I agree,' said Lindy. 'You agree too, don't you, Ivor?'

Ivor jumped. 'Oh yes, quite.' He was a little bemused, not understanding why Matilda should have gathered such a devoted fan club so quickly.

'Do you really think so?' said Kelvin. 'What about that jaw of hers?'

Lindy was having some difficulty in stomaching this cold dissection of Matilda. She may also have been harbouring doubts about the morality of this exercise in manipulation. At any rate, she let her mask of goodwill slip a little. 'You're a fine one to start criticizing Matilda,' she snapped.

'I think her jaw is fine – most beguiling,' said Dennis hastily, frowning at Lindy. If one started to prod at the great tottering blancmange that was Kelvin's vanity, he could become unmanageable. Fortunately, his hearing was highly selective and he chose to ignore Lindy's remark.

'Hmm,' said Kelvin, but he looked happier than he had done when he had first arrived at the party and he went over to top up Matilda's drink. The obvious appreciation of his contemporaries had burnished up her appeal in his eyes and he stood by her side for the rest of the evening, looking on with slightly puzzled pride as the villagers, one by one at Dennis's prompting, went up and made manifest how delightful they all found Matilda to be.

We had underestimated Matilda. Ivor met her on the platform of the station on Monday morning. He was going up for a Milk Marketing Board meeting and she was going home. Kelvin had offered her the job and had indicated that it could lead to a great deal more, but Matilda had not been seduced by the idea of becoming his housekeeper and still less had she been willing to be seduced by the man himself.

'A miserable old bastard,' was her pithy summing up. 'I'm better off with my husband.'

It was a pity, but we quite understood her point of view. She walked off with £500 as well. Kelvin could not report it as he had not declared it to the Inland Revenue. The sympathy he received was underwhelming.

Chapter Nine

'YOU KNOW HOW we country people are different from those who live in towns, don't you?' asked Muriel, carefully measuring another couple of inches of gin into her glass.

'God! She's going to get boring again,' replied her sister Barbara.

'Do shut up, dear. It's because we need to make money through our own initiative. In towns all you have to do is go out and work for someone else. Out here, nobody gives you money. You have to go and get it for yourself.'

We were sitting round their kitchen table at 10.30 in the morning. It was hard work visiting the sisters. Whatever time of the day or night, one was never offered tea or coffee, but only alcohol. They drank gin while visitors were offered cooking sherry. This was an economy measure. Most visitors never touched or never finished the vast drinks that were pressed upon them and it hurt less to pour bad sherry down the drain than good gin.

The sisters were both widows and bickered furiously with each other. Muriel had taken me aside once to tell me what lay at the foundation of their disagreements: 'I was the clever one when we were girls and I had curly hair. Barbara was stupid and had straight hair and so she was very jealous of me. And she has never got over it.'

Muriel had married a sailor and had produced a stream of amiably unsuccessful children whom she despised. Barbara had married a colonial judge who had died of a heart attack the day the unthinkable had happened and his colony had achieved its independence. When they reached their seventies, they had come together again to continue the ritual they had begun in childhood of being extremely rude to each other and the ritual they had adopted in adulthood of spending as many of their waking moments as possible in a state that would have melted the bottom of a breathalyser bag.

I had called to return the tortoise. It had come with the house which had been an old smithy at the edge of the village. The reptile had been there the ten years that the sisters had been living there and a yellowing photograph showed the animal beside the last blacksmith. Its name, Bleriot, indicated that it had probably been around for the best part of a century. The creature was even mentioned in the house deeds as part of the fixtures and fittings of the establishment, but nobody had asked the tortoise whether it approved of the arrangement. It had dug itself into the rose-bed one winter and, when it woke up in the spring, it had a new owner. It had been rudely disturbed by Muriel's Afghan which had been in the process of burying a bone.

The Afghan had only been a puppy then, but it had been love at first sight. The dog's idea of a blissfully consummated relationship was to go for a long country walk with the freaked-out tortoise, frantically waving its legs, firmly clasped between its jaws. There was never a problem when they met other dogs. After a brief examination of the block-mouthed, growling Jellicoe, one could see them dismiss him with the thought of 'nutter'.

Bleriot decided early on that the best solution to his difficulties lay in emigrating and, whenever Jellicoe was not concentrating, he would plod grimly down the garden path and head south towards a better world. Unfortunately for him, his route took him past our front door and he would invariably be fielded by ourselves, by Jellicoe in a lather of panicked excitement, or by a motorist, happy enough to flatten hedgehogs but unwilling to risk his tyres or suspension on a large tortoise.

On this occasion, I had given the reptile twenty-four hours of peace amid our lettuces before returning it to its rightful owners and having to undergo the obligatory sherry. The sisters were arguing as usual when I came through the door and they both gave me imperious – if unfocused – glances as I entered.

'Thank you,' said Barbara, graciously accepting the errant creature. 'Such a pity they're inedible, isn't it?'

'Barbara! How could you! Poor Bleriot.'

Poor Bleriot was looking as if his consumption would have been a merciful release. He was lying underneath the kitchen table, upside down, firmly anchored beneath Jellicoe's paw, while the dog was peering earnestly into his shell, slapping his face with a long pink tongue whenever he dared to poke it out. I rose to leave, abandoning the latter half of my sherry.

'Oh yes,' said Barbara as I moved towards the door. She turned round in her chair, overbalanced and slid to the ground.

'Shit,' she said, but continued from the floor: 'We are looking for a way of earning some more money. It would be appreciated if you would come up with some ideas.'

A tallish order, off the back foot, I thought.

Muriel looked at me hopefully. 'The trouble is that our expenses are so high. We have certain little luxuries to which we have become accustomed.' She carefully topped up her gin from the litre bottle on the table in front of her. Her speech and her bleary gaze gave the impression that she was on the point of collapse, but the iron grip with which she held the bottle was as steady as that of a surgeon scrabbling around amid someone's brains.

'How about buying your little luxuries wholesale?' I suggested. Mick at the cafe had a daily delivery run, supplying spirits by the crate-load to the army of retired who lived in the village and the surrounding countryside. He charged full retail prices and slapped on a whacking delivery charge. A significant proportion of the pensions paid out by the Ministry of Defence and the civil service must eventually end up in the glens of the Scottish Highlands and in their distilleries.

'Buy wholesale? But how would we pick it up?' asked Barbara. That was the 'Catch-22' which was enabling Mick to get rich. From 10.00 am to midnight, most of those over sixty-five in the district were well beyond the legal driving limit. 'No, we want to earn money. Quite apart from anything else, it would give us something to do.'

'Are you serious?' I asked.

'Well, fairly serious. We wouldn't want to do anything strenuous. There's our 10-acre field out the back, for example. There must be something more profitable that we can do with it than just rent it out to Dick Hunniford so he can cover it with his sheep.'

'Cover it with your own sheep. That's got to be more profitable.'

'Don't be so stupid. I am willing to look at sheep from my bedroom window and I am even prepared to eat selected parts of the creatures, but I have no desire to become more closely involved with such a moronic species of animal. You can run along now.'

So I ran along.

A couple of weeks later, there was a bit of excitement in the village. An enormous yellow bulldozer was seen crabbing its way down the side of one of the hills that surrounded us. Such visitations were uncommon. The narrow lanes kept out most heavy vehicles. It was a blessing in many respects, until an ignorant driver managed to penetrate as far as the village itself when he would get himself into an inextricable articulated tangle at the corner of the pub and the post office, while Land Rovers and horseboxes backed up for half a mile on either side

311

of him. It brought out the beast in Percy when he tried to sort it out.

Bulldozers roamed the countryside on the back of huge flat-bed lorries, grubbing out hedges and scouring the bottom of slurry pits wherever they stopped. Their lorry would get them as close to their destination as possible and then they set off by themselves in a bee-line to wherever they wished to go. Oddly enough, although there was plenty of sound and fury as they travelled and it looked as though their tracks would leave great tramlines slashed across the landscape, once the belching, roaring machine had disappeared over the horizon, there would be a tingling silence; the crushed vegetation and saplings would cautiously unfold themselves and, within a couple of hours, it was as if the machine had never passed.

The bulldozer on this particular visitation clanked its way to the bottom of the hill, cautiously edged its way into the river and gingerly crossed through the summer-low water before triumphantly snorting its way out on the far side and climbing into Barbara and Muriel's field. What on earth was going on?

The jungle drums muttered and rumbled in their quest for intelligence, but none of the usual sources could come up with any information. The machine crunched to a halt by the edge of the stream that ran down the centre of the precipitous field, and its operator disembarked and walked over to the house. The watchers – not twitching their lace curtains so much as standing in the fields and their gardens with binoculars clamped to their eyes – relaxed, knowing that the driver would now be sitting at the kitchen table with a tumblerful of cheap sherry in front of him and would soon be incapable of any further work for the day.

However, within an hour, people tumbled out of their houses again as an echoing blare bounced round the valley to announce that the jaundiced behemoth had restarted its engine. It was rootling about with its blade on the bed of the stream, was the report: digging a pond, clearly.

That did not last long. The water authority was inundated with calls from local citizens who felt it their duty to ascertain that proper permission had been obtained for such action and

Ivor, in his role of parish councillor, turned up on the smithy doorstep to advise Barbara and Muriel that it was in their interest to halt the work until the proper permission had been obtained. It took some time to sort out the red tape and it took some time for Ivor to recover from the effects of having a tortoise bounced off his head, but work eventually restarted.

The sisters had permission to dig out a large pond, fed by the stream, into which they were going to place rainbow trout. These were to be caught by visiting anglers who would be charged by the pound, at a higher rate than the fish would cost them if purchased from a fishmonger. It was quite a bright idea, another neat method of separating the tourists from their money.

The bulldozer roared and puffed for a week. Barbara supervised for a day and then had to delegate to Muriel after she had annoyed the driver to such an extent that he chased her round the field, trying to swat her with the blade of his machine.

When the work was completed, it had all the charm of a bomb site. It formed a massive scar on the hillside which was glaringly obvious as one came along the road leading to the bridge into the village. Its colour was what created the eyesore: most of the valley was a vivid grass-green, but the bulldozer had dragged up the subsoil which was clay in blue and yellow layers and had piled it up to dam the stream. Right in the centre of this garish protuberance was an ominous band of grey.

This band gave rise to problems. It was good porous shale, through which the stream continued to chuckle its merry way down to the river, refusing, with complete self-assurance, even to consider spreading itself across the carefully prepared floor of the pond which remained sparsely and sullenly puddled. The delivery of trout was postponed and I, returning Bleriot yet again, was called in to advise.

I had the reputation of being quite an expert at this sort of thing, having spent a few years of my life trying to persuade a slurry pit to leak gently and economically into the environment and thus save me the expense of having to hire a bulldozer to empty it. However, this was a reversal of my accustomed role and I was not sure that my experience was up to stopping flows rather than encouraging them.

I managed to avoid more than a single sip of sherry, Jellicoe emptying my glass while Barbara's back was turned. We walked out through the glass door that led from the kitchen into the garden where I carefully placed the tortoise in the middle of the lawn and watched him for a second or two until he collected himself and began to plod determinedly back towards the gate that led into the lane. The garden halted abruptly about 10 yards from the smithy and became a 4-foot-high expanse of nettles – 'The nature reserve,' said Barbara airily, as we raised our arms above our heads and cautiously waded through the alien, sour smell of the crushed plants marking our progress.

'You're going to have to make some sort of an entrance for the fishermen,' I said. 'You can't have them wading through this lot.'

'All in good time.'

We reached the fence by the edge of the field. Already it had changed its character. Gone was the St Andrews-quality fairway that had been created by the tenant sheep, their cropping keeping the grass down to a springy couple of inches. The animals had been evicted before the arrival of the bulldozer and the field was in danger of becoming an extension of the nature reserve with thistles, docks, nettles and buttercups seizing the opportunity to spring up to compete with the rank grass for air space. We walked across to the edge of the pond.

'Well, there seems to be a decent flow of water,' I said, watching the stream as it gurgled across the pond and disappeared into the wall, emerging, like magic, on the other side.

'I can see that,' said Barbara, scathingly. 'But it's supposed to fill the pond rather than go straight across. How do I stop it?'

I was a bit wary. I had a feeling that plugging leaks in ponds might be a bit like hammering a nail into a brick wall – something that led to much heartache and little success. I was not sure that I wanted to take on this particular responsibility.

'There are several things you could try,' I said non-committally.

'Yes. We've thought of trying to spread clay over the shale, or putting down a sheet of butyl rubber or even a sheet of polythene.'

'Yes. That's the sort of thing I would have recommended.'

'Which do you think would be best?'

'Well, they all have certain points in their favour. What would they all cost?'

'The clay puddling would be cheapest in itself, but it would probably mean bringing back the bulldozer to make a decent job of it.' Barbara must have had lengthy periods of sobriety recently to collate this sort of information. 'That would cost quite a lot. The rubber is meant to be jolly good, but it's expensive too and that just leaves the plastic.'

'It sounds like the plastic, then.'

'Do you really think so? I had come to that conclusion as

well. After all, it's not likely that water will be able to get through polythene.'

I was not quite so sure. Polythene was all very well, in my experience, until it got a hole in it, and it only took one wasp in a filthy temper to make a hole.

'You will come and help lay it, won't you?' asked Barbara.

The sisters did not waste much time. An immense roll of black agricultural polythene was dumped outside their front gate a couple of days later and I was ordered to assist with the laying thereof that afternoon. There were three of us, Frank Mattock who farmed up behind the smithy and whose land bordered the field, the commander and myself.

The commander was still a bit of an agricultural virgin in spite of his market garden, and it soon showed. 'Let's get that polythene off the road, first,' he said, marching up to the roll of plastic and bending down to pick up one end.

'Hang on a minute, Commander,' said Frank, but it was too late. The commander grasped the roll and tried to lift it. Half-way up, his face turned white. He then sank back to his knees, put the plastic down and rested his hands on the ground. Jellicoe and the sisters had come out to greet their workforce and the dog went up to the commander and started to lick his face. Barbara looked at him suspiciously. He appeared to be deep in prayer, facing Mecca, and was ignoring Jellicoe whose tongue must have smelled of tortoise if not of his own intimate orifices.

'Are you all right?' asked Muriel.

'I think I'm going to be sick,' came the faint reply.

'Don't be silly,' said Barbara.

'I'm fairly sure I'm going to be sick.'

Barbara bent down and tried to examine the commander's face.

'Good Lord! I do believe the fellow's pissed. How utterly lamentable!'

Frank and I looked at her in astonishment and even the commander wearily turned his head and tried to see her through the spray of Jellicoe's saliva. It was a superb example of the pot calling the kettle black, but she appeared unconscious of the irony.

'I'm not drunk,' said the commander in a strained voice. 'I've just put my back out.'

'Nonsense,' boomed Barbara. 'You're just a bloody shirker.'

A vague pink wash of incipient fury suffused the commander's cheeks, but an attempt to rise to his feet rapidly drained this flicker of life from his face and he sank back to his knees with a moan. Frank and I were sympathetic. For the male sex, no pain can equal that moment of exquisite, pure agony which you experience when you first put your back out. Break a leg, be mauled by a puma, and the shock of the injury masks the pain, but there is no natural anaesthetic when the back goes. And it is a pain that almost every working countryman has had to live through. The commander began to giggle.

'Christ! It must be bad,' said Frank.

'It's bad,' agreed the commander. The giggle is a well-known reaction to the onset of severe back trouble. It is the origin of the saying 'If I don't laugh, I'll cry' at the sheer outrage to the nervous system.

'Humph,' said Barbara, striding over to the commander,

kicking Jellicoe out of the way as she approached. 'Let me give you a hand up.'

'Get away from me,' said the sufferer, as he fought to control his laughter. It is not funny when you start to laugh when your back goes. You want to be utterly still to minimize the pain and the last thing you need is for your belly and your diaphragm to start heaving about. 'Just leave me alone, please,' he begged.

'But we can't leave you on your hands and knees in the middle of the road,' said Barbara.

'Yes, you can. The bloody tortoise can walk round me.'

We left him to his agony. It apparently took him half an hour to recover sufficiently to move, another half-hour to walk home, and then his wife made the fatal mistake of persuading him to take to his bed. With that degree of back trouble, if you take to your bed, you are liable to stay there forever. The only cure is to force yourself to your feet and keep moving.

With the commander out of action, Frank and I carefully picked up either end of the plastic roll while the ladies supported the middle and we all tottered round the side of the smithy into the field where the pond lay. It was like carrying a cannon: every undulation of the ground made us stagger off course as we fought against gravity and the random forces exerted by the ladies. We came to the pond and, while the ladies bickered as to the best place to put down the burden, Frank and I pre-empted them by dropping it with a toe-crunching thud.

The pond had potential. It was a good size – about 30 yards by 50 with a thistle-covered island carefully left by the bulldozer, slightly off-centre to allow the stream to flow past on the starboard side. With a slight effort, one could imagine the clay covered by rippling water, damsel flies flitting round the vegetation of the water margin and rings left by the rising trout. But all that required a leak-proof bed and, at that moment, the pond was a desolation of blue and yellow clay.

'I suggest,' said Barbara, confidently, 'that we place the roll of plastic on the dam wall and just unroll it upstream to the edge of the pond.'

I had forgotten my gumboots, but it was a warm and sunny day and there were worse ways of passing it than dabbling around in water with squidgy clay oozing between my toes.

Frank had not yet understood the basis on which he had been recruited. 'I'm not sure that starting down here would be the best way, Barbara. If we unroll it from the top, it would be a damn sight easier and the water would be less likely to get under the sheet.'

'Don't argue with me,' said Barbara with tight-lipped patience. 'Just do what I say, please, Frank.'

Barbara still lived in those legendary golden days of yesteryear when the lower orders knew their place while the gentry benignly cared for them, saving them from the folly of their feckless ways, and all that was asked in return was a slavish subservience. Frank was helping out for nothing. He could have bought her out without even having to tug his forelock in the direction of the bank manager and, whereas Barbara's knowledge of the behaviour of liquids was confined to the 75cl within the average bottle of spirits, Frank farmed many acres within a 65-inch rainfall belt. The effective control and disposal of water was as important a part of his job as being able to tell the difference between a sheep and a cow. For a few seconds, I thought he might tell Barbara precisely what she could do with her roll of polythene, but then he caught my eye and winked.

'If that's the way you want it, Missus. But remember, I can only help you today. I start combining tomorrow.'

'That's the way I want it,' replied Barbara.

So we began to unroll the sheet and carefully spread the polythene over the shale on the bank up to the level of a drainage pipe that had been laid to take care of the overflow. Then we ran it up the stream across the floor of the pond up to the point where it shelved back into the field; in theory, the stream was now running over a waterproof plastic bed. It took less than half an hour.

'Right,' said Barbara. 'That was very easy. Thank you so much.'

'May I make a suggestion?' said Frank.

'Certainly,' responded Barbara graciously.

'It might be a good idea to dig the edges of the sheet into the clay to provide a watertight seal.'

'You worry too much, Frank. It won't be necessary. The water is not going to get underneath the sheet.'

'Whatever you say. But remember, I'm combining for the rest of the week.'

'I'll remember,' replied Barbara patiently, and we walked back to the smithy to be given a glass of sherry – finest British ruby sweet oloroso – in payment for our services.

At 10.00 am the following morning, Barbara summoned me. She was not in a good mood. There was quite a respectable puddle on the plastic underneath the dam wall – at least as big as the shubunkin pool in front of Mandyandkeith's – but the pond ought to have been virtually full and even spilling out through the overflow by this time.

'There are obviously holes in the sheet. It's a scandal that they should supply faulty goods like this.'

'It strikes me that it's far more likely that the water is going under the sheet.'

'Nonsense.'

'Barbara, if you look, you will observe that the water is running down the polythene very nicely and spreading out until it comes to the edge. Then it spreads no further. For heaven's sake, the sheet of plastic is even floating at the edge.'

Barbara looked. 'Humph! I suppose it is possible. What's to be done?'

'Frank suggested digging the sheet into the clay.'

'Oh no. There's no need to go to all that trouble. It just needs a few stones round the edge to hold it down and stop it floating.'

'I doubt if that will do the trick.'

'Of course it will.'

Of course it did not. Barbara and Muriel spent much of the day trundling rocks across the bed of the pond and placing them so that they anchored the sheet. I was dismissed for being insufficiently positive in my thinking, but was recalled the next morning when it had become obvious that Frank's advice would have to be followed. The first task was to remove all the rocks that had been placed by the sisters the day before. I was aided by a grumbling Barbara while Muriel, who was slightly better at winning friends and influencing people, went into the village to try to rustle up some labour.

The Grabber, whom she had cornered in the post office while he was posting his pools entry, was all she could come up with. Nobody else was in a position to drop everything and come running in order to be cursed by Barbara.

The Grabber, who had earned his nickname through his behaviour at barn dances in his youth, was a hedge-layer, and he had been able to make a very good living at it. It was still an important skill in the village which was surrounded by mile after mile of great hedge banks, taking up a disproportionate amount of agricultural land. These banks had been established a thousand years ago by the pioneers who had first cleared the land round about in order to grow their crops. Stones and boulders had been laboriously prised out of the ground and piled up in neat rows where it had been decided to make the field boundaries. Over the centuries, these walls had grown over and become hedges, completely stockproof and giving shelter to the animals like no barbed-wire fence ever could. The old craftsmen had proved to be more perishable than their landscape. Men like the Grabber could approach a neglected hedge, crowned by a spindly line of 20-foot saplings through which both wind and sheep could pass without impediment, and transform it with a few strokes of the billhook into a tight, living barrier of woven branches, once again providing shelter to a score of species of animals and birds.

During the previous decade, the price applicable to the piecework of hedge laying had risen spectacularly since the skills needed for the job were disappearing much faster than the hedges themselves. An untrained layer would take twice as long as the Grabber, and those of his ilk, to do the job and the rate had to be high enough to persuade the non-specialist to take on the work. So both the Grabber and the local pub had grown prosperous.

Then the Grabber had been asked to do a job on the family farm. The farm, operated by a cousin, had been owned by the family since the days of the Tudors. Our part of the country had never attracted the great barons who bought up or expropriated vast tracts of land which they parcelled out to their feudal retainers. We were too far from the centre of power in London and the land was not good enough. So we had a tradition of independent yeoman farmers, each with 100–200 acres, who did not need to bow down to anyone.

Such farmers tended to take a long view of their business and the Grabber's family was no exception. On the farm, there was one 10-acre patch that had been allowed to revert to scrubland. This patch seemed to have gone in and out of production as circumstances demanded since it had first been cleared by the Grabber's Saxon forebears. Its recent history had been recorded. It had grown wheat during the Napoleonic Wars and was then left alone until the 1860s when it had grown potatoes. It became scrub again until the First World War, when it was growing oats, and was left to its own devices during the Depression of the nineteen-thirties until the Second World War, when it had grown barley. When the civil servants of the War Agricultural Commission had returned to their offices, it had been allowed to revert once again.

The Grabber's cousin decided to bring this piece of land back into production as he wished to expand his beef herd, and the Grabber was called in to tame the hedges and re-hang the gates while the trees, which had crept over the couple of fields that were there, were being cleared.

Then problems had arisen. A retired architect, who wrote a column called 'Mother Nature's News' for a group of local newspapers in the Midlands, had heard about the plans and had lobbied against them so successfully that the 10 acres had been designated a Site of Special Scientific Interest with the result that nobody was to be allowed to farm them ever again. In vain was it pleaded that there was nothing natural about the few acres. They had been thoroughly farmed, albeit on and off, for a millennium and the ancient hedgerows were there to prove it. Even if the land was cleared, there was little doubt that it would revert back to bog and scrubby woodland after a decade or two. All that made it botanically interesting was the frequent change in the type of habitat that it provided and that specialness would be destroyed if it was decided to fossilize the site in such an arbitrary way.

The decree was passed, however. The bemused farmer was offered a management agreement which undertook to pay him a certain sum of money in perpetuity provided that he left that corner of the farm alone. The Grabber was disgusted and hung up his billhook for good. As he had said, what was the point of trying to do a decent job any more, if any ignorant booby could come along and tell you to ruin the land and even pay you good money to do it? The Grabber had retired to his cabbages, his courgettes, his cider and his post as assistant verger at the church, but he still liked to keep his hand in, and was always willing to join in anything that was going on, so he was delighted to answer Muriel's call for aid.

The sisters had only one spade which I used, but the Grabber had brought his fork and we worked our way round the edge of the sheet. It was rather satisfying, a bit like digging peat, as the spade slipped easily into the clay to remove a neat, brick-shaped clod. We carefully dug a shallow trench all the way round the sheet into which we placed the edges of the polythene before replacing the clods and carefully treading them in. It was a three-hour job but, by the end of it, the bed of the pond was well and truly watertight. There was nothing now to prevent the sisters ordering a tankload of silvery trout which could be tumbled into the pool from the back of a Land Rover and their bonanza could begin.

The Grabber and I went to sit on the island to watch the stream, frustrated in its attempts to escape, sullenly start to spread itself over the edge of the sheet and across the base of the pond. Barbara and Muriel came to join us, bearing a couple of deckchairs and cider as a more appropriate drink for labourers who had completed their allotted task than the customary gin or sherry.

'I'd really like to thank you both for all your work,' said Muriel.

'To tell the truth I was quite glad to get away from the garden,' replied the Grabber. 'It makes a bit of a change. Now that I'm an old man, I don't get out that much.'

'You're an old fraud, Grabber,' I said. 'You're in the pub

323

twice a day and you follow every pack of hounds within a 20-mile radius.'

The Grabber shook his head with a sigh. 'No, I don't follow the hunt these days. I suppose it's because I'm getting on and I'm happy now to let all God's creatures live in peace. I don't hold with hunting like I used to.'

'For heaven's sake,' I exclaimed, 'you sound just like Walter Gabriel!'

'Leave the old boy alone,' said Barbara, ignoring the fact that he was ten years younger than her. 'I know exactly how he feels. When you get to our age, life becomes precious and you learn to live from day to day. I used to hunt when I was a big younger, but I wouldn't dream of it now. I like to see living things around me.'

This lump-in-the-throat stuff, coming from two of the most outrageously hard-boiled characters in the community, was too much to endure. I was not going to let them get away with it, particularly Barbara. 'If life is so sacred now that you are in your dotage, Barbara, why are you encouraging tourists to lure your fish to their doom?'

Barbara sighed and was echoed by the Grabber with whom she exchanged a glance that pitied my lack of understanding. 'Don't think that it is by choice. We are often forced into situations that we regret by economic circumstances. I wish there had been another way, but Muriel and I have to live.'

Muriel poured us another drink out of a gallon plastic container. It was rough farmhouse scrumpy – so rough that the label was not even printed, but hand-written. She had brought out a picnic lunch of bread and cheese and Scotch eggs which she passed round. I lay on my back, listening to the sound of the stream and watching the tiny dots of the larks against the blue of the sky. 'Oh look! There's a rat,' said Muriel.

'What?' I asked, not really listening, since I was trying to calculate the mean speed of skylark droppings when they hit the ground if released from a height of 200 feet.

'Look. Over there. There's a rat.'

I propped myself up on my elbow. So there was. It was a young rat, half-grown – because no adult rodent would be stupid enough to walk about in the middle of the day in full view of a group of people. It was sniffing around on the highly unpromising territory of the bed of the pond. It was rather sweet, really.

Barbara put down the newspaper she had been reading and looked over the top of her spectacles. She looked and she saw. She sank her foot into the dozing Grabber's ribs. He sat up, rubbed the sleep from his eyes and looked round and saw.

'Bloody hell!' said the Grabber. He struggled to his feet, snatched up his fork and plunged down the bank of the island in pursuit. The rat stopped sniffing and watched him come, waving his fork and uttering inarticulate cries. It was a very laid-back rodent. It allowed him to get within 10 yards before it decided that the Grabber might not be a dedicated member of the League Against Cruel Sports and so it turned and ambled off across the pond. The Grabber steamed after it while Barbara, now on her feet, jumped up and down with excitement.

'Kill it! Go on, kill it!' she shrieked.

The Grabber was doing his best. He had virtually caught up with the rat which was still showing a remarkably casual attitude to the business of its own survival. Perhaps it realized that the Grabber was still dazed by sleep and cider and not much of a threat. He was plunging his fork again and again into the ground, trying to spear the animal, but his aim was lousy.

The rat reached the stream and paused with its pursuer only a yard or two behind. Muriel closed her eyes so that she would not have to witness the bloody deed. I watched in resigned fascination while Barbara continued to scream encouragement. There was no need to worry. The animal placed its paw delicately in the water, decided that it was too cold and turned, scuttling between the Grabber's legs, and wandered off up the side of the stream to disappear in the long grass at the pond's edge. The Grabber puffed his way back to the island.

'Bad luck,' said Barbara. 'That was jolly exciting. You very nearly got it.'

The Grabber collapsed on the grass. 'Blooming heck. I haven't run like that for years. D'you see the little bugger jink? He was a right fly one, that. I reckon someone must have chased him before.'

Muriel still had her eyes closed and was now muttering a prayer for strength and patience beneath her breath. So I took it upon myself to break the bad news.

'There's just one problem, Grabber.'

'Oh yes?'

'The watertight plastic sheet. I would guess, conservatively, that it now has about a hundred fork holes in it.'

The Grabber and Barbara stared out over the bed of the pond. There was a rumbling sound from Barbara and the volcano burst. Muriel and I clapped our hands over our ears while people throughout the village anxiously inspected the sky for thunderclouds.

'You unbelievably stupid old fart!' she bellowed. 'You've ruined it!'

'You were encouraging me.'

Muriel and I left them to it and walked back to the smithy. I made sure that I was not around when the sheet was removed and the shale was covered in a layer of clay.

Chapter Ten

IT WAS KELVIN who coined the expression 'swallows'. Swallows were the people who came to live in the village and the surrounding area who had not actually been born there. The typical swallow was a thrusting young executive and his wife who would buy a cottage, do it up, live in it for a few years and then find that the education of their children, or the demands of his career, or even the mind-boggling boredom of having to mix with country bumpkins at the weekends, meant that they had to sell up and move on to somewhere else. Swallows flitted prettily about the community for a season or two without putting down roots and migrated on to sunnier climes.

The Jarretts were the epitome of the swallow. They had bought an extremely rough cottage in River Lane, a couple of doors down from Mandyandkeith, for a price that had still been the talk of the country estate agents' annual dinner-dance a couple of years later. They had then gutted it, removing what few period charms it may have possessed, and converted its interior into a fine example of High Islington Camp.

They had little to do with the village at first. In their thirties, they were both small and pretty and they commuted to teaching jobs in the market town on the back of a huge Japanese motorcycle, wearing matching scarlet overalls and crash helmets.

Then, during their first summer, on one of those still, warm evenings when the swifts screamed through the streets and even the yawn of a stretching dog seemed to echo off the front of the cottages, the sound of loud rock music was heard emerging through their Georgian-style windows. Jimmy had craned his neck to look in as he made his delicately septuagenarian way up to the pub. He had not been quite able to make out what the Jarretts were up to, but they weren't sitting in front of an organ like Mandy had been.

'All I could see was two arses poking in the air.'

'Were they on top of each other, Jimmy?' Kelvin had asked.

'No, I can't say that they were. More side by side.'

'That's a bit strange. Side by side and not on top of each other. Especially on a Sunday evening,' chuckled Billy. He worked as a mechanic in the local garage and fancied himself as the local Lothario.

'Not everyone's like you, Billy,' said Kelvin.

'I bet they wish they were,' replied Billy, with the self-satisfied macho smirk of the inadequate cocksman trying to reassure himself that he was otherwise. Jimmy shot him a look of distaste before continuing. The art of successful gossip lies in delicately leaving room for the vulgar or bitchy interpretation to be made, should the listener so desire. This fragile and subtle creation is cheapened if the receiver of gossip lacks sensitivity and crudely spells it out.

'They were dressed and pointing up at the ceiling and sort of wobbling in time to the music.'

'The Jarretts?' asked the publican.

'No, their backsides.'

'It sounds pretty innocuous to me. I should think that most people in this pub do some pretty strange things with their spouses when they think they are in private.'

'I know they do,' said Lindy. This caused a thoughtful silence. Lindy, as district nurse, was an unexploded minefield of gossip. Through her job, she had learned just about everything about everyone for miles around and had a habit of staring at you with an enigmatic smile playing at the corner of her lips. It could be highly disconcerting and was the only known device for halting Kelvin in full conversational flow.

Consequently there was silence until the commander came through the door. 'There are strange things going on at the bottom of the village,' he said, as he eased himself on to a stool. 'Some American lady in the Jarretts' house yelled at me to throw my shoulders back and lift my chin as I went past. She sounded just like the drill instructor at Dartmouth. It gave me a very nasty turn.'

It was duly noted that their house in River Lane was worth keeping an eye on, but no pub-frequenting villager could dream up a good enough excuse to get inside to find out what was happening. This was rectified a few weeks later when a notice appeared on the board in the post office announcing that the local branch of the SDP was being set up, with its inaugural meeting to be held at the Jarretts' when an election of officers would take place. Dick Hunniford and Ivor both went along as the respective chairmen of the Liberals and

Tories, as did Lindy who rather fancied Dr Owen. She had had a *penchant* for comely medics ever since her days as a student nurse.

Dick was the one who managed to sort out the problem of the loud American. He had been quietly driven into a corner by the fixed smile and determined brightness of Emily Jarrett who had wanted to know in what way Dick thought that Liberal policies differed from those of the SDP. Dick could not have told her the difference between Liberal policies and those of the Tories, so the conversation had been frustrating for both parties. However, he did manage to catch a glimpse of the Jarrett music centre while his eyes were casting around for a way out and, there on top of it, was the sleeve of a record.

'It had a picture of a lady grinning like a monkey on the front. She had a funny pointed backside and was wearing only a striped vest and long black stockings. It was called "Jane Fondle's Work Record" and she was upside down with her legs in the air. I reckon they were doing exercises like that when Jimmy looked through their window.'

With that problem safely pigeon-holed, the Jarretts seemed to take a higher profile. They donned his'n'hers tracksuits and ran about the streets of the village at odd hours of the day and night, frequently giving the older inhabitants nasty shocks when they erupted round the corner of a house, their trainer-clad feet pounding the tarmac with an assortment of village curs snapping at their heels. They would flash past, leaving nothing but the impression of their bright smiles shimmering in the air behind them and, perhaps, a few drops of sweat flicked into the faces of their beholders.

Nobody quite knew what to make of this until Frank Mattock came across them trotting up the road one day and managed to flag them down. They did not actually have much option since the lane was choked by his herd of dairy cows, undulating at a snail's pace towards the milking parlour, and there was no way of getting through them.

Frank's herd had achieved a certain notoriety when, the previous summer, it had encountered coming in the opposite direction many thousands of pounds' worth of customized white Porsche containing our local tycoon, Ross. Ross had sensibly stopped in the narrow lane to allow the cows to pass but had, less sensibly, brayed his horn when the tight fit led to some of them having to brush against his paintwork. The cows had panicked, with appalling consequences.

Cows, contrary to popular belief, are extremely emotional animals and they display their emotions by becoming loose in the bowel. The toot of Ross's horn literally scared them shitless. It was Ross's misfortune that the customizing of his motorcar had included turning it into a convertible and, by the time that the herd had passed and the car again came into view, neither Ross, nor his wife, nor the car were white any longer and all three were steaming gently in the still air.

The Jarretts were forced to slow to a walk beside Frank.

'Evening,' he said.

'Evening,' replied the Jarretts.

Frank looked at them curiously. They did not seem to be out of breath. 'Nice evening,' he added.

'Isn't it?' answered the Jarretts, smiling happily. The village knew what they did in their spare time but nobody knew why they did it. Nobody could think of any good reason why they should spend so much time running about and jumping up and down. Bill thought that the most likely explanation was that it had something to do with their religion. The communards, who seemed to change their religion rather more often than they probably changed their underwear, had made us aware of such matters. However, Frank thought he would try to get to the bottom of their motivation.

'Nice evening for a walk,' he said.

'We were jogging, actually,' replied Emily.

'Jogging? Is that what it's called?' Frank savoured the word. 'Jogging. And why would you be jogging?'

'For exercise.'

'For exercise?' Frank was a windsucker, blessed with a local characteristic. Its exponents tended to repeat what was being said to them and then drew air sharply in through their pursed lips with an audible sucking sound. In spite of his *penchant* for gold rings, bracelets and displaying his hairy chest, Frank was still very much a ponderous, careful-thinking countryman. 'And why would you be wanting to take exercise?' No countryman takes exercise for its own sake or even considers it: it comes as a by-product of the way of life.

'I exercise so that I am comfortable in my body,' replied Emily.

Frank continued to plod along after the swaying rumps of his cows, his stick driving holes in the verge where the grass took over from the tarmac.

'I don't quite understand that,' he said, after a bit of thought.

'What?'

'How exercise can make you more comfortable in your body. I mean, I can see your body and, if Mr Jarrett doesn't mind me saying so, it looks very nice —'

'No, I don't mind at all,' said Malcolm Jarrett.

'— But whether you're comfortable or not depends on whether you're sitting on a hard tractor seat or a tin-tack. So comfort is something that happens outside it, not in it.'

'That's not what I meant,' said Emily. 'You see, my body has to be listened to and strengthened.'

Frank looked sideways at Emily rather ruminatively. In the village, we were beginning to get used to this sort of conversation. The communards always managed to turn a remark as mundane as a comment on the weather into a major obscurantist philosophical discussion.

'The only time I am able to listen to my body is when my belly rumbles,' said Frank, 'or when I fart.'

'You obviously don't understand.'

'S'right,' agreed Frank.

'These days, we need to be on top of our bodies so that we can lead the intense multi-faceted lives that we demand with greater clarity and balance.'

Frank picked a grass stalk out of the hedgerow and chewed at it. He had nothing to do other than to walk along behind his cows, so he thought he might as well continue the conversation. 'It's a sort of religion, is it? All this rushing about and listening to your body.'

'No, certainly not. We have a right and a duty to be physically fit.'

'I always reckoned that staying healthy was a matter of luck.'

'Not at all. Anyone can control their own health and the length of their life. It's a matter of diet and maintaining a positive attitude,' replied Malcolm Jarrett.

'Is that right?' asked Frank.

They continued to follow the cows. Frank swished idly at the cow parsley in the hedgerow while the Jarretts skipped up and down so that they wouldn't stiffen up. It was like taking a couple of dogs for a walk, Frank reported later. They were dancing all round him, covering a dozen yards to every one of his. Still, Emily was wearing a white tracksuit and her bum was undeniably nicer to look at than those of the cows.

The Jarretts' profile continued to be high. They organized evenings of classical record music at home, although Winnie was the only regular attender. Jimmy and the Grabber turned up once just to see if there were any free drinks going, but there weren't. They achieved a certain notoriety by writing letters to the local paper condemning hunting after their motorbike, returning home from work, had been forced to stop at a road junction to allow sixty horsemen, thirty-eight motorcycle followers, 132 cars, and a woman on foot carrying a baby, to cross in front of them, all baying for blood in pursuit of an extremely knackered stag.

Most swallows went through a period when they were vociferously opposed to hunting, although not many went as far as writing rude letters to the papers about it. Hunting was such an imporant part of life in the area that it was difficult to avoid it. However, it was an unfortunate fact, that most came to realize, that the large numbers of deer in the vicinity would have been wiped out by the farmers for their depredations on crops had it not been for the love of hunting that the farmers had, bred deep in their bones over the centuries of indulgence in the sport.

It was difficult to deny that there was something distinctly odd about people who spent so much money and received so much pleasure from chasing and killing such splendid animals, but the deer probably had a better deal than the cattle who ended up in the inevitable ignominy of the slaughterhouse. The deer, at least, had a chance of living in freedom to a ripe old age and, if they met their end through a huntsman's bullet after the hounds had brought them to bay, that death was a celebration rather than mere routine.

The Jarretts' newspaper correspondence was regarded indulgently by the locals. Anti-hunting was a stage that many newcomers had to go through and it was hoped that, when they had grown out of it, they would take their natural place at the bottom of the social pyramid from where they could slowly ascend as the passing of the years turned them into figures of some significance in the community – provided they stayed long enough. It would never be possible for them to reach the eminence of people like Kelvin and Jimmy who had actually been born in the village, but others like Ivor and Lindy had risen remarkably quickly. Lindy was regarded as an equal by most of the locals and she had lived in the area for only fifteen years, while the dazzling example of the commander, who had managed to get on the committee of the horticultural society within five years of moving to the village, was an inspiration to all swallows and a solid refutation of the charge that the locals were inclined to be hostile to newcomers.

However, it took time for incomers to learn their place in society and, during that first year or two, their social judgement tended to be poor. The Jarretts soon went above their station in life again. In the late autumn, another notice appeared on the board in the post office. 'Challenge', it was headed, followed by 'The Social Democratic Party challenges the Liberal and Conservative Parties to a Grand Quiz'.

Ivor and Dick and their committees went into a huddle to agree a mutual strategy. They concluded that, although it would probably be wiser to ignore these social and political upstarts, it was just within the dignity of their respective parties to approach the issuers of the challenge and find out what they had in mind. It was devastatingly simple. There would be a panel of three people to represent each party. A quizmaster was to be found who would be mutually acceptable and members of the public would be charged an admission fee of 50p. The winning team would take the kitty to add to party funds.

It was felt that the challenge could not be ignored, although there were obvious difficulties. The Jarretts were both teachers and therefore must be awesomely bright. They listened to classical music and took both the *Observer* and the *Sunday Times* at the weekend. Who would be the questionmaster? This was a really knotty one which nearly caused the whole idea to founder. In the end, it was decided that the quiz would be divided into three parts, each section presided over by a different questioner to be nominated by each party. It was further agreed that there should be no prior collusion between the team and its questionmaster and that there should be a ten-minute break between each section to allow drinks to be replenished. The venue was to be the church hall and the date the week before Christmas. A book was opened in the pub: the SDP evens, Tories 2 to 1 against and Liberals 3 to 1. The excitement was intense.

Chapter Eleven

THE CHURCH HALL was normally used only once a month for meetings of the parochial church council. It had once been used for parish council meetings, but its members had passed a unanimous vote just before the war which changed their venue to a room in the pub. This was a great aid to the free exchange of ideas and had considerably increased the quantity, if not the quality, of the oratory. The hall itself was a dank, miserable room used primarily for the storage of trestle tables and chairs that had last seen the light of day at the jubilee of King George V. It also had a pile of old saucepans in one corner which a previous vicar had collected with the intention of transforming them into a Spitfire, but the war had ended before a sufficient quantity had accumulated to make it worthwhile for them to be pressed into service.

There were two items on the walls that could be considered decorative. On one side of the room hung a splendid Georgian wall clock and, opposite, was a large print entitled *The Light of the World*, with the figure of Christ holding up his lamp, looking as if he were trying to peer through the fly spots that dotted the picture-glass to read the time on the clock.

There was always a thick layer of dust over everything. The caretaker, whose responsibility it was to keep the place clean, was also clock winder and organist at the church, but he had been corrupted by his part-time assistant, the Grabber.

The latter kept an eye out for coach parties arriving in the village. When they appeared he would rush up to the caretaker's cottage from where they would both repair to the church. As the tourists entered the church, the high spot of any tour of the village, they would be greeted by the caretaker playing tunes on the organ like *Bless this House* and *Danny Boy* with every ounce of pathos that he could deliver and, just as they were about to reach for their hankies, the Grabber would emerge from the vestry, bearing a collection plate and intoning, 'Give alms to the poor of the parish.' The two of them made a fortune during the tourist season and it all passed across the bar in the pub.

By the time the contestants gathered in the pub on the evening of the contest, it had become a real needle match as the Tories had let slip that they had obtained a letter from the Sniffer MP thanking the other two parties for contributing to Conservative funds. This was to be read out in the event of their victory. Their team consisted of Dennis, the commander and Kelvin, which immediately caused their odds to lengthen to 6 to 1 against during a flurry of late-struck bargains. The SDP had the Jarretts and Winnie, their only other paid-up member, while the Liberals had Dick Hunniford, Mary Mowbray and Lindy.

Business in the pub boomed. In fact, the evening became a testimony to the amount that the local citizenry could drink, once they put their minds to it. Most of the contestants were already there loosening up their brain cells, while the spectators were stoking up for a long evening ahead. The Jarretts had obviously given up training for the day and were downing large quantities of whisky, which was an encouraging sign that they might be preparing to participate properly in this, the most important cultural activity of the community. They and the rest of the protagonists were standing to one side of the bar trying to look blasé and important while the future audience examined them to try to pick up hints as to their future form.

Mary Mowbray came in through the pub door and fought her way to the bar. Her ruddy complexion was highlighted by a large piece of white sticking plaster across her forehead.

'What happened to you, Mary?' asked the commander.

'I walked into a door,' she replied grimly.

'What a shame! Can I buy you a drink?'

'Just an orange juice, please. The doctor told me to lay off for a few days.'

'That's dreadful. If I were you, I'd change my doctor.'

The commander handed her an orange juice and she looked round the raucously crowded pub. 'Where's Dennis? I've got a bone to pick with him.'

'He should be along any minute,' answered Ivor. 'What's he done?'

'Never you mind. Ah! Here he comes now.'

Dennis elbowed his way up to the bar. 'What ho, chaps!' he said. 'Ready for the fray?' Dennis sometimes used expressions that were rather old-fashioned. He had once called a tourist whom he had nearly run down 'old bean', which had been construed as a deadly insult and had brought out a volley of abuse. He saw Mary and her plaster. 'Mary! What on earth has happened to you? Grenville did not mention anything about it last night. They must be dangerous, those WI meetings.'

'I thought it must have been you,' said Mary. 'Who else came out last night?'

'Frank Mattock was along. Why? What's this about?'

'You should be ashamed of yourself! It's all your fault that I've hurt my head.'

Dennis looked a bit bewildered. 'I don't quite understand.

All we did was have a few drinks and help Grenville pluck your chickens because you were at your meeting.'

'A few drinks! Grenville was in a drunken stupor – it was quite disgraceful. And as for that trick you played, it was quite disgusting! And damned irresponsible.'

'Oh, you saw that did you?'

'I did.'

'What's all this about?' asked the commander.

Dennis looked a bit embarrassed. 'Well, you know, we had a few drinks and plucked and gutted a few chickens and had a few more drinks and Grenville fell asleep in front of the Aga. It was all very harmless.'

'That doesn't sound that awful,' said the commander.

'And what about that chicken neck?' demanded Mary. 'I suppose that was your idea?'

'Oh no. That was Frank's.'

'What about a chicken neck?' prompted the commander.

'Well, Frank had this idea for a joke, you see. Grenville was asleep and just before we went he put this chicken neck so that it was poking out of Grenville's trousers. It looked jolly realistic. We thought it might give him a bit of a fright when he woke up.' There was a guffaw of laughter from round the bar.

'That's not so bad, Mary,' said the commander. 'Where's your sense of humour?'

'I left it in the doctor's surgery,' replied Mary. 'When I got home, I went into the kitchen and there was Grenville, still sound asleep, and there was the neck. I could have handled that all right, but when I went in the dog was sitting in front of my dear husband chewing it and when I screamed, it pulled it out. I fainted and cracked my head on the Aga. And don't anyone dare laugh.'

'Heavens!' said Dennis, spluttering a bit. 'How absolutely appalling for you. I'm most dreadfully sorry. We should have thought of that and shut the dog out of the kitchen. It is a cocker spaniel after all. And what's its name again?'

'Willy,' said the commander.

One we had wiped the orange juice off the commander and Dennis, the pub emptied as we repaired across the road to the church hall. It had been transformed for the occasion. Two paraffin heaters had been working for most of the day and the chill had been driven back to the corners of the room. It had been dusted down and Winnie had arranged vases of flowers on the four tables – one for each team and one for the questionmasters – which had been erected in front of sixty or so chairs. There was an expectant hum of conversation as people settled themselves in partisan groups.

The vicar was quizmaster for the SDP, the squire for the Tories and the Liberals had chosen Muriel, which had annoyed her sister Barbara, both because she had not been selected and because Muriel had no business in supporting the Liberals. The questioners went into a huddle to establish the order of play and the vicar was selected to open the bowling.

It immediately became clear why the SDP had chosen him. His opening question brought dismayed looks from the Liberals and Tories and a buzz of consternation ran round all those who had put money on the two outsiders.

'Who was the son of Jephunneh?'

Who indeed? Who or perhaps even *what* is or was Jephunneh? The question was rapidly passed down the line of Tories and Liberals to the SDP and Emily Jarrett looked expectantly at Winnie. With the cat-at-the-cream look adopted by every smart Alec on every TV quiz show, she trotted out, 'Joshua the son of Nun, and Caleb the son of Jephunneh, were the only two, who ever got through, to the land of milk and honey.'

'Ting' went Ivor on his little bell and the SDP received bonus marks, putting them five points in the lead. The Tories and Liberals swallowed nervous gulps of their drinks to bolster their confidence, while the SDP celebrated with whisky and a discreet sip of sherry for Winnie. The publican had taken the precaution of establishing a team of runners at the door and there was no danger that the contestants might be stricken by drought.

Winnie's father had been a Methodist lay preacher and the first dozen questions were aimed mercilessly at her sphere of knowledge: who was Zelophehad?; name eight of the tribes of Israel; how old was Methuselah when he finally shuffled off his mortal coil? The Liberals were nowhere and the Tories were only saved from a whitewash when Dennis managed to dredge the names of the three who were stuffed into the fiery furnace from the depths of his subconscious mind and elicited the first round of applause of the evening from all those who had backed his team at 6 to 1.

The vicar's second round was literature. The Jarretts answered all their questions and scavenged hungrily for bonus points among the wreckage of the answers hesitantly submitted by the other teams. Dennis again saved the Tories by displaying an unexpected knowledge of the works of Charles Dickens and Lindy managed to break the Liberal duck by knowing that the Jabberwock was slain by a vorpal sword. The vicar's third and final round of questions was more even. He had chosen to concentrate on science and technology and none of the contestants was able to differentiate between a byte and a ram, Cobol or Basic, or was capable of hazarding an intelligent guess as to what the letters of the word laser might stand for. Lindy scored the only points when he strayed into biology, while both Jarretts were overruled by Ivor when they tried to dispute the length of time required to burn up the calories in an ounce of butter if one was playing squash.

The vicar's incumbency of the chair ended with the SDP scoring sixty-five points, the Tories fifteen and the Liberals ten. The ten-minute break was a desperate business. Bill closed the book on the SDP and he could find nobody prepared to back either of the other teams. Even Dick Hunniford refused to back himself at 33 to 1. The pub was packed as the interval stretched to twenty minutes and the unfortunate Mary Mowbray was the only member of either team who was still entirely sober by the time that the bell tinged to announce the squire's term of office. His first question was to the SDP.

'Who saw him die?'

'I beg your pardon?' asked Malcolm Jarrett, the team captain.

'Who saw him die?' repeated the squire.

The team went into a huddle. 'We don't quite understand the question,' said the captain.

341

The squire reddened a bit. 'It's a perfectly simple question. Who saw him die?'

'Who saw who die?'

'Don't be so damn silly. If I told you who saw who die, then I'd be giving you the answer. That's your job. Mine's to do the asking.'

'But there isn't enough information in the question to give a sensible answer. There could be hundreds of answers. Hardy saw Nelson die, for example.'

'Wrong. I offer it for a bonus.'

'Mr Umpire, I would like to enter a protest.'

The audience was enjoying this. It was not much fun watching other people showing off, but it was lovely when they could not get the answers and began to lose their cool.

'Overruled,' said Ivor. 'The answer's obviously "the fly". It's from *Cock Robin*, isn't it, squire? "I, said the fly, with my little eye." '

'Quite right, Ivor. Next question —'

'The fly,' said Kelvin.

The squire paused. 'What are you talking about?'

'You offered it for a bonus and the answer's "the fly".'

'But the correct answer's already been given.'

'Ah yes, but Ivor's not playing. He's just the umpire. I'm the first contestant to give it.'

'Don't be absurd,' said the squire.

'Actually, I think Kelvin's right,' said Ivor. 'You did offer it for a bonus and it was wrong of me to answer. Did you know what the right answer was before I gave it, Kelvin?'

'Yes,' replied Kelvin stoutly.

'In that case, I award you a bonus point.'

'I protest,' said Malcolm Jarrett.

'So do I,' said Dick. 'Anyone could have said "the fly".'

'But Kelvin was the only person who did. Anyway, that's the first question he has answered and how many others do you think he's going to get right?'

The other contestants could hardly argue with that and as the audience thought that Kelvin deserved his point as well, the squire moved on. 'Mrs Jarrett, what have cow, horse and goat got in common?'

There was another SDP huddle. 'They are all grass-eating quadrupeds which could well be ruminants and they can be seen in the British countryside. They're all domesticated mammals . . . Is that enough?'

'No. I offer it —'

'Hang on,' said Emily, 'we haven't finished yet . . . er . . . they can all be found within the parish. They can all be eaten . . . er . . .'

'Ting' went Ivor. 'Your time is up. I offer it for a bonus.'

'The second letter of each word is "o",' said Mary.

'Right,' said the squire.

'That's ridiculous,' said Malcolm indignantly.

'If you abuse the questionmaster, you'll have points deducted,' warned Ivor.

Malcolm, the unaccustomed whisky coursing through his veins, opened his mouth to say more in spite of some hissing from all those spectators who were backing the other teams, but Emily obviously and painfully kicked him on the ankle and he shut up.

'Next question,' said the squire. 'When did mains electricity come to the village?'

'1959,' said Dick promptly.

Malcolm avoided his wife's foot and spoke up again. 'How could we be expected to know that?'

'How could we be expected to know all that stuff about books that the vicar asked?' said Dick.

'That's common knowledge to everyone who's well-read.'

'The electricity is common knowledge to everyone who lives round here.'

'Nonsense,' said Malcolm belligerently.

The squire was getting cross. 'If there's one thing I hate, it's someone who belly-aches. Kindly control yourself.'

'Piss off,' said Malcolm.

Ivor tinged his bell. 'Any further unwarranted interruptions or abuse will result in the deduction of points,' he warned.

Malcolm glared, but held his peace.

The squire cleared his throat. 'What are the colours of the old Etonian tie?'

'Light and dark blue,' answered Dennis.

'And the colours of a Guards tie, Mr Jarrett?'

'Blue, with a British Rail symbol on it.'

'I meant the Brigade of Guards – the army brigade.'

Malcolm muttered, 'Ridiculous old fascist,' under his breath but refused to try a guess.

'Dark red and dark blue,' said Dennis.

'Well done, Dennis. You're doing jolly well,' said the squire approvingly. 'Dick, how many rows of pews are there in the church?'

Dick looked blank.

'Eighteen,' yelled the Grabber from the audience.

'Eighteen,' said Dick.

'Quite correct.'

Ivor frowned at the spectators. 'I must ask the audience to keep quiet.'

'Mary,' said the squire, 'who commanded the first British unit into Brussels during the last war?'

'How on earth am I supposed to know that?' she asked.

Malcolm smirked rather drunkenly.

'It's an important part of military history,' said the squire.

'Well, I've no idea. Montgomery?'

'No, I offer it for a bonus.' There was silence. 'I did.'

'You did what?' asked Mary.

'I commanded the first British unit into Brussels.'

Mandyandkeith in the audience began to clap, but nobody else joined in. The squire looked a bit disappointed.

The squire's round brought the Tories up to within twenty points of the SDP, but the odds that Bill was offering on the Liberals in the pub during the interval were now 50 to 1. Muriel managed to change all that, however. Instead of the bits of paper that the others had fumbled through in order to ask their questions, she was equipped with a tray covered in a lacy tablecloth. When Ivor tinged to announce the opening the session, she whisked off the cloth.

'I couldn't think of any questions and so we shall have a memory test. On this tray are forty-five everyday objects. Each team can examine it for one minute and then they have five minutes to list as many of those objects as they can remember.'

The Liberals won, of course, taking home £22.50, less the cost of the tea and biscuits that were on offer at the end of the evening. Mary Mowbray was the only person on either team who was sufficiently sober by Muriel's round to remember more than half a dozen of the objects. She managed thirty, while Dennis and Malcolm Jarrett were so appalled by the task confronting them that they both fell asleep before the end of their five minutes. The real winners were the publican, who had one of the best evenings of the year, and Muriel. She had placed a £3 bet at 50 to 1 and soaked up all the profits that Bill had been counting on. She donated £5 of it to party funds.

Chapter Twelve

THE COMMANDER had had a bad week. His pig had escaped only a few days before it was due to be hacked into small pieces and hung up in the chimney to smoke. The beast had found his cauliflowers and had rampaged up and down their neatly regimented rows before breaking into a shed and eating a packet of weed killer. He was now gloomily waiting for it to die. That was not all. He had sold some eggs to the hotel, one of which had contained an almost fully developed chick that had sent the chef, an ex-debutante graduate of a Cordon Bleu cookery course, into hysterics and quite ruined a batch of meringues.

The commander had been coming into the pub in an ill temper all week and his mood had grown increasingly foul as he poured the barley wines down his throat.

'It's a backwater, this place. Nothing but a backwater. Nothing has changed and nothing has happened for centuries. I sometimes wonder what the hell I'm doing here.'

'Making a living?' proffered Dennis cautiously.

'Making a living! That's a joke for a start. I could have gone into industry or into the City when I left the navy. Man management: that's what I'm qualified for. I could take men half-way round the world and they were willing to fight and die when they got there.'

'Pigs are different, though,' said Kelvin. 'Pigs aren't as easy to handle as people. They don't know what's good for them.'

The commander brooded for a bit. 'My brain is turning to porridge. You can't help turning into a country bumpkin out here. There's no stimulation. What is there to talk about? Tell me that?'

'Money, sex, politics, religion, sport, human nature, current affairs, literature, art,' said Lindy. 'It's very restrictive.'

'I know. It's dreadful. This area is a cultural desert. There isn't a theatre for miles.'

Malcolm Jarrett, our local intellectual, had been holding his peace until now, but felt he could contribute here. 'There's nothing to stop you going up to Stratford.'

'Ah,' said the commander. 'If only I could afford it. But it's so far away and it would just cost too much to get there.'

'I suppose you couldn't spare the time, either.'

'It's not so much that. After all, the cabbages will keep on growing whether I'm there to watch them or not. It's just that I can't justify the cost.'

'Aye. That's the trouble, it's the expense,' agreed Kelvin.

That was the attitude which made the usual scruffy assortment of characters round the bar, nursing their glasses of beer, worth about ten times their urban counterparts. They were willing to spend any amount of money on their businesses, but virtually nothing on their leisure, pleasure or what might make their lives or those of their families more comfortable.

'Yes,' said Dennis, getting into the spirit of things. 'If only I could afford to go, I would love it.'

'That's easy enough to arrange,' said Malcolm. 'We've got an "A" level class going up from the college next week and there'll be plenty of spare seats on the bus. You could all come if you wanted.'

There was a short silence. Malcolm looked enquiringly at the commander. 'Oh,' he said, 'I'm rather busy next week. What day is it going up?'

'What days can't you manage?' asked Malcolm cruelly.

'Let's think,' said the commander, a bit embarrassed about finding himself on the spot. 'Well, Thursday's market day. Couldn't do that.'

'No, couldn't do Thursday,' echoed Kelvin.

'If that bloody pig survives, I'm hoping to take it to the abattoir on Tuesday, and on Friday I've got the VAT man coming round. What day is the bus going up?'

'I think it's Wednesday.'

'What a shame! That's when I have to get stuff ready to take to market.'

'Isn't it a pity,' said Dennis. 'I would have loved to go up as well. If only it had been Monday.'

'Yes,' chorused half those in the pub. 'If only it had been Monday.'

'I'd've liked a nice bit of Shakespeare,' said Kelvin, who sounded as if he equated it with a nice bit of pork. 'Monday would be my only free day.'

Malcolm Jarrett had got it wrong, of course. It had been Monday all along and he was wise enough in the ways of the village to contact all those who had expressed an interest by telephone to prevent any further collusion on excuses. There were some rather glum meetings in the street and in the post office where it was discovered just who was in for a large dose of culture.

The commander was going, as were Kelvin, myself, Lindy, Dennis, Mary Mowbray and an ancient couple who were cousins of some kind to Kelvin. It was never safe to inquire too closely into relationships between 'cousins' or even nieces and nephews. It all too often uncovered details that would have caused instant combustion to the relevant page of the Book of Common Prayer.

We all met outside the post office at 7.30 am, late enough to allow the morning agricultural chores to have been completed. We were not a particularly happy bunch. It was late October; it was still fairly dark and there was frost on the ground. Most of us were muffled in coats or padded jackets, but Kelvin was wearing his smart suit with a thick woolly pullover beneath. We had to go into town to meet the bus and so we all piled into the commander's estate car – one of those foreign eight-seater jobs – which he used to transport courgettes and mushrooms to market and bring back piles of rotting horse manure to give the aforesaid mushrooms something to feed on.

Town was half an hour away, but it was only fifteen minutes before Kelvin's cousins began to fall apart. This was a phenomenon I had heard about, but never witnessed. The village had housed a famous old lady who had died ten years earlier at the age of ninety-five. In all her years, she had never been more than 1½ miles from the house in which she had been born; she had never seen the sea, which was only 10 miles away across the moor. Kelvin's cousins were out of the same mould. They had been to town before, but now they were faced by a four-hour journey up the motorway to Stratford. They had been able to come to terms with the idea in abstract, but the reality proved too much for them. They were gentle old people, so there was nothing loud or raucous about their funny turns. The old woman, who had been introduced as Mercy, leaned politely over the back of her seat and was sick over Kelvin's going-to-the-theatre trousers.

Kelvin had been contemplating the slowly lightening morning with a certain foreboding himself, but Mercy's action brought his attention back to current matters. 'You daft old biddy,' he yelled.

The commander had been having his difficulties as well. He had been quietly swearing to himself about the instability of his car due to the abnormal weight of his seven passengers, but the sudden sensory shocks brought about by the violent assault of Kelvin's yell on his eardrums and on his olfactory nerves by Mercy's regurgitation of her breakfast Rice Krispies made him swerve violently across the bows of one of the many milk tankers that ply the country lanes in the early morning. He pulled up by the hedge.

The doors of the car were flung open and, before the wondering gaze of the tanker driver who had been forced to stop, we all jumped out of the vehicle. The commander seemed to have lost his cool completely, which made one feel thankful on behalf of those matelots whom he expected to fight and die for him that his nerve had never been put to the test under fire. He was standing in the middle of the road, wringing his hands.

'My car, my poor car. It'll never be the same again. It'll stink for as long as I own it.'

Kelvin's cousins were standing on the verge, he with his arm round her, looking like a pair of elderly dormice. 'Mercy's very sorry. But her nerves got the better of her.'

'What can I do? What can I do?' moaned the commander.

Lindy went over to check on Mercy and then peered into the car at Kelvin. After his initial outburst, he appeared to be in a state of shock. The tanker driver switched on his hazard warning lights and climbed down from his cab.

'What the hell's going on?' he asked. 'Oh, hullo, Dennis.'

Before he had decided that he did not like work, Dennis had been one of the farmers from whom the driver had collected milk. Farmers all tried to remain on excellent terms with their tanker drivers because it was they who decided how much milk was actually picked up each day and thus had considerable influence on their incomes. At Christmas, milk lorries groaned under the weight of gift bottles of whisky and gin.

'Good morning, Vic,' replied Dennis. 'One of our passengers has been sick.'

'All over the interior of my car,' moaned the commander.

Some strangled grunts brought it to our notice that Kelvin was coming round. They developed into an indignant squawk. 'It's not your bloody car that's suffered, it's my trousers!' he shouted as he bent himself into contortions extricating himself from the dicky seat of the car.

'Really?' said the commander, perking up a bit. He pushed Kelvin out of the way so that he could see into the car. 'Oh, wonderful! It seems to be all right. Your trousers seem to have taken it all. Isn't that a relief?'

'Now we've got that cleared up, hadn't we better be getting on our way?' said Lindy. 'Otherwise we'll miss the bus.'

'I think Mercy and I would be better off going home,' said Kelvin's cousin.

'And if you think I'm going to spend the rest of the day in these trousers, you're wrong,' said Kelvin, who was gingerly trying to hold them away from his legs. 'I'm going home to change.'

'But we'll miss the bus,' said the commander.

'What's all this about?' asked the driver. He was waving cars past his lorry.

'We're all supposed to be meeting a bus in town but Kelvin wants to go home to change his trousers and those two just want to go home. If we take them back, we'll miss the bus,' said Ivor.

'That's no problem. The three of them can squeeze into the cab with me. I'm on my way up to the village.'

'But how will I get back in time for the bus?' asked Kelvin.

'You won't.'

'That's not fair,' he said, reverting to childhood.

Vic had the solution. 'I know. Why don't you change trousers with the old man? You're much the same size.' Both Kelvin and the old man looked horrified. The idea of exposing any of their flesh or their undergarments in public was too awful to contemplate. They belonged to the old school and were reluctant even to roll up their shirt sleeves on a sunny day.

'His trousers won't match my jacket,' said Kelvin.

Lindy, used to dealing with such people, understood their difficulty. 'That won't matter, Kelvin. I suggest that all the men form a circle round you. Like they do at rugby internationals when someone loses their shorts.'

Kelvin, with his back to the wall, was capable of rising to the occasion. 'I'm not stripping off in the middle of the road. What I'm going to do is change in the cab of the lorry.' He climbed up to unveil himself and the rest of us moved over to the old man to persuade him to do the same.

Then a police car arrived. The situation could have been better. The road at this point was too narrow to merit a white line to define the centre and the commander's car and the milk tanker were causing a considerable impediment to the free flow of traffic. Not that there was much traffic, but that was not the point. The policeman pulled up behind the lorry and came up to tap on the window of the cab.

Kelvin, had he had any sense, would have wound down the window and explained that he was a retired special constable, a man of great integrity and probity who was in the process of examining his longjohns to see whether they, too, needed to be changed. It seemed, though, that he looked briefly up and said, 'Get knotted.'

The policeman had rather a short fuse and he began to beat on the cab door. Kelvin, somewhat alarmed by this display, locked it. We became aware of the disturbance and moved round from the front of the lorry to see what was going on.

'What the hell do you think you're playing at, hitting my door like that?' asked the driver.

'So it's your door, is it?' said the policeman. The sort of policemen that we knew travelled around in Land Rovers or rusty Ford Escorts and were given short shrift if they tried to 'come the copper' on us. This particular one seemed to be rather far from his native habitat. He was wearing an orange jacket and his vehicle was one of those large saloons that are normally to be seen sliding down the fast lane of motorways, all flashing lights and dayglo paint, with the back seat piled high with traffic cones.

'I've just said so, you daft pillock. Look,' Vic said, pointing at his overall, 'it says "Milk Marketing Board" on my pocket and it says "Milk Marketing Board" on the lorry.'

The policeman strode over to Vic and loomed at him, menacingly. 'Who are you calling a daft pillock?'

'Who was it who was thumping on the door of my lorry? You could have damaged it.'

'*If* it's your lorry. What's that bloke doing in the cab, then?'

'He's taking off his trousers.'

That rocked the policeman a bit, but he was not about to let it interfere with his duty. 'Whatever he's up to, get this road cleared or else I'll book you for obstruction.' He would have been inhuman had he left matters there, however. 'Why's he taking off his trousers anyway?'

'Because she was sick on them.'

The policeman turned to inspect the guilty 'she'. Mercy, who was behind the commander's car, was tugging at her husband's boots as he lay on the ground.

'What's she doing?'

'What does it look like? She's trying to get his boots off.'

'Why's she taking off his boots?'

'So that he can get his trousers off.'

The policeman looked suspiciously at Vic. 'Are you taking the mickey?'

'No.'

'OK, then, why does that one want to get his trousers off?'

'So that the one in the cab taking his trousers off can go to Stratford to see Shakespeare.'

The policeman thought for a bit. These town bobbies, as this one surely was, have to learn that the rural brain works rather differently from the urban brain. The city villain is always looking for ways to go round the law so that he can commit an offence that he knows is naughty. The rural villain constantly finds the law putting itself between him and something that he considers perfectly all right – such as poaching – or else niggling away at the outcroppings of bureaucracy in the case of tractor licences and checking that the pub stops serving drinks at closing time. The police tend to be looked at as interfering busy-bodies rather than menacing figures of authority.

'You'll have to come up with a better story than that. He can't be going to see Shakespeare. He's been dead for years.'

Satisfying this guardian of the law was a very complicated business, but eventually we passed the old man's trousers through the lorry window to Kelvin. Dennis, grumbling at the sacrilege, gave up a couple of sheets of his *Times* to fabricate a kilt for the de-trousered one to appease the policeman's sense of decency. The boy in blue then led us, carving through the non-existent traffic with his light flashing, and we made the bus with minutes to spare.

The trip up was very peaceful. The students were provincial punk, daringly stretching to a stud in one ear, and many of them were nice, clean-living members of the Young Farmers' Club. They sat in the back of the coach where they giggled, played mini-computer games and listened to Abba on their personal stereos. We were under the control of Martha, a lecturer in the English department of the college. Dennis fell asleep. The commander and Kelvin looked out of the window and marvelled at all the rich farmland we were passing, and Mary lectured Martha on the finer points of dressage.

By the time we reached Stratford, we had found out that the play was *Julius Caesar*, that we had to pay for our seats since the munificence of the education authority only went as far as the bus, and that Kelvin had a deep passion for the actress playing Portia, having had her imprinted on his brain as she was the first moving object that he had ever seen on television when he had finally decided to buy one – 26-inch colour with a built-in cocktail cabinet – six years earlier.

The students vanished as soon as they disembarked from the bus while the adults stood round in an uncertain circle, wondering just how to occupy themselves until the play started at 7.30. It dawned on me that we were tourists, part of that despised under-race that clogged the streets of the village during the summer months. The commander was the only one of us who had ever had experience of being one of this breed in the past and his tourism had taken place in the gut of Valetta, the reeking opium dens of Macao and possibly even a gracious bordello or two in New Orleans. He was not much good at the home-grown variety. He and Dennis moved across the road from the bus station and gazed with horror into a shop window filled with dolls dressed as beefeaters, Anne Hathaways and all the members of the royal family.

'Right,' said Martha. 'What does everyone want to do?'

'I came here to go to the theatre,' said Kelvin.

'Yes, we all did. But the play doesn't start for seven hours.'

'We could have left later, then, and I wouldn't have had that awful rush to feed the stock this morning.'

'You mean for Prudence to feed the stock while you drank your tea,' said Dennis.

354

'Bloody cheek!' said Kelvin.

Martha clapped her hands together. 'Come on, now. Pay attention.' She had realized that the group she was with would be as difficult to control as any of her students. 'What I would suggest is that we all have lunch together and then go and see some of the sights.'

We strolled up the street, casting indifferent eyes over half-timbered Tudor buildings and making disparaging comments about the displayed menus and the ugliness of the passers-by as opposed to those back home.

'How about a Chinese meal?' suggested the commander.

'Foreign muck,' said Kelvin automatically.

'I'm told they always have English food on the menu and they're usually very cheap.'

Kelvin was overruled and we trooped suspiciously upstairs into the first-floor restaurant. Martha, fortunately, was a true child of our urban culture, which meant that she knew her way round a Chinese menu. A town of at least five thousand people is needed to support a Chinese restaurant and our village was 15 miles from such a conurbation. So the subtle mysteries of foo yung, chow mein and chop suey were as veiled to members of our community as the cuisine of the highlands of New Guinea. There was an uneasy silence as we studied the menu.

'What's sweet-and-sour?' asked Dennis.

Martha looked up from her menu with a startled expression. 'Sweet-and-sour? You must know. Deep-fried bits of pork or whatever coated in batter in a sweet-and-sour sauce.'

'But is it nice?'

'Yes, I suppose so. It's not what I go for, personally, but it's probably the most popular Chinese dish.'

'I once spent a fortnight in Hong Kong,' said the commander. 'But I don't remember any of this sort of stuff. I had some sea-snake once and the lady I was with had a thousand-year egg, but she said it was nothing like as old as that. It had probably been laid in the past decade.'

Kelvin's alarm bells were ringing. 'You mean they serve you snakes and rotten eggs?'

'They're considered a great delicacy.'

'But an egg that old wouldn't even be rotten. It would have dried up completely.'

'I don't think it can have done. Anyway I don't suppose a rotten egg is any worse than some of the things you eat.'

'Nonsense. I eat good fresh food.'

'And you have to get Prudence to shake the maggots off the venison you poach.'

'That's different.'

'So's a thousand-year egg.'

The neatly-bottomed waiter, wearing the manic grin of his branch of the profession, appeared at the end of our table. 'Order, Sir?' he asked in an oriental approximation of a Midlands accent.

'We're not quite ready yet,' said Martha. He bowed politely and withdrew, padding down to the other end of the restaurant, past the sprinkling of businessmen insulating themselves from the embarrassment of having to catch each other's eyes behind copies of the morning papers. The waiter straightened out a napkin and glided back to our table.

'We're still not ready,' said the commander testily, trying to equate his memories of Hong Kong with the Chinglish of the menu. The waited bowed and withdrew a couple of yards to scrutinize us with infinite contempt.

'Shall I order for us all?' suggested Martha.

'That sounds like a good idea,' said Lindy.

'I want a steak and an omelette,' announced Kelvin. 'They can't muck up that.'

'All right. I'll order Chinese for the rest of us and you can be on your own.' The waiter, who had been quivering beside us like a Labrador waiting for the order to retrieve, jumped forward. 'We'd like a 67, a 32, a 43 —'

The waiter peered over her shoulder at the menu. '67, that is sliced duck and bean shoots. What is 32?'

They laboriously worked out the order.

'I never know why they bother to give the dishes numbers,' said Martha, after the waiter had retreated to a hatch and bawled the order through. 'They never know them.'

'Perhaps it's something to do with their accounts,' said Dennis. 'Ivor is a tax commissioner and he was telling me that there was a Chink up in front of them who claimed he fed his family on the leftovers from the customers' plates. He got away with it, too.'

'Well, I'll make sure I spit on anything that I leave behind,' said Kelvin. 'Just because these people are foreigners, there's no reason why they should be allowed to get away with not paying their taxes.'

It was doubtful whether Kelvin had ever paid any tax in his life. Even within the last couple of years, on the rare occasions that he put his hand into his pocket, he often pulled out one of the old white fivers. Up to five years previously, he had even been in the habit of paying with a gold sovereign, no doubt hoarded away by a tax-avoiding ancestor. That had been very popular locally until some spoil-sport of a visitor had told him in the pub that they were now worth more than fifty times the face value.

We sat and waited for our food. Martha occupied us by providing a crash course on the life and times of William Shakespeare with particular reference to Stratford and to a well-practised outline of the plot and deeper meaning of *Julius*

Caesar. The waiter returned, bringing steaming trays of food which he laid down on the table.

'It's certainly very colourful,' said Mary critically. It was certainly that: lurid reds, yellows and greens – all that was missing was blue, which has never been a wildly popular colour for food. We had oval plates while Kelvin's was round with his omelette reposing in the middle of it. He looked at it mournfully.

'Where's my steak?' he asked. The waiter had done his waiting and had gone behind the bar to pick his teeth and examine the breasts of the foreign devil on page 3. Kelvin tried to catch his eye and failed, so he summoned him as he was wont to summon his sheepdog – by sticking a couple of gnarled fingers in his mouth and emitting a whistle. The whistle was designed to catch the attention of an elderly, half-deaf canine a couple of fields away and it sliced through the chapel-like silence of the restaurant and almost knocked the waiter off his stool. There was a rustle of disapproving *Daily Telegraph*s from the other tables, which was silenced by a glare from Kelvin. Dennis and Martha looked pained.

'You can be really uncouth,' complained Dennis.

'Don't blame me. Blame that waiter for not bringing me the dinner that I asked for,' replied Kelvin.

'Lunch,' murmured Dennis as the waiter approached.

'Sah?' said the waiter. 'You whistle?'

'That's right, chum. I whistle. Where's my steak?'

The waiter looked at Kelvin's plate. 'You order omelette and there is omelette.'

'I also order steak. Isn't that right?' Kelvin appealed for support from round the table with limited success since the rest of us were fully absorbed in the engrossing task of trying to help ourselves to precisely one fifth of everything whilst trying to make the fifths closer to quarters in the case of the more interesting dishes. 'Well, I did, anyway.'

The waiter gave Kelvin a supercilious look but picked up his order book and leafed through it. 'Ah so!' he said in the best Charlie Chan manner. 'Quite ri'. You do order steak. See there.'

Kelvin looked at the relevant calligraphy which could have

been Greek to him, if it hadn't already been Chinese. 'Good. Well, where is it, then?'

The waiter looked carefully up and down the table. There was definitely no steak to be seen. 'I order steak so you must have eaten it already.'

'Don't be daft,' said Kelvin. 'You've only just brought my plate. How could I have possibly had time to eat it? I haven't even dirtied my fork yet.'

The waiter picked up Kelvin's fork and took it over to the window where he held it up to the light and carefully examined it. He returned. 'So you eat steak with your fingers.'

The rest of us were now agog. It was a lovely conversation to listen in to.

Kelvin, remarkably, was holding on to his temper. He seemed to be more baffled than angry. He shifted uneasily in his chair. 'Look. If you want your bill to be paid, just stop messing about and go and get me my steak.'

That was a threat that will cow waiters the world over. Ours scurried back behind the bar and engaged in a bellowed conversation with the guardian of the hatch. It did not seem to satisfy him and he came back with an aggressive glint in his eye. 'Cook say he give you steak.'

'Well, Cook's got it bloody well wrong!' said Kelvin in exasperation.

'He didn't get his steak, you know,' said Lindy. The majority of the meal was now distributed and we could afford to join in.

The waiter looked round at us, his eyes peering at each of us in turn. 'You all say he not got steak?'

'Yes!' we chorused.

'You all not pay for steak?'

'We all not pay for steak,' agreed the commander.

'Excuse me,' said the waiter and he withdrew back to the hatch where a furious altercation ensued.

'He seems to be remarkably scrutable for his race,' observed Dennis.

There was a crash as the hatch was slammed shut and a door beside the bar flew open. We turned to see what the fuss was about and observed a Chinese wearing a white apron and overalls burst into the restaurant waving his arms around and shouting at the waiter. The waiter pointed out Kelvin and shouted back. They both came over to the table.

'You're on your own, Kelvin,' murmured Lindy.

The cook stopped by Kelvin and stabbed his finger at the plate. 'Omelette,' he hissed.

'Yes,' agreed Kelvin cautiously.

The chef grasped the omelette in both hands and pulled. It was a bit like a conjuring trick. The egg peeled away to reveal a steak nestling inside. 'Steak, bloody steak. You see bloody steak, yes? Steak omelette, what waiter man ask for.'

The waiter burst into impassioned speech which cannot have been polite as the chef struck him a clumsy blow on the chest. The waiter retaliated and this drew forth a shriek of fury from the chef who chased the waiter round the table and pursued him into the kitchen where bangs and crashes revealed that the disagreement was continuing.

'They can get a bit excited, these people,' observed the commander.

Kelvin was looking sadly at his steak omelette. 'I don't think I want it now,' he said. 'Not after that chap has fingered it.'

'I wouldn't worry,' said Mary. 'He was the chef, after all. He's bound to have fingered everything.'

'That's not the same. He fingered it in public. And there's a dirty great thumbprint in the middle of the steak.'

'Bad luck,' said Dennis, thoughtfully examining a wrinkled brown object that he had speared with his fork. 'I've no idea what this is, but it's really rather good.'

With the waiter out of the restaurant and, judging by the noise, likely to be absent for a while, the businessmen began to fold their newspapers and tiptoe away. Kelvin shovelled his mangled steak omelette on to a side-plate and began to tour the remains of the other dishes. The commander saw him coming and snatched up the last two morsels of lemon chicken. Frustrated and hungry, Kelvin returned to his omelette, deciding to pick at the bits untouched by human hand.

The waiter eventually re-emerged and toured the tables

vacated by the businessmen, harvesting pound notes and piles of luncheon vouchers before coming to our table and handing the bill to Kelvin who was just mopping up the last remaining morsel on his plate. Some of the starch had been knocked out of the waiter, a button was missing from his white jacket and he carried a napkin in front of his mouth. The bill was extremely modest and the commander took it and carefully added it up.

'He hasn't charged you for the steak omelette.'

'I no charge for steak omelette. Bloody chef mess it up. It is on the house.'

'Oh, I see,' said the commander. 'That is very generous.'

'Thank you,' said the waiter, withdrawing. We divided the bill by six. There was a debate about the tip. Some felt that nothing was deserved under the circumstances, but the free steak omelette which Kelvin had eaten swayed the majority and 10 per cent was agreed upon. We laid down our money and left, waiting half-way down the stairs while Martha and the commander visited their respective loos.

'Interesting sort of meal, that,' observed Dennis.

'Yes,' said Mary. 'It was very different and surprisingly good. I think I might go to a Chinese restaurant again.'

Suddenly there was a scream from the floor above us. We craned our necks to see the waiter leaning over the bannisters and looking down at us. 'Ho!' he yelled and threw something down the central well of the staircase towards us. We instinctively ducked, but Mary was struck on the head. It was three screwed-up pound notes. 'I don't want tip. Bloody cook gives you steak omelette. That is bad. I only take tips when the job is good.' He turned away leaving us gazing, dumbfounded, after him.

'Heavens!' said Dennis. 'A waiter refusing a tip! The earth must have wobbled on its axis.'

'Look out!' said Mary. 'He's back.'

The waiter was leaning over the bannisters again, the napkin still covering his nose. 'You are stupid, stupid people!' he yelled.

Dennis waved and smiled at him. 'Hullo, hullo, thank you very much.'

'What are you doing?' asked Mary.

'Humouring him. I've read about these orientals. They can run amok if you don't keep them sweet.'

'What's amok?' asked Kelvin.

'They pick up an axe and rush about chopping people up until somebody kills them. I think it's the Chinese who do it. Or it may be the Malays.' Judging by the sudden burst of foreign tongues above us, the chef had joined the waiter and the amok was about to take place.

'Shall we wait outside for the others?' suggested Mary.

'I think that might be the wisest course,' agreed Dennis, and we all scuttled down the rest of the stairs to wait in the street for the commander and Martha.

'I'm not sure I'd go to another Chinese restaurant,' said Kelvin. 'I thought they behaved rather strangely.' There was nobody to say, 'They're not all like that,' because for all we knew they probably were.

'Let's go and see Shakespeare's birthplace,' said Martha.

'How long before the play starts?' asked Lindy.

'Five and a half hours,' was the grim response.

We strolled across the town, gently burping up our bean sprouts like cows savouring the cud, towards the hallowed birthplace of the bard. It seemed to be very suburban as we approached.

'That's handy,' remarked Mary, 'he was born just up the road from the library. I bet that's what made him decide to be a writer.'

There was an entry charge so we did not go in but trailed back towards the town centre.

'I could have gone out hunting today,' said Mary.

'You can go out hunting every day, but it's not every day that you have the opportunity to see a great play,' replied Dennis.

'Do you really hunt?' asked Martha, as we scuffed through the great drifts of fallen leaves along the edge of the river.

'Yes. Two or three times a week usually.'

'Don't you feel a bit uncomfortable about it?'

'No, not really. One is used to it now. One's backside gets hardened quite quickly.'

'No, I don't mean that. I mean uncomfortable about the principle of hunting foxes. I think it's disgraceful that it still goes on in this day and age.'

'Hunting foxes? Oh no. I would never dream about going fox hunting. Dreadful pompous conceited lot who do, and they know nothing about the countryside.'

'That's good,' said Martha with relief. 'I find fox hunting indefensible.'

'So do I,' concurred Mary heartily. 'You spend your time sitting about in the freezing cold for hours beside a covert waiting for something to happen. I haven't done it for years. It bores me witless.'

'I suppose you drag hunt, then?'

'Heavens no! I go stag hunting. Much more fun. Better chase and a decent kill at the end of the day to show for it rather than a ratty scrap of red fur well chewed over by the hounds. You ought to come out with us for a day.'

'No, thank you,' said Martha faintly, as disturbed as only a *Guardian*-reading, liberal-arts college lecturer could be, confronted by one who flouted all the shibboleths so brazenly.

We entered the church where the bard was interred. A custodian seated in the chancel solicited a donation before we could go through to the grave.

'Is that all?' said Kelvin. 'It's not much to look at, is it? Just a bit of paving stone with a rope round it. You can't even read the writing on it.'

Martha was shocked. 'It's the grave of William Shake-speare.'

'I know that, but so what?'

'So what? You're standing a few yards from the skull that housed the brain of one of the greatest geniuses that the world has ever known.'

'Yes, but the skull's been vacant for a good while now and, personally, I'd rather read the fatstock prices than *Romeo and Juliet*.'

'You're just a boor, Kelvin,' said the commander, who was standing reverently to attention beside the steps that led to the grave and the altar.

'Is he just? Well, when did you last read anything by Shakespeare?' asked Lindy.

'Er . . . not for a bit.'

'Not since you left school, I'll bet. And what play was it that you last read?'

'*Antony and Cleopatra.*'

'Is that the one that had Sid James as Antony?' asked Kelvin.

'That's right, and Kenneth Williams played Caesar. It was quite funny,' replied the commander.

'I think that was a "Carry On" film,' said Dennis. 'It was Burton and Taylor who did the original.'

'Oh yes. Quite right,' said the commander.

Martha decided to educate us. 'That's probably the best likeness of Shakespeare that we have,' she said, indicating the bust high in its niche on the wall to the left of the grave.

We examined it critically. 'He looks a bit like a doctored cat,' said Kelvin.

'He does, doesn't he?' replied Dennis. 'I expect the chap who carved it wasn't very good.'

'Well, if he wasn't very good, how do we know that Shakespeare looked like that?' said Kelvin. 'It's like that chap with a squint who's a woodcarver up at the commune. He keeps doing busts of people that always end up looking like monkeys.'

'We have other portraits,' said Martha. 'Like the ones we would have seen back at the birthplace.'

'When were they done?' asked Dennis.

'I suppose the earliest was produced about twenty years after his death.'

'I bet they just copied that ratty little carving up there. For all we know, Shakespeare may have had one eye and his nose spread over his face.'

Kelvin, having spread scorn over one of our national shrines, stumped back to one of the pews and ostentatiously pulled out a copy of *Farmers Weekly* from the enormous poacher's pocket built into his jacket, put on his reading glasses, licked his fingers and began to study the afore-mentioned fatstock prices. Dennis slipped out of the chancel to join him and persuaded him to turn to the crossword in which they became absorbed.

The mourners round the grave became restive. 'How long until the play starts?' asked Mary.

'Four hours,' replied Martha.

'What can we do now?' asked the commander.

'I know what I'd like to do,' said Mary. 'I'd like to have a go on that organ.'

We looked at her in surprise. 'I didn't know you could play,' said Lindy.

'I quite often play in chapel on Sunday, but I've never managed to play on an instrument as good as that.' 'That' was a great bank of pipes stuck above the aisle with a small playing booth to the right of the pulpit.

'I didn't know you went to chapel,' said Lindy.

'Yes. I enjoy playing on the organ.'

Religion was a subject that was largely avoided in our community because the diversity of beliefs could have led to serious disagreements. We had a few recusants whose needs were ministered to by a decrepit priest who fancied himself as an intellectual theologian. There was the C. of E. but it had never recovered from the excesses of its clergy a century ago when they had had a whale of a time drinking, hunting and whoring, leaving the souls of their parishioners as easy pickings for Wesley and a host of evangelical imitators who left their places of worship scattered along the lanes, as common as Dutch barns. If you weren't established, you tended to worship at the nearest chapel dedicated to some obscure Old Testament figure or other and hope that transgression of the fundamental stricture that was common to all of them – never to let a drop of alcohol pass between your lips – might be forgiven on the day of judgement.

Mary moved hungrily towards the organ and rattled at the door that kept casual fingers away from its keys.

'I'd leave it alone,' said Martha nervously, looking round the interior of the church. The guardian of Shakespeare's tomb seemed half-asleep and unlikely to object, but there were a couple of semi-official Women's Institute types peddling *memento mori* at the entrance of the church and they were

365

looking at Kelvin and Dennis with some disapproval. Dennis had taken over the crossword while Kelvin had stretched himself out along the pew for a quick nap.

'Don't be silly,' said Mary. 'What's an organ for if it's not to be played? Commander!' Like Kelvin's whistle in the restaurant, Mary's voice had been evolved to control hounds during the bedlam of the kill and to summon her husband from several fields away when he was riding the tractor in his earmuffs. It was probably the loudest noise, including the organ, to have pierced the dim religious quiet for centuries and the bust of the bard tottered on its perch. The commander hurried to her side. 'Commander, can you break into this organ?'

Mary, although she had lowered her voice, was clearly audible throughout the church. The WI ladies twittered to each other about whether they ought to interfere, but they were occupied by a large group of Japanese tourists who had entered and were hissing their way round the souvenirs. A few of them had decided to follow Kelvin's example and were now stretched along the pews with their eyes closed. They must have thought this was the western way of worship or how one showed respect to the tombs of famous forefathers.

The commander, with deft fingers that had probably unlocked the Polaris firing mechanisms, opened up the organ loft and, with Martha almost in tears at the lack of respect being shown by her charges, Mary switched on the lights and fiddled with the stops. There was a preliminary blare that woke the wondering children of Nippon and Mary was off in a rousing rendition of *D'ye ken John Peel?*.

Martha pulled Mary from the stool. 'For heaven's sake, if you must play, at least choose something more appropriate. This is a church, after all.'

'Oh very well,' said Mary. 'What do you suggest?'

'How about *Eternal Father Strong to Save?*' suggested the commander.

'Right.' Mary pulled out all the stops and let it rip. She and the commander bellowed out the accompaniment while Martha retreated to the back of the church to dissociate herself from them. In consideration of the nature of the

366

congregation, Mary then switched to selections from *The Mikado* and Kelvin, mindful of the amount of money that the Grabber sometimes came to the pub with, rousted out the guardian of the chancel, who was quite enjoying the concert, and the two of them went amidst the tourists with a collection plate. They made enough to pay for the complete refurbishment of the bust in luminous paint, with sufficient over to re-carve the bardic slab.

We wandered back to the town in a pleasantly mellow mood. Dennis had finished his crossword and all, save Martha, had thoroughly enjoyed *The Mikado* and the few excerpts from *Madame Butterfly* which had been the encore when it was discovered how generous the tourists had been in donating to church funds.

We had tea in a shoppe, mooched round a bookshop and peered over the wall at the son or the grandson of the sacred tree under which the bard was wont to sit, eventually gravitating to the Memorial Theatre to sit in the relentlessly stylish cafe where we played 'Animal, vegetable and mineral' to while away the time. As 7.30 approached, the cafe began to fill with people, mainly with scores of children.

'It's not a kiddies' play, is it?' asked Kelvin.

'Oh no,' replied Martha. 'They're all probably doing it for "O" or "A" level this year. Any Shakespeare play you go to has an audience that is full of young people.'

'Does the theatre make a profit?' asked Mary.

'No, the Arts Council and all sorts of other organizations have to subsidize it. But I believe Stratford is closer to break-even point than most theatres that put on Shakespeare.'

Kelvin was puzzled. 'But if it doesn't make a profit, why don't they put on plays that people want to see?'

Martha was shocked. 'This is the Shakespeare Memorial Theatre. It has to stage Shakespeare. His plays are part of our national culture.'

'It seems a bit daft to me. If it wasn't for all these kids, there'd be nobody here and they're only here because they're forced to be. I reckon this Shakespeare has only survived because of the bloody examiners making people do him at school.'

Our seats were up in the gods, or should have been. The gods were crammed by shrieking teenagers pinching each other's bottoms, hitting each other with programmes and hurling peanuts across the aisle. It looked as though the atmosphere of the Colosseum would be effortlessly achieved. Martha stayed there to keep an eye on her pupils, but none of the rest of us was prepared to endure the vertigo brought on by looking down the precipitous slope of tiered seats, bristling with punk haircuts, towards the tiny stage far below.

As the curtain rose, so did we, clattering our way down the steps from the upper circle that led to the street outside. Back in through the main entrance we went, where we bluffed our way past the attendants into the stalls. It was both more peaceful and more comfortable there, and we settled down to look at the stage.

'I thought this was supposed to be *Julius Caesar*,' said Kelvin.

'So did I,' said Dennis, leaning over to look at the programme belonging to an American in the row in front. It had been decided that quite enough had been spent without buying fripperies like programmes. 'It is.'

'But it can't be. Bugger me, it is! That fat chap has just said something about a holiday to see Caesar.'

There were people saying 'shhh' in a variety of foreign tongues all round us.

'But Romans are supposed to wear things like bedsheets,' persisted Kelvin.

'Togas,' said Dennis.

'That's right. But this lot are wearing brown uniforms and jackboots. They surely never wore gear like that.'

'Perhaps they can't afford to buy the right sort of costume,' suggested Dennis.

'I think it's a bloody disgrace,' said Mary. 'When we did *The Mikado*, it was no trouble to ask people to make up their own costumes. They could have at least done the same. And look at that photograph.' The stage was dominated by a huge photograph of a face, presumably of Caesar himself. 'They didn't have photos in those days. It's ridiculous.'

We sat there in silence for a bit, seething with discontent.

'Can you make out what they're saying?' asked Dennis.

'Not very well,' said Kelvin. He cupped his hands and yelled across the hallowed air towards the stage, 'Speak up!'

The commander and I could take no more of this and moved several rows further back. Caesar himself had arrived on stage and strode about saying 'ha' and 'ho' for a bit until the soothsayer arrived. There were snorts of delight from the groundlings in front of us.

'He's the spitting image of Jimmy,' announced Kelvin loudly. One of the usherettes came down to read the riot act and an uneasy peace descended until Caesar and his entourage arrived on stage bizarrely decked in gold polythene. 'I bet they got these costumes from a job lot of *Dr Who* stuff,' said Kelvin very audibly, and received an appropriately dagger-like glare from Brutus across the footlights. 'What the hell's that noise meant to be?' A most curious tweeting sound

369

was echoing around the theatre, which a discussion among the rustics eventually identified as the sound of scores of electronic watches all deciding that it was 8.00 pm at roughly the same moment.

It was not really the play that we should have gone to see. Kelvin went to sleep after his TV star had had her moment on stage and revealed quite a lot of thigh for quite a long time while she was showing her scars. He slept through thunderstorm, assassination and Mark Antony's speech and only the electric excitement generated by Dennis at the prospect of having a drink, brought him, snorting, out of his doze just before the interval.

Afterwards, Mary and Dennis both joined him in sleep. Even Martha agreed later that they had not missed all that much. The most memorable, if embarrassing, moment of the production took place when Brutus committed hara-kiri. He pounced on his sword with an enthusiasm weirdly akin to the way that Kelvin would have jumped on Matilda, had he ever had the chance. There was a moment of stunned silence before the gods erupted in laughter which spread as far as the stalls.

We did not get home until 2.00 am, but it was generally agreed that it had been worth going. Mary got the producer's job in *Blithe Spirit* on the strength of it. Dennis was asked to speak to four WIs on the experience and Kelvin bored the local pub about it for weeks. There is some talk about booking a coach to go to see *No Sex, Please, We're British* next year.